ST

D0319489

Rover Metro Owners Workshop Manual

Jeremy Churchill

Models covered
Rover Metro models with 1118 cc and 1397 cc 'K-series'
engines, including 16- valve and special/limited editions

*Does not cover later GTi 16v with multi-point fuel-injection system or
automatic transmission models*

ABCDE
FGHIJ
KLMNO
PQRST

Haynes Publishing Group
Sparkford Nr Yeovil
Somerset BA22 7JJ England

Haynes Publications, Inc
861 Lawrence Drive
Newbury Park
California 91320 USA

Acknowledgements
Thanks are due to the Champion Sparking Plug Company Limited who supplied the illustrations showing spark plug conditions, to Holt Lloyd Limited who supplied the illustrations showing bodywork repair, and to Duckhams Oils who provided lubrication data. Certain other illustrations are the copyright of Rover Group Limited, and are used with their permission. Thanks are also due to Sykes-Pickavant Limited, who provided some of the workshop tools, and to all those people at Sparkford who helped in the production of this manual.

© **Haynes Publishing Group 1991**

A book in the **Haynes Owners Workshop Manual Series**

Printed by J. H. Haynes & Co. Ltd., Sparkford, Nr Yeovil, Somerset BA22 7JJ, England

ISBN 1 85010 711 4

British Library Cataloguing in Publication Data
A catalogue record for this book is available from the British Library

Whilst every care is taken to ensure that the information in this manual is correct, no liability can be accepted by the authors or publishers for loss, damage or injury caused by any errors in, or omissions from, the information given.

Contents

Rover Metro 1.1C model

Rover Metro 1.4GS model

About this manual

Its aim

The aim of this manual is to help you get the best value from your vehicle. It can do so in several ways. It can help you decide what work must be done (even should you choose to get it done by a garage), provide information on routine maintenance and servicing, and give a logical course of action and diagnosis when random faults occur. However, it is hoped that you will use the manual by tackling the work yourself. On simpler jobs it may even be quicker than booking the car into a garage and going there twice, to leave and collect it. Perhaps most important, a lot of money can be saved by avoiding the costs a garage must charge to cover its labour and overheads.

The manual has drawings and descriptions to show the function of the various components so that their layout can be understood. Then the tasks are described and photographed in a clear step-by-step sequence.

Its arrangement

The manual is divided into Chapters, each covering a logical sub-division of the vehicle. The Chapters are each divided into Sections, numbered with single figures, eg 5; and the Sections into paragraphs (or sub-sections), with decimal numbers following on from the Section they are in, eg 5.1, 5.2, 5.3 etc.

It is freely illustrated, especially in those parts where there is a detailed sequence of operations to be carried out. There are two forms of illustration: figures and photographs. The figures are numbered in sequence with decimal numbers, according to their position in the Chapter – eg Fig. 6.4 is the fourth drawing/illustration in Chapter 6. Photographs carry the same number (either individually or in related groups) as the Section or sub-section to which they relate.

There is an alphabetical index at the back of the manual as well as a contents list at the front. Each Chapter is also preceded by its own individual contents list.

References to the 'left' or 'right' of the vehicle are in the sense of a person in the driver's seat, facing forward.

Unless otherwise stated, nuts and bolts are removed by turning anti-clockwise, and tightened by turning clockwise.

Vehicle manufacturers continually make changes to specifications and recommendations, and these, when notified, are incorporated into our manuals at the earliest opportunity.

Whilst every care is taken to ensure that the information in this manual is correct, no liability can be accepted by the authors or publishers for loss, damage or injury caused by any errors in, or omissions from, the information given.

Project vehicles

The main project vehicle used in the preparation of this manual, and appearing in many of the photographic sequences was a 1990 1.4GS. Additional work was carried out and photographed on a 1990 GTi 16v.

Introduction to the Rover Metro

The Rover Metro covered in this manual is a much-developed version of the original Austin Metro first launched in October 1980. These models, first seen in May 1990, are all fitted with the new 'K' series engine in either 1.1 or 1.4 litre sizes, with either SU KIF carburettors or Rover/Motorola Modular Engine Management System single-point fuel-injection (MEMS-SPi). The engine is able to accept a full range of emission control systems, up to and including a three-way regulated catalytic converter, and is designed to require the minimum of servicing.

The transmission, a joint development by Rover and Peugeot engineers, is of Peugeot design and produced by Rover in four- and five-speed forms; it is fitted to the left-hand end of the engine. The complete engine/transmission assembly is mounted transversely across the front of the car and drives the front wheels through unequal-length driveshafts.

The suspension is by the Hydragas system, with the units being linked front-to-rear on each side, and is heavily revised with wishbone-type lower arms. The suspension components at front and rear are rubber-mounted on separate subframes.

Braking is by discs at the front and drums at the rear, with a dual-circuit hydraulic system.

The body is available in three- or five-door Hatchback versions, with a wide range of fittings and interior trim depending on the model's specification.

General dimensions and weights

Dimensions

Overall length	3521 mm
Overall width (including mirrors)	1775 mm
Overall height (at kerb weight and specified ride height)	1377 mm
Wheelbase	2269 mm
Front track	1475 mm
Rear track	1470 mm
Turning circle:	
GTa, GTi 16v	10 710 mm
All other models	9890 mm

Weights

Kerb weight – car unladen, less options, but with full fuel tank, coolant and all fluids, tools and spare wheel:

1.1C – three-door	815 kg
1.1L – three-door	820 kg
1.1S – three-door	825 kg
1.1C – five-door	830 kg
1.1L – five-door, 1.4SL – three-door	835 kg
1.1S – five-door	840 kg
GTa – three-door	845 kg
1.4SL – five-door	850 kg
1.4GS, GTa – five-door	860 kg
GTi 16v	875 kg

Note: *Add 5 kg if a catalytic converter is fitted*

Maximum gross vehicle weight	1290 kg
Maximum roof rack load	50 kg
Maximum towing weight – with braked trailer:	
1.1 models	700 kg
1.4 models	800 kg
Towing hitch downward load	50 kg

Jacking, towing and wheel changing

To change a wheel, have the car parked on firm, level ground, apply the handbrake firmly and select first or reverse gear. Ask any passengers to get out of the car and to stay clear, then remove the spare wheel, tools and jack from the luggage compartment.

Remove the roadwheel trim (where fitted) and slacken the roadwheel nuts through half to one turn each, working in a diagonal sequence (photo). Using chalk or similar, mark the relationship of the roadwheel to the hub.

Place chocks at the front and rear of the roadwheel diagonally opposite the one to be changed, then locate the jack head in the jacking point nearest to the wheel to be changed; if side skirts/sill extensions are

fitted, it may be necessary to use the alternative jacking point provided by the larger hole inboard of the normal jacking point. Ensure that the jack base is located on firm ground and jack up the car (photos).

When the wheel is clear of the ground remove the nuts and lift off the wheel. Check that the threads and the wheel-to-hub mating surfaces are clean and undamaged. The threads may be cleaned with a brass wire brush if rusty. Apply a thin smear of anti-seize compound (Holts Copaslip) to the threads (and also to the roadwheel-to-hub mating surfaces) to prevent the formation of corrosion and clean the inside of the roadwheel to be fitted.

On refitting, align the marks made on removal (if the same

Slacken roadwheel nuts in diagonal sequence

With jack base on firm ground, locate jack head ...

... in normal jacking point 'A' – note alternative point 'B'

Tighten roadwheel nuts to specified torque wrench setting

Rear towing eye – for towing light vehicles only

Jacking, supporting and towing points

1   Central jack location pad
2   Front suspension subframe
    longitudinals
3   Jacking/support point
4   Jacking/support point
5   Jacking/support point
6   Jacking/support point
7   Underbody longitudinal
    sections
8   Rear suspension subframe
    bolts
9   Rear suspension subframe
    reinforced areas
10 Front towing eyes
11 Transporter lashing points
12 Rear towing eye

roadwheel is being fitted) and moderately tighten the nuts. Lower the car and then tighten securely the nuts, working in progressive stages and in a diagonal sequence, to the specified torque wrench setting if possible (photo).

Refit the roadwheel trim (where applicable) and check the tyre pressure. With the spare wheel in position, remove the chocks and stow the jack and tools. If a new roadwheel has been fitted, have it balanced as soon as possible. If the roadwheel nuts were tightened using the car's wheelbrace, check as soon as possible that they are tightened to the specified torque wrench setting.

When jacking up the car to carry out repair or maintenance tasks position the jack as follows; see the accompanying illustration for details:

If the front of the car is to be raised, place the jack head under point 1, or on a jacking beam placed across points 2; axle stands should be placed at points 3 and 4 or points 7.

To raise the rear of the car, place the jack head on a jacking beam placed across points 8; axle stands should be placed at points 5 and 6 or points 9.

To raise the side of the car, place the jack head under point 3 or 4 at the front, point 9 at the rear, with axle stands at points 5, 6 or 7, as appropriate.

Never work under, around or near a raised car unless it is adequately supported in at least two places with axle stands or suitable sturdy blocks.

The car may be towed for breakdown recovery purposes, but only using the towing eyes positioned at the front and rear of the vehicle (photo). These eyes are intended only for towing other vehicles (or being towed by them) and must not be used for lifting the car either directly or indirectly.

Buying spare parts and vehicle identification numbers

Buying spare parts

Spare parts are available from many sources; for example, Rover garages, other garages and accessory shops, and motor factors. Our advice regarding spare part sources is as follows.

Officially appointed Rover garages – This is the best source for parts which are peculiar to your car, and are not generally available (eg complete cylinder heads, internal gearbox components, badges, interior trim etc). It is also the only place at which you should buy parts if the vehicle is still under warranty. To be sure of obtaining the correct parts, it will be necessary to give the storeman your car's vehicle identification number, and if possible, take the old parts along for positive identification. Many parts are available under a factory exchange scheme – any parts returned should always be clean. It obviously makes good sense to go straight to the specialists on your car for this type of part, as they are best equipped to supply you.

Other garages and accessory shops – These are often very good places to buy materials and components needed for the maintenance of your car (eg oil filters, spark plugs, bulbs, drivebelts, oils and greases, touch-up paint, filler paste, etc). They also sell general accessories, usually have convenient opening hours, charge lower prices and can often be found not far from home.

Motor factors – Good factors will stock all the more important components which wear out comparatively quickly (eg exhaust systems, brake pads, seals and hydraulic parts, clutch components, bearing shells, pistons, valves etc). Motor factors will often provide new or reconditioned components on a part exchange basis – this can save a considerable amount of money.

Vehicle identification numbers

Modifications are a continuing and unpublicised process in vehicle manufacture, quite apart from major model changes. Spare parts manuals and lists are compiled upon a numerical basis, the individual vehicle identification numbers being essential to correct identification of the component concerned.

Vehicle identification plate on bonnet lock platform

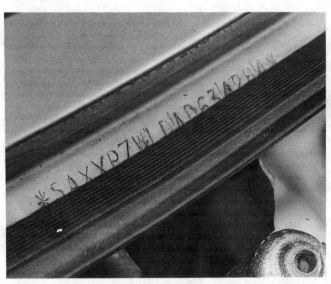

Vehicle identification number in drain channel at rear of bonnet

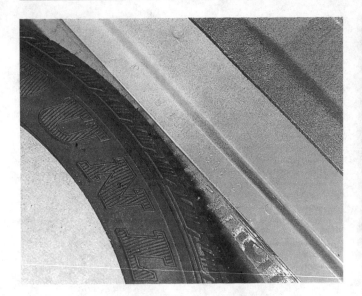

Vehicle body number on right-hand lip of spare wheel well

Engine number on front of cylinder block/crankcase

When ordering spare parts, always give as much information as possible. Quote the car model, year of manufacture, body and engine numbers as appropriate.

The *vehicle identification plate* is located on the bonnet lock platform (photo). It gives the VIN (vehicle identification number), vehicle weight information and paint and trim colour codes.

The *vehicle identification number* is given on the vehicle identification plate and is repeated, stamped into the drain channel at the rear edge of the bonnet, above the braking system master cylinder (photo).

The *body number* is stamped into a plate fixed to the right-hand lip of the spare wheel well, in the luggage compartment (photo).

The *engine number* is stamped into a raised pad on the front left-hand end of the cylinder block/crankcase, next to the transmission (photo).

The *transmission number* is marked on a label stuck on the top of the transmission, near the clutch cable abutment.

The *carburettor number* is stamped into a metal identification tag attached to one of the carburettor suction chamber screws.

Safety first!

However enthusiastic you may be about getting on with the job in hand, do take the time to ensure that your safety is not put at risk. A moment's lack of attention can result in an accident, as can failure to observe certain elementary precautions. There will always be new ways of having accidents, and the following points do not pretend to be a comprehensive list of all dangers; they are intended rather to make you aware of the risks and to encourage a safety-conscious approach to all work you carry out on your vehicle.

Essential DOs and DON'Ts

DON'T rely on a single jack when working underneath the vehicle. Always use reliable additional means of support, such as axle stands, securely placed under a structural part of the vehicle that you know will not give way.

DON'T attempt to loosen or tighten high-torque nuts (eg wheel hub nuts) while the vehicle is on a jack; it may be pulled off.

DON'T start the engine without first ascertaining that the transmission is in neutral (or 'Park' where applicable) and the handbrake applied.

DON'T suddenly remove the filler cap from a hot cooling system – cover it with a cloth and release the pressure gradually first, or you may get scalded by escaping coolant.

DON'T attempt to drain oil, automatic transmission fluid, or coolant until you are sure it has cooled sufficiently to avoid scalding you.

DON'T grasp any part of the engine, exhaust or catalytic converter without first ascertaining that it is sufficiently cool to avoid burning you.

DON'T allow brake fluid or antifreeze to contact vehicle paintwork.

DON'T syphon toxic liquids such as fuel, brake fluid or antifreeze by mouth, or allow them to remain on your skin.

DON'T inhale dust – it may be injurious to health (see *Asbestos* below).

DON'T allow any spilt oil or grease to remain on the floor – wipe it up straight away, before someone slips on it.

DON'T use ill-fitting spanners or other tools which may slip and cause injury.

DON'T attempt to lift a heavy component which may be beyond your capability – get assistance.

DON'T rush to finish a job, or take unverified short cuts.

DON'T allow children or animals in or around an unattended vehicle.

DON'T park vehicles with catalytic converters over combustible materials such as dry grass, oily rags, etc if the engine has recently been run. As catalytic converters reach extremely high temperatures, any such materials in close proximity may ignite.

DON'T run vehicles equipped with catalytic converters without the exhaust system heat shields fitted.

DO wear eye protection when using power tools such as an electric drill, sander, bench grinder etc, and when working under the vehicle.

DO use a barrier cream on your hands prior to undertaking dirty jobs – it will protect your skin from infection as well as making the dirt easier to remove afterwards; but make sure your hands aren't left slippery. Note that long term contact with used engine oil can be a health hazard.

DO keep loose clothing (cuffs, tie etc) and long hair well out of the way of moving mechanical parts.

DO remove rings, wristwatch etc, before working on the vehicle – especially the electrical system.

DO ensure that any lifting tackle or jacking equipment used has a safe working load rating adequate for the job, and is used precisely as recommended by the manufacturer.

DO keep your work area tidy – it is only too easy to fall over articles left lying around.

DO get someone to check periodically that all is well when working alone on the vehicle.

DO carry out work in a logical sequence and check that everything is correctly assembled and tightened afterwards.

DO remember that your vehicle's safety affects that of yourself and others. If in doubt on any point, get specialist advice.

IF, in spite of following these precautions, you are unfortunate enough to injure yourself, seek medical attention as soon as possible.

Asbestos

Certain friction, insulating, sealing, and other products – such as brake linings, brake bands, clutch linings, gaskets, etc – contain asbestos. *Extreme care must be taken to avoid inhalation of dust from such products since it is hazardous to health.* If in doubt, assume that they *do* contain asbestos.

Fire

Remember at all times that petrol is highly flammable. Never smoke, or have any kind of naked flame around, when working on the vehicle. But the risk does not end there – a spark caused by an electrical short-circuit, by two metal surfaces contacting each other, by careless use of tools, or even by static electricity built up in your body under certain conditions, can ignite petrol vapour, which in a confined space is highly explosive.

Whenever possible disconnect the battery earth terminal before working on any part of the fuel or electrical system, and never risk spilling fuel on to a hot engine or exhaust. Catalytic converters run at extremely high temperatures, and consequently can be an additional fire hazard. Observe the precautions outlined elsewhere in this section.

It is recommended that a fire extinguisher of a type suitable for fuel and electrical fires is kept handy in the garage or workplace at all times. Never try to extinguish a fuel or electrical fire with water.

Note: *Any reference to a 'torch' appearing in this manual should always be taken to mean a hand-held battery-operated electric lamp or flashlight. It does NOT mean a welding/gas torch or blowlamp.*

Fumes

Certain fumes are highly toxic and can quickly cause unconsciousness and even death if inhaled to any extent, especially if inhalation takes place through a lighted cigarette or pipe. Petrol vapour comes into this category, as do the vapours from certain solvents such as trichloroethylene. Any draining or pouring of such volatile fluids should be done in a well ventilated area.

When using cleaning fluids and solvents, read the instructions carefully. Never use materials from unmarked containers – they may give off poisonous vapours.

Never run the engine of a motor vehicle in an enclosed space such as a garage. Exhaust fumes contain carbon monoxide which is extremely poisonous; if you need to run the engine, always do so in the open air or at least have the rear of the vehicle outside the workplace. Although vehicles fitted with catalytic converters have greatly reduced toxic exhaust emissions, the above precautions should still be observed.

If you are fortunate enough to have the use of an inspection pit, never drain or pour petrol, and never run the engine, while the vehicle is standing over it; the fumes, being heavier than air, will concentrate in the pit with possibly lethal results.

The battery

Batteries which are sealed for life require special precautions which are normally outlined on a label attached to the battery. Such precautions are primarily related to situations involving battery charging and jump starting from another vehicle.

With a conventional battery, never cause a spark, or allow a naked light, in close proximity to it. It will normally be giving off a certain amount of hydrogen gas, which is highly explosive.

Whenever possible disconnect the battery earth terminal before working on the fuel or electrical systems.

If possible, loosen the filler plugs or cover when charging the battery from an external source. Do not charge at an excessive rate or the battery may burst. Special care should be taken with the use of high charge-rate boost chargers to prevent the battery from overheating.

Take care when topping up and when carrying the battery. The acid electrolyte, even when diluted, is very corrosive and should not be allowed to contact clothing, eyes or skin.

Always wear eye protection when cleaning the battery to prevent the caustic deposits from entering your eyes.

Mains electricity and electrical equipment

When using an electric power tool, inspection light, diagnostic equipment etc, which works from the mains, always ensure that the appliance is correctly connected to its plug and that, where necessary, it is properly earthed. Do not use such appliances in damp conditions and, again, beware of creating a spark or applying excessive heat in the vicinity of fuel or fuel vapour. Also ensure that the appliances meet the relevant national safety standards.

Ignition HT voltage

A severe electric shock can result from touching certain parts of the ignition system, such as the HT leads, when the engine is running or being cranked, particularly if components are damp or the insulation is defective. Where an electronic ignition system is fitted, the HT voltage is much higher and could prove fatal, especially to wearers of cardiac pacemakers.

Jacking and vehicle support

The jack provided with the vehicle is designed primarily for emergency wheel changing, and its use for servicing and overhaul work on the vehicle is best avoided. Instead, a more substantial workshop jack (trolley jack or similar) should be used. Whichever type is employed, it is essential that additional safety support is provided by means of axle stands designed for this purpose. Never use makeshift means such as wooden blocks or piles of house bricks, as these can easily topple or, in the case of bricks, disintegrate under the weight of the vehicle. Further information on the correct positioning of the jack and axle stands is provided in the *Jacking, towing and wheel changing* section.

If removal of the wheels is not required, the use of drive-on ramps is recommended. Caution should be exercised to ensure that they are correctly aligned with the wheels, and that the vehicle is not driven too far along them so that it promptly falls off the other ends or tips the ramps.

General repair procedures

Whenever servicing, repair or overhaul work is carried out on the car or its components, it is necessary to observe the following procedures and instructions. This will assist in carrying out the operation efficiently and to a professional standard of workmanship.

Joint mating faces and gaskets

When separating components at their mating faces, never insert screwdrivers or similar implements into the joint between the faces in order to prise them apart. This can cause severe damage which results in oil leaks, coolant leaks, etc upon reassembly. Separation is usually achieved by tapping along the joint with a soft-faced hammer in order to break the seal. However, note that this method may not be suitable where dowels are used for component location.

Where a gasket is used between the mating faces of two components, ensure that it is renewed on reassembly and fit it dry unless otherwise stated in the repair procedure. Make sure that the mating faces are clean and dry with all traces of old gasket removed. When cleaning a joint face, use a tool which is not likely to score or damage the face, and remove any burrs or nicks with an oilstone or fine file.

Make sure that tapped holes are cleaned with a pipe cleaner and keep them free of jointing compound, if this is being used, unless specifically instructed otherwise.

Ensure that all orifices, channels or pipes are clear and blow through them, preferably using compressed air.

Oil seals

Oil seals can be removed by levering them out with a wide flat-bladed screwdriver or similar implement. Alternatively, a number of self-tapping screws may be screwed into the seal and these used as a purchase for pliers or some similar device in order to pull the seal free.

Whenever an oil seal is removed from its working location, either individually or as part of an assembly, it should be renewed.

The very fine sealing lip of the seal is easily damaged and will not seal if the surface it contacts is not completely clean and free from scratches, nicks or grooves. If the original sealing surface of the component cannot be restored, and the manufacturer has not made provision for slight relocation of the seal relative to the sealing surface, the component should be renewed.

Protect the lips of the seal from any surface which may damage them in the course of fitting. Use tape or a conical sleeve where possible. Lubricate the seal lips with oil before fitting and, on dual-lipped seals, fill the space between the lips with grease.

Unless otherwise stated, oil seals must be fitted with their sealing lips toward the lubricant to be sealed.

Use a tubular drift or block of wood of the appropriate size to install the seal and, if the seal housing is shouldered, drive the seal down to the shoulder. If the seal housing is unshouldered, the seal should be fitted with its face flush with the housing top face (unless otherwise instructed).

Screw threads and fastenings

Seized nuts, bolts and screws are quite a common occurrence where corrosion has set in, and the use of penetrating oil or releasing fluid will often overcome this problem if the offending item is soaked for a while before attempting to release it. The use of an impact driver may also provide a means of releasing such stubborn fastening devices when used in conjunction with the appropriate screwdriver bit or socket. If none of these methods works, it may be necessary to resort to the careful application of heat, or the use of a hacksaw or nut splitter device.

Studs are usually removed by locking two nuts together on the threaded part and then using a spanner on the lower nut to unscrew the stud. Studs or bolts which have broken off below the surface of the component in which they are mounted can sometimes be removed using a proprietary stud extractor. Always ensure that a blind tapped hole is completely free from oil, grease, water or other fluid before installing the bolt or stud. Failure to do this could cause the housing to crack due to the hydraulic action of the bolt or stud as it is screwed in.

When tightening a castellated nut to accept a split pin, tighten the nut to the specified torque, where applicable, and then tighten further to the next split pin hole. Never slacken the nut to align the split pin hole unless stated in the repair procedure.

When checking or retightening a nut or bolt to a specified torque setting, slacken the nut or bolt by a quarter of a turn, and then retighten to the specified setting. However, this should not be attempted where angular tightening has been used.

For some screw fastenings, notably cylinder head bolts or nuts, torque wrench settings are no longer specified for the latter stages of tightening, 'angle-tightening' being called up instead. Typically, a fairly low torque wrench setting will be applied to the bolts/nuts in the correct sequence, followed by one or more stages of tightening through specified angles.

Locknuts, locktabs and washers

Any fastening which will rotate against a component or housing in the course of tightening should always have a washer between it and the relevant component or housing.

Spring or split washers should always be renewed when they are used to lock a critical component such as a big-end bearing retaining bolt or nut. Locktabs which are folded over to retain a nut or bolt should always be renewed.

Self-locking nuts can be reused in non-critical areas, providing resistance can be felt when the locking portion passes over the bolt or stud thread. However, it should be noted that self-locking stiffnuts tend to lose their effectiveness after long periods of use, and in such cases should be renewed as a matter of course.

Split pins must always be replaced with new ones of the correct size for the hole.

When thread-locking compound is found on the threads of a fastener which is to be re-used, it should be cleaned off with a wire brush and solvent, and fresh compound applied on reassembly.

Special tools

Some repair procedures in this manual entail the use of special tools such as a press, two or three-legged pullers, spring compressors etc. Wherever possible, suitable readily available alternatives to the manufacturer's special tools are described, and are shown in use. In some instances, where no alternative is possible, it has been necessary to resort to the use of a manufacturer's tool and this has been done for reasons of safety as well as the efficient completion of the repair operation. Unless you are highly skilled and have a thorough understanding of the procedures described, never attempt to bypass the use of any special tool when the procedure described specifies its use. Not only is there a very great risk of personal injury, but expensive damage could be caused to the components involved.

Environmental considerations

When disposing of used engine oil, brake fluid, antifreeze etc, give due consideration to any detrimental environmental effects. Do not, for instance, pour any of the above liquids down drains into the general sewage system or onto the ground to soak away. Many local council refuse tips provide a facility for waste oil disposal as do some garages. If none of these facilities are available, consult your local Environmental Health Department for further advice.

With the universal tightening-up of legislation regarding the emission of environmentally harmful substances from motor vehicles, most current vehicles have tamperproof devices fitted to the main adjustment points of the fuel system. These devices are primarily designed to prevent unqualified persons from adjusting the fuel/air mixture with the chance of a consequent increase in toxic emissions. If such devices are encountered during servicing or overhaul, they should, wherever possible, be renewed or refitted in accordance with the vehicle manufacturer's requirements or current legislation.

Tools and working facilities

Introduction

A selection of good tools is a fundamental requirement for anyone contemplating the maintenance and repair of a motor vehicle. For the owner who does not possess any, their purchase will prove a considerable expense, offsetting some of the savings made by doing-it-yourself. However, provided that the tools purchased meet the relevant national safety standards and are of good quality, they will last for many years and prove an extremely worthwhile investment.

To help the average owner to decide which tools are needed to carry out the various tasks detailed in this manual, we have compiled three lists of tools under the following headings: *Maintenance and minor repair*, *Repair and overhaul*, and *Special*. Newcomers to practical mechanics should start off with the *Maintenance and minor repair* tool kit and confine themselves to the simpler jobs around the vehicle. Then, as confidence and experience grow, more difficult tasks can be undertaken, with extra tools being purchased as, and when, they are needed. In this way, a *Maintenance and minor repair* tool kit can be built up into a *Repair and overhaul* tool kit over a considerable period of time without any major cash outlays. The experienced do-it-yourselfer will have a tool kit good enough for most repair and overhaul procedures and will add tools from the *Special* category when it is felt that the expense is justified by the amount of use to which these tools will be put.

Maintenance and minor repair tool kit

The tools given in this list should be considered as a minimum requirement if routine maintenance, servicing and minor repair operations are to be undertaken. We recommend the purchase of combination spanners (ring one end, open-ended the other); although more expensive than open-ended ones, they do give the advantages of both types of spanner.

Combination spanners:
   Metric – 8, 9, 10, 11, 12, 13, 14, 15, 17 & 19 mm
Adjustable spanner – 35 mm jaw (approx)
Spark plug spanner (with rubber insert)
Spark plug gap adjustment tool

Set of feeler gauges
Brake-adjusting spanner
Brake bleed nipple spanner
Screwdrivers:
   Flat blade – approx 100 mm long x 6 mm dia
   Cross blade – approx 100 mm long x 6 mm dia
Combination pliers
Hacksaw (junior)
Tyre pump
Tyre pressure gauge
Grease gun
Oil can
Oil filter removal tool
Fine emery cloth
Wire brush (small)
Funnel (medium size)

Repair and overhaul tool kit

These tools are virtually essential for anyone undertaking any major repairs to a motor vehicle, and are additional to those given in the *Maintenance and minor repair* list. Included in this list is a comprehensive set of sockets. Although these are expensive, they will be found invaluable as they are so versatile – particularly if various drives are included in the set. We recommend the ½ in square-drive type, as this can be used with most proprietary torque wrenches. If you cannot afford a socket set, even bought piecemeal, then inexpensive tubular box spanners are a useful alternative.

The tools in this list will occasionally need to be supplemented by tools from the *Special* list.

Sockets (or box spanners) to cover range in previous list
Reversible ratchet drive (for use with sockets) (photo)
Extension piece, 250 mm (for use with sockets)
Universal joint (for use with sockets)
Torque wrench (for use with sockets)
Self-locking grips
Ball pein hammer
Soft-faced mallet (plastic/aluminium or rubber)

Sockets and reversible ratchet drive

Spline bit set

Spline key set

Valve spring compressor

Piston ring compressor

Piston ring removal/installation tool

Cylinder bore hone

Three-legged hub and bearing puller

Micrometer set

Vernier calipers

Dial test indicator and magnetic stand

Stroboscopic timing light

Compression testing gauge

Vacuum pump and gauge

Screwdrivers:
    Flat blade – long & sturdy, short (chubby), and
    narrow (electricians) types
    Cross blade – long & sturdy, and short (chubby) types
Pliers:
    Long-nosed
    Side cutters (electricians)
    Circlip (internal and external)
Cold chisel – 25 mm
Scriber
Scraper
Centre punch
Pin punch
Hacksaw
Brake hose clamp
Brake bleeding kit
Selection of twist drills
Steel rule/straight-edge
Allen keys (inc. splined/Torx type) (photos)
Selection of files
Wire brush
Axle-stands
Jack (strong trolley or hydraulic type)
Light with extension lead

Special tools

The tools in this list are those which are not used regularly, are expensive to buy, or which need to be used in accordance with their manufacturers' instructions. Unless relatively difficult mechanical jobs are undertaken frequently, it will not be economic to buy many of these tools. Where this is the case, you could consider clubbing together with friends (or joining a motorists' club) to make a joint purchase, or borrowing the tools against a deposit from a local garage or tool hire specialist. It is worth noting that many of the larger DIY superstores now carry a large range of special tools for hire at modest rates.

The following list contains only those tools and instruments freely available to the public, and not those special tools produced by the vehicle manufacturer specifically for its dealer network. You will find occasional references to these manufacturers' special tools in the text of this manual. Generally, an alternative method of doing the job without the vehicle manufacturer's special tool is given. However, sometimes there is no alternative to using them. Where this is the case and the relevant tool cannot be bought or borrowed, you will have to entrust the work to a franchised garage.

    Valve spring compressor (photo)
    Valve grinding tool
    Piston ring compressor (photo)
    Piston ring removal/installation tool (photo)
    Cylinder bore hone (photo)
    Balljoint separator
    Coil spring compressors (where applicable)
    Two/three-legged hub and bearing puller (photo)
    Impact screwdriver
    Micrometer and/or vernier calipers (photos)
    Dial test indicator/dial gauge (photo)
    Stroboscopic timing light (photo)
    Dwell angle meter/tachometer
    Universal electrical multi-meter
    Cylinder compression gauge (photo)
    Hand-operated vacuum pump and gauge (photo)
    Clutch plate alignment set (photo)
    Brake shoe steady spring cup removal tool (photo)
    Bush and bearing removal/installation set (photo)
    Stud extractors (photo)
    Tap and die set (photo)
    Lifting tackle
    Trolley jack

Buying tools

For practically all tools, a tool factor is the best source since he will

Clutch plate alignment set

Brake shoe steady spring cup removal tool

Bush and bearing removal/installation set

Stud extractor set

Tap and die set

have a very comprehensive range compared with the average garage or accessory shop. Having said that, accessory shops often offer excellent quality tools at discount prices, so it pays to shop around.

Remember, you don't have to buy the most expensive items on the shelf but it is always advisable to steer clear of the very cheap tools. There are plenty of good tools around at reasonable prices, but always aim to purchase items which meet the relevant national safety standards. If in doubt, ask the proprietor or manager of the shop for advice before making a purchase.

Care and maintenance of tools

Having purchased a reasonable tool kit, it is necessary to keep the tools in a clean and serviceable condition. After use, always wipe off any dirt, grease and metal particles using a clean, dry cloth, before putting the tools away. Never leave them lying around after they have been used. A simple tool rack on the garage or workshop wall for items such as screwdrivers and pliers is a good idea. Store all normal spanners and sockets in a metal box. Any measuring instruments, gauges, meters, etc, must be carefully stored where they cannot be damaged or become rusty.

Take a little care when tools are used. Hammer heads inevitably become marked and screwdrivers lose the keen edge on their blades from time to time. A little timely attention with emery cloth or a file will soon restore items like this to a good serviceable finish.

Working facilities

Not to be forgotten when discussing tools is the workshop itself. If anything more than routine maintenance is to be carried out, some form of suitable working area becomes essential.

It is appreciated that many an owner mechanic is forced by circumstances to remove an engine or similar item without the benefit of a garage or workshop. Having done this, any repairs should always be done under the cover of a roof.

Wherever possible, any dismantling should be done on a clean, flat workbench or table at a suitable working height.

Any workbench needs a vice; one with a jaw opening of 100 mm (4 in) is suitable for most jobs. As mentioned previously, some clean dry storage space is also required for tools, as well as for any lubricants, cleaning fluids, touch-up paints and so on, which become necessary.

Another item which may be required, and which has a much more general usage, is an electric drill with a chuck capacity of at least 8 mm ($\frac{5}{16}$ in). This, together with a good range of twist drills, is virtually essential for fitting accessories.

Last, but not least, always keep a supply of old newspapers and clean, lint-free rags available, and try to keep any working area as clean as possible.

Spanner jaw gap and bolt size comparison table

Jaw gap – in (mm)	Spanner size	Bolt size
0.197 (5.00)	5 mm	M 2.5
0.216 (5.50)	5.5 mm	M 3
0.218 (5.53)	$\frac{7}{32}$ in AF	
0.236 (6.00)	6 mm	M 3.5
0.250 (6.35)	$\frac{1}{4}$ in AF	
0.275 (7.00)	7 mm	M 4
0.281 (7.14)	$\frac{9}{32}$ in AF	
0.312 (7.92)	$\frac{5}{16}$ in AF	
0.315 (8.00)	8 mm	M 5
0.343 (8.71)	$\frac{11}{32}$ in AF	
0.375 (9.52)	$\frac{3}{8}$ in AF	
0.394 (10.00)	10 mm	M 6
0.406 (10.32)	$\frac{13}{32}$ in AF	
0.433 (11.00)	11 mm	M 7
0.437 (11.09)	$\frac{7}{16}$ in AF	$\frac{1}{4}$ in SAE
0.468 (11.88)	$\frac{15}{32}$ in AF	
0.500 (12.70)	$\frac{1}{2}$ in AF	$\frac{5}{16}$ in SAE
0.512 (13.00)	13 mm	M8
0.562 (14.27)	$\frac{9}{16}$ in AF	$\frac{3}{8}$ in SAE
0.593 (15.06)	$\frac{19}{32}$ in AF	
0.625 (15.87)	$\frac{5}{8}$ in AF	$\frac{7}{16}$ in SAE
0.669 (17.00)	17 mm	M 10
0.687 (17.44)	$\frac{11}{16}$ in AF	
0.709 (19.00)	19 mm	M 12
0.750 (19.05)	$\frac{3}{4}$ in AF	$\frac{1}{2}$ in SAE
0.781 (19.83)	$\frac{25}{32}$ in AF	
0.812 (20.62)	$\frac{13}{16}$ in AF	
0.866 (22.00)	22 mm	M 14
0.875 (22.25)	$\frac{7}{8}$ in AF	$\frac{9}{16}$ in SAE
0.937 (23.79)	$\frac{15}{16}$ in AF	$\frac{5}{8}$ in SAE
0.945 (24.00)	24 mm	M 16
0.968 (24.58)	$\frac{31}{32}$ in AF	
1.000 (25.40)	1 in AF	$\frac{11}{16}$ in SAE
1.062 (26.97)	1 $\frac{1}{16}$ in AF	$\frac{3}{4}$ in SAE
1.063 (27.00)	27 mm	M 18
1.125 (28.57)	1 $\frac{1}{8}$ in AF	
1.182 (30.00)	30 mm	M 20
1.187 (30.14)	1 $\frac{3}{16}$ in AF	
1.250 (31.75)	1 $\frac{1}{4}$ in AF	$\frac{7}{8}$ in SAE
1.260 (32.00)	32 mm	M 22
1.312 (33.32)	1 $\frac{5}{16}$ in AF	
1.375 (34.92)	1 $\frac{3}{8}$ in AF	
1.418 (36.00)	36 mm	M 24
1.437 (36.49)	1 $\frac{7}{16}$ in AF	1 in SAE
1.500 (38.10)	1 $\frac{1}{2}$ in AF	
1.615 (41.00)	41 mm	M 27

Booster battery (jump) starting

When jump starting a car using a booster battery, observe the following precautions:

(a) *Before connecting the booster battery, make sure that the ignition is switched off.*
(b) *Ensure that all electrical equipment (lights, heater, wipers etc) is switched off.*
(c) *Make sure that the booster battery is the same voltage as the discharged one in the vehicle.*
(d) *If the battery is being jump started from the battery in another vehicle, the two vehicles MUST NOT TOUCH each other.*
(e) *Make sure that the transmission is in Neutral (manual gearbox) or Park (automatic transmission).*

Connect one jump lead between the positive (+) terminals of the two batteries. Connect the other jump lead first to the negative (-) terminal of the booster battery, and then to a good earthing point on the vehicle to be started, such as a bolt or bracket on the engine block, at least 45 cm (18 in) from the battery if possible. Make sure that the jump leads will not come into contact with the fan, drivebelts or other moving parts of the engine.

Start the engine using the booster battery, then with the engine running at idle speed, disconnect the jump leads in the reverse order of connection.

Jump start lead connections for negative-earth vehicles – connect leads in order shown

Conversion factors

Length (distance)
Inches (in)	X	25.4	= Millimetres (mm)	X	0.0394	= Inches (in)
Feet (ft)	X	0.305	= Metres (m)	X	3.281	= Feet (ft)
Miles	X	1.609	= Kilometres (km)	X	0.621	= Miles

Volume (capacity)
Cubic inches (cu in; in^3)	X	16.387	= Cubic centimetres (cc; cm^3)	X	0.061	= Cubic inches (cu in; in^3)
Imperial pints (Imp pt)	X	0.568	= Litres (l)	X	1.76	= Imperial pints (Imp pt)
Imperial quarts (Imp qt)	X	1.137	= Litres (l)	X	0.88	= Imperial quarts (Imp qt)
Imperial quarts (Imp qt)	X	1.201	= US quarts (US qt)	X	0.833	= Imperial quarts (Imp qt)
US quarts (US qt)	X	0.946	= Litres (l)	X	1.057	= US quarts (US qt)
Imperial gallons (Imp gal)	X	4.546	= Litres (l)	X	0.22	= Imperial gallons (Imp gal)
Imperial gallons (Imp gal)	X	1.201	= US gallons (US gal)	X	0.833	= Imperial gallons (Imp gal)
US gallons (US gal)	X	3.785	= Litres (l)	X	0.264	= US gallons (US gal)

Mass (weight)
Ounces (oz)	X	28.35	= Grams (g)	X	0.035	= Ounces (oz)
Pounds (lb)	X	0.454	= Kilograms (kg)	X	2.205	= Pounds (lb)

Force
Ounces-force (ozf; oz)	X	0.278	= Newtons (N)	X	3.6	= Ounces-force (ozf; oz)
Pounds-force (lbf; lb)	X	4.448	= Newtons (N)	X	0.225	= Pounds-force (lbf; lb)
Newtons (N)	X	0.1	= Kilograms-force (kgf; kg)	X	9.81	= Newtons (N)

Pressure
Pounds-force per square inch (psi; lbf/in^2; lb/in^2)	X	0.070	= Kilograms-force per square centimetre (kgf/cm^2; kg/cm^2)	X	14.223	= Pounds-force per square inch (psi; lbf/in^2; lb/in^2)
Pounds-force per square inch (psi; lbf/in^2; lb/in^2)	X	0.068	= Atmospheres (atm)	X	14.696	= Pounds-force per square inch (psi; lbf/in^2; lb/in^2)
Pounds-force per square inch (psi; lbf/in^2; lb/in^2)	X	0.069	= Bars	X	14.5	= Pounds-force per square inch (psi; lbf/in^2; lb/in^2)
Pounds-force per square inch (psi; lbf/in^2; lb/in^2)	X	6.895	= Kilopascals (kPa)	X	0.145	= Pounds-force per square inch (psi; lbf/in^2; lb/in^2)
Kilopascals (kPa)	X	0.01	= Kilograms-force per square centimetre (kgf/cm^2; kg/cm^2)	X	98.1	= Kilopascals (kPa)
Millibar (mbar)	X	100	= Pascals (Pa)	X	0.01	= Millibar (mbar)
Millibar (mbar)	X	0.0145	= Pounds-force per square inch (psi; lbf/in^2; lb/in^2)	X	68.947	= Millibar (mbar)
Millibar (mbar)	X	0.75	= Millimetres of mercury (mmHg)	X	1.333	= Millibar (mbar)
Millibar (mbar)	X	0.401	= Inches of water (inH$_2$O)	X	2.491	= Millibar (mbar)
Millimetres of mercury (mmHg)	X	0.535	= Inches of water (inH$_2$O)	X	1.868	= Millimetres of mercury (mmHg)
Inches of water (inH$_2$O)	X	0.036	= Pounds-force per square inch (psi; lbf/in^2; lb/in^2)	X	27.68	= Inches of water (inH$_2$O)

Torque (moment of force)
Pounds-force inches (lbf in; lb in)	X	1.152	= Kilograms-force centimetre (kgf cm; kg cm)	X	0.868	= Pounds-force inches (lbf in; lb in)
Pounds-force inches (lbf in; lb in)	X	0.113	= Newton metres (Nm)	X	8.85	= Pounds-force inches (lbf in; lb in)
Pounds-force inches (lbf in; lb in)	X	0.083	= Pounds-force feet (lbf ft; lb ft)	X	12	= Pounds-force inches (lbf in; lb in)
Pounds-force feet (lbf ft; lb ft)	X	0.138	= Kilograms-force metres (kgf m; kg m)	X	7.233	= Pounds-force feet (lbf ft; lb ft)
Pounds-force feet (lbf ft; lb ft)	X	1.356	= Newton metres (Nm)	X	0.738	= Pounds-force feet (lbf ft; lb ft)
Newton metres (Nm)	X	0.102	= Kilograms-force metres (kgf m; kg m)	X	9.804	= Newton metres (Nm)

Power
Horsepower (hp)	X	745.7	= Watts (W)	X	0.0013	= Horsepower (hp)

Velocity (speed)
Miles per hour (miles/hr; mph)	X	1.609	= Kilometres per hour (km/hr; kph)	X	0.621	= Miles per hour (miles/hr; mph)

Fuel consumption
Miles per gallon, Imperial (mpg)	X	0.354	= Kilometres per litre (km/l)	X	2.825	= Miles per gallon, Imperial (mpg)
Miles per gallon, US (mpg)	X	0.425	= Kilometres per litre (km/l)	X	2.352	= Miles per gallon, US (mpg)

Temperature

Degrees Fahrenheit = (°C x 1.8) + 32

Degrees Celsius (Degrees Centigrade; °C) = (°F − 32) x 0.56

It is common practice to convert from miles per gallon (mpg) to litres/100 kilometres (l/100km), where mpg (Imperial) x l/100 km = 282 and mpg (US) x l/100 km = 235

Fault diagnosis

Contents

Introduction

The vehicle owner who does his or her own maintenance according to the recommended service schedules should not have to use this section of the manual very often. Modern component reliability is such that, provided those items subject to wear or deterioration are inspected or renewed at the specified intervals, sudden failure is comparatively rare. Faults do not usually just happen as a result of sudden failure, but develop over a period of time. Major mechanical failures in particular are usually preceded by characteristic symptoms over hundreds or even thousands of miles. Those components which do occasionally fail without warning are often small and easily carried in the vehicle.

With any fault finding, the first step is to decide where to begin investigations. Sometimes this is obvious, but on other occasions a little detective work will be necessary. The owner who makes half a dozen

haphazard adjustments or replacements may be successful in curing a fault (or its symptoms), but will be none the wiser if the fault recurs and ultimately may have spent more time and money than was necessary. A calm and logical approach will be found to be more satisfactory in the long run. Always take into account any warning signs or abnormalities that may have been noticed in the period preceding the fault – power loss, high or low gauge readings, unusual smells, etc – and remember that failure of components such as fuses or spark plugs may only be pointers to some underlying fault.

The pages which follow provide an easy reference guide to the more common problems which may occur during the operation of the vehicle. These problems and their possible causes are grouped under headings denoting various components or systems, such as Engine, Cooling system, etc. The Chapter and/or Section which deals with the problem is also shown in brackets. Whatever the fault, certain basic principles apply. These are as follows:

Verify the fault. This is simply a matter of being sure that you know what the symptoms are before starting work. This is particularly important if you are investigating a fault for someone else who may not have described it very accurately.

Don't overlook the obvious. For example, if the vehicle won't start, is there petrol in the tank? (Don't take anyone else's word on this particular point, and don't trust the fuel gauge either!) If an electrical fault is indicated, look for loose or broken wires before digging out the test gear.

Cure the disease, not the symptom. Substituting a flat battery with a fully charged one will get you off the hard shoulder, but if the underlying cause is not attended to, the new battery will go the same way. Similarly, changing oil-fouled spark plugs for a new set will get you moving again, but remember that the reason for the fouling (if it wasn't simply an incorrect grade of plug) will have to be established and corrected.

Don't take anything for granted. Particularly, don't forget that a 'new' component may itself be defective (especially if it's been rattling around in the boot for months), and don't leave components out of a fault diagnosis sequence just because they are new or recently fitted. When you do finally diagnose a difficult fault, you'll probably realise that all the evidence was there from the start.

1   Engine

Engine fails to rotate when attempting to start
- Battery terminal connections loose or corroded (Chapter 12).
- Battery discharged or faulty (Chapter 12).
- Broken, loose or disconnected wiring in the starting circuit (Chapter 12).
- Defective starter solenoid or switch (Chapter 12).
- Defective starter motor (Chapter 12).
- Starter pinion or flywheel ring gear teeth loose or broken (Chapter 12).
- Engine earth strap broken or disconnected (Chapter 12).

Engine rotates but will not start
- Fuel tank empty.
- Battery discharged (engine rotates slowly) (Chapter 12).
- Battery terminal connections loose or corroded (Chapter 12).
- Ignition components damp or damaged (Chapters 1 and 5).
- Broken, loose or disconnected wiring in the ignition circuit (Chapters 1 and 5).
- Worn, faulty or incorrectly gapped spark plugs (Chapter 1).
- Choke mechanism sticking, incorrectly adjusted, or faulty (Chapter 4).
- Major mechanical failure (eg camshaft drive) (Chapter 2).

Engine difficult to start when cold
- Battery discharged (Chapter 12).
- Battery terminal connections loose or corroded (Chapter 12).
- Worn, faulty or incorrectly gapped spark plugs (Chapter 1).
- Choke mechanism sticking, incorrectly adjusted, or faulty (Chapter 4).
- Other ignition system fault (Chapters 1 and 5).
- Low cylinder compressions (Chapter 2).

Engine difficult to start when hot
- Air filter element dirty or clogged (Chapter 1).
- Choke mechanism sticking, incorrectly adjusted, or faulty (Chapter 4).
- Carburettor float chamber flooding (Chapter 4).
- Low cylinder compressions (Chapter 2).

Starter motor noisy or excessively rough in engagement
- Starter pinion or flywheel ring gear teeth loose or broken (Chapter 12).
- Starter motor mounting bolts loose or missing (Chapter 12).
- Starter motor internal components worn or damaged (Chapter 12).

Engine starts but stops immediately
- Insufficient fuel reaching carburettor (Chapter 4).

- Loose or faulty electrical connections in the ignition circuit (Chapters 1 and 5).
- Vacuum leak at the carburettor or inlet manifold (Chapter 4).
- Blocked carburettor jet(s) or internal passages (Chapter 4).

Engine idles erratically
- Incorrectly adjusted idle speed and/or mixture settings (Chapter 1).
- Air filter element clogged (Chapter 1).
- Vacuum leak at the carburettor, inlet manifold or associated hoses (Chapter 4).
- Worn, faulty or incorrectly gapped spark plugs (Chapter 1).
- Uneven or low cylinder compressions (Chapter 2).
- Camshaft lobes worn (Chapter 2).
- Timing belt incorrectly tensioned (Chapter 2).

Engine misfires at idle speed
- Worn, faulty or incorrectly gapped spark plugs (Chapter 1).
- Faulty spark plug HT leads (Chapter 1).
- Incorrectly adjusted idle mixture settings (Chapter 1).
- Incorrect ignition timing (Chapter 1).
- Vacuum leak at the carburettor, inlet manifold or associated hoses (Chapter 4).
- Distributor cap cracked or tracking internally (Chapter 1).
- Uneven or low cylinder compressions (Chapter 2).
- Disconnected, leaking or perished crankcase ventilation hoses (Chapters 1 and 4).

Engine misfires throughout the driving speed range
- Blocked carburettor jet(s) or internal passages (Chapter 4).
- Carburettor worn or incorrectly adjusted (Chapters 1 and 4).
- Fuel filter choked (Chapter 1).
- Fuel pump faulty or delivery pressure low (Chapter 4).
- Fuel tank vent blocked or fuel pipes restricted (Chapter 4).
- Vacuum leak at the carburettor, inlet manifold or associated hoses (Chapter 4).
- Worn, faulty or incorrectly gapped spark plugs (Chapter 1).
- Faulty spark plug HT leads (Chapter 1).
- Distributor cap cracked or tracking internally (Chapter 1).
- Faulty ignition coil (Chapter 5).
- Uneven or low cylinder compressions (Chapter 2).

Engine hesitates on acceleration
- Worn, faulty or incorrectly gapped spark plugs (Chapter 1).
- Carburettor accelerator pump faulty (Chapter 4).
- Blocked carburettor jets or internal passages (Chapter 4).
- Vacuum leak at the carburettor, inlet manifold or associated hoses (Chapter 4).
- Carburettor worn or incorrectly adjusted (Chapters 1 and 4).

Engine stalls
- Incorrectly adjusted idle speed and/or mixture settings (Chapter 1).
- Blocked carburettor jet(s) or internal passages (Chapter 4).
- Vacuum leak at the carburettor, inlet manifold or associated hoses (Chapter 4).
- Fuel filter choked (Chapter 1).
- Fuel pump faulty or delivery pressure low (Chapter 4).
- Fuel tank vent blocked or fuel pipes restricted (Chapter 4).

Engine lacks power
- Incorrect ignition timing (Chapter 1).
- Carburettor worn or incorrectly adjusted (Chapter 1).
- Timing belt incorrectly fitted or tensioned (Chapter 2).
- Fuel filter choked (Chapter 1).
- Fuel pump faulty or delivery pressure low (Chapter 4).
- Uneven or low cylinder compressions (Chapter 2).
- Worn, faulty or incorrectly gapped spark plugs (Chapter 1).
- Vacuum leak at the carburettor, inlet manifold or associated hoses (Chapter 4).
- Brakes binding (Chapters 1 and 9).
- Clutch slipping (Chapter 6).

Engine backfires
- Ignition timing incorrect (Chapter 1).
- Timing belt incorrectly fitted or tensioned (Chapter 2).

- Carburettor worn or incorrectly adjusted (Chapter 1).
- Vacuum leak at the carburettor, inlet manifold or associated hoses (Chapter 4).

Oil pressure warning light illuminated with engine running
- Low oil level or incorrect grade (Chapter 1).
- Faulty oil pressure switch (Chapter 12).
- Worn engine bearings and/or oil pump (Chapter 2).
- High engine operating temperature (Chapter 3).
- Oil pressure relief valve defective (Chapter 2).
- Oil pick-up strainer clogged (Chapter 2).

Engine runs-on after switching off
- Idle speed excessively high (Chapter 1).
- Faulty anti-run-on solenoid (Chapter 4).
- Excessive carbon build-up in engine (Chapter 2).
- High engine operating temperature (Chapter 3).

Engine noises
Pre-ignition (pinking) or knocking during acceleration or under load
- Ignition timing incorrect (Chapter 1).
- Incorrect grade of fuel (Chapter 4).
- Vacuum leak at the carburettor, inlet manifold or associated hoses (Chapter 4).
- Excessive carbon build-up in engine (Chapter 2).
- Worn or damaged distributor or other ignition system component (Chapter 5).
- Carburettor worn or incorrectly adjusted (Chapter 1).

Whistling or wheezing noises
- Leaking inlet manifold or carburettor gasket (Chapter 4).
- Leaking exhaust manifold gasket or pipe to manifold joint (Chapter 1).
- Leaking vacuum hose (Chapters 4, 5 and 9).
- Blowing cylinder head gasket (Chapter 2).

Tapping or rattling noises
- Faulty hydraulic tappets (Chapter 1 or 2).
- Worn valve gear or camshaft (Chapter 2).
- Worn timing belt or tensioner (Chapter 2).
- Ancillary component fault (water pump, alternator etc) (Chapters 3 and 12).

Knocking or thumping noises
- Worn big-end bearings (regular heavy knocking, perhaps less under load) (Chapter 2).
- Worn main bearings (rumbling and knocking, perhaps worsening under load) (Chapter 2).
- Piston slap (most noticeable when cold) (Chapter 2).
- Ancillary component fault (alternator, water pump etc) (Chapters 3 and 12).

2 Cooling system

Overheating
- Insufficient coolant in system (Chapter 3).
- Thermostat faulty (Chapter 3).
- Radiator core blocked or grille restricted (Chapter 3).
- Electric cooling fan or thermostatic switch faulty (Chapter 3).
- Pressure cap faulty (Chapter 3).
- Timing belt worn, or incorrectly tensioned (Chapter 2).
- Ignition timing incorrect (Chapter 1).
- Inaccurate temperature gauge sender unit (Chapter 3).
- Air lock in cooling system (Chapter 1).

Overcooling
- Thermostat faulty (Chapter 3).
- Inaccurate temperature gauge sender unit (Chapter 3).

External coolant leakage
- Deteriorated or damaged hoses or hose clips (Chapter 1).

- Radiator core or heater matrix leaking (Chapter 3).
- Pressure cap faulty (Chapter 3).
- Water pump seal leaking (Chapter 3).
- Boiling due to overheating (Chapter 3).
- Core plug leaking (Chapter 2).

Internal coolant leakage
- Leaking cylinder head gasket (Chapter 2).
- Cracked cylinder head or cylinder bore (Chapter 2).

Corrosion
- Infrequent draining and flushing (Chapter 1).
- Incorrect antifreeze mixture or inappropriate type (Chapter 1).

3 Fuel and exhaust system

Excessive fuel consumption
- Air filter element dirty or clogged (Chapter 1).
- Carburettor worn or incorrectly adjusted (Chapter 4).
- Choke cable incorrectly adjusted or choke sticking (Chapter 4).
- Ignition timing incorrect (Chapter 1).
- Tyres underinflated (Chapter 1).

Fuel leakage and/or fuel odour
- Damaged or corroded fuel tank, pipes or connections (Chapter 1).
- Carburettor float chamber flooding (Chapter 4).

Excessive noise or fumes from exhaust system
- Leaking exhaust system or manifold joints (Chapter 1).
- Leaking, corroded or damaged silencers or pipe (Chapter 1).
- Broken mountings causing body or suspension contact (Chapter 1).

4 Clutch

Pedal travels to floor – no pressure or very little resistance
- Broken clutch cable (Chapter 6).
- Faulty clutch pedal self-adjust mechanism (Chapter 6).
- Broken clutch release bearing or fork (Chapter 6).
- Broken diaphragm spring in clutch pressure plate (Chapter 6).

Clutch fails to disengage (unable to select gears)
- Faulty clutch pedal self-adjust mechanism (Chapter 6).
- Clutch friction plate sticking on transmission input shaft splines (Chapter 6).
- Clutch friction plate sticking to flywheel or pressure plate (Chapter 6).
- Faulty pressure plate assembly (Chapter 6).
- Transmission input shaft seized in crankshaft spigot bearing (Chapter 2).
- Clutch release mechanism worn or incorrectly assembled (Chapter 6).

Clutch slips (engine speed increases with no increase in vehicle speed)
- Faulty clutch pedal self-adjust mechanism (Chapter 6).
- Clutch friction plate friction material excessively worn (Chapter 6).
- Clutch friction plate friction material contaminated with oil or grease (Chapter 6).
- Faulty pressure plate or weak diaphragm spring (Chapter 6).

Judder as clutch is engaged
- Clutch friction plate friction material contaminated with oil or grease (Chapter 6).
- Clutch friction plate friction material excessively worn (Chapter 6).
- Clutch cable sticking or frayed (Chapter 6).
- Faulty or distorted pressure plate or diaphragm spring (Chapter 6).

- Worn or loose engine or gearbox mountings (Chapter 2).
- Clutch friction plate hub or transmission input shaft splines worn (Chapter 6).

Noise when depressing or releasing clutch pedal
- Worn clutch release bearing (Chapter 6).
- Worn or dry clutch pedal bushes (Chapter 6).
- Faulty pressure plate assembly (Chapter 6).
- Pressure plate diaphragm spring broken (Chapter 6).
- Broken clutch friction plate cushioning springs (Chapter 6).

5 Transmission

Noisy in neutral with engine running
- Input shaft bearings worn (noise apparent with clutch pedal released but not when depressed) (Chapter 7).*
- Clutch release bearing worn (noise apparent with clutch pedal depressed, possibly less when released) (Chapter 6).

Noisy in one particular gear
- Worn, damaged or chipped gear teeth (Chapter 7).*

Difficulty engaging gears
- Clutch fault (Chapter 6).
- Worn or damaged gear linkage (Chapter 7).
- Incorrectly adjusted gear linkage (Chapter 7).
- Worn synchroniser units (Chapter 7).*

Jumps out of gear
- Worn or damaged gear linkage (Chapter 7).
- Incorrectly adjusted gear linkage (Chapter 7).
- Worn synchroniser units (Chapter 7).*
- Worn selector forks (Chapter 7).*

Vibration
- Lack of oil (Chapter 1).
- Worn bearings (Chapter 7).*

Lubricant leaks
- Leaking driveshaft oil seal (Chapter 7).
- Leaking housing joint (Chapter 7).*
- Leaking input shaft oil seal (Chapter 7).*

Although the corrective action necessary to remedy the symptoms described is beyond the scope of the home mechanic, the above information should be helpful in isolating the cause of the condition so that the owner can communicate clearly with a professional mechanic

6 Driveshafts

Clicking or knocking noise on turns (at slow speed on full lock)
- Lack of constant velocity joint lubricant (Chapter 8).
- Worn outer constant velocity joint (Chapter 8).

Vibration when accelerating or decelerating
- Worn inner constant velocity joint (Chapter 8).
- Bent or distorted driveshaft (Chapter 8).

7 Braking system

Note: *Before assuming that a brake problem exists, make sure that the tyres are in good condition and correctly inflated, the front wheel alignment is correct and the vehicle is not loaded with weight in an unequal manner*

Vehicle pulls to one side under braking
- Worn, defective, damaged or contaminated front or rear brake pads/shoes on one side (Chapter 1).

- Seized or partially seized front or rear brake caliper/wheel cylinder piston (Chapter 9).
- A mixture of brake pad/shoe lining materials fitted between sides (Chapter 1).
- Brake caliper mounting bolts loose (Chapter 9).
- Rear brake backplate mounting bolts loose (Chapter 9).
- Worn or damaged steering or suspension components (Chapter 10).

Noise (grinding or high-pitched squeal) when brakes applied
- Brake pad or shoe friction lining material worn down to metal backing (Chapter 1).
- Excessive corrosion of brake disc or drum, especially if the vehicle has been standing for some time (Chapter 1).
- Foreign object (stone chipping etc) trapped between brake disc and splash shield (Chapter 1).

Excessive brake pedal travel
- Faulty master cylinder (Chapter 9).
- Air in hydraulic system (Chapter 9).

Brake pedal feels spongy when depressed
- Air in hydraulic system (Chapter 9).
- Deteriorated flexible rubber brake hoses (Chapter 1 or 9).
- Master cylinder mounting nuts loose (Chapter 9).
- Faulty master cylinder (Chapter 9).

Excessive brake pedal effort required to stop vehicle
- Faulty vacuum servo unit (Chapter 9).
- Disconnected, damaged or insecure brake servo vacuum hose (Chapter 9).
- Primary or secondary hydraulic circuit failure (Chapter 9).
- Seized brake caliper or wheel cylinder piston(s) (Chapter 9).
- Brake pads or brake shoes incorrectly fitted (Chapter 1).
- Incorrect grade of brake pads or brake shoes fitted (Chapter 1).
- Brake pads or brake shoe linings contaminated (Chapter 1).

Judder felt through brake pedal or steering wheel when braking
- Excessive run-out or distortion of front discs or rear drums (Chapter 9).
- Brake pad or brake shoe linings worn (Chapter 1).
- Brake caliper or rear brake backplate mounting bolts loose (Chapter 9).
- Wear in suspension, steering components or mountings (Chapter 9).

Brakes binding
- Seized brake caliper or wheel cylinder piston(s) (Chapter 9).
- Incorrectly adjusted handbrake mechanism or linkage (Chapter 1).
- Faulty master cylinder (Chapter 9).

Rear wheels locking under normal braking
- Rear brake shoe linings contaminated (Chapter 1).
- Faulty brake pressure regulator (Chapter 9).

8 Suspension and steering systems

Note: *Before diagnosing suspension or steering faults, be sure that the trouble is not due to incorrect tyre pressures, mixtures of tyre types or binding brakes*

Vehicle pulls to one side
- Defective tyre (Chapter 1).
- Excessive wear in suspension or steering components (Chapter 10).
- Incorrect front wheel alignment (Chapter 10).
- Accident damage to steering or suspension components (Chapter 10).

Wheel wobble and vibration
- Front roadwheels out of balance (vibration felt mainly through the steering wheel) (Chapter 10).

- Rear roadwheels out of balance (vibration felt throughout the vehicle) (Chapter 10).
- Roadwheels damaged or distorted (Chapter 10).
- Faulty or damaged tyre (Chapter 10).
- Worn steering or suspension joints, bushes or components (Chapter 10).
- Wheel nuts loose (Chapter 1).

Excessive pitching and/or rolling around corners or during braking
- Defective Hydragas units and/or dampers (where fitted) (Chapter 10).
- Broken or weak suspension component (Chapter 10).
- Worn or damaged anti-roll bar or mountings (Chapter 10).

Wandering or general instability
- Incorrect front wheel alignment (Chapter 10).
- Worn steering or suspension joints, bushes or components (Chapter 10).
- Roadwheels out of balance (Chapter 10).
- Faulty or damaged tyre (Chapter 10).
- Wheel nuts loose (Chapter 1).
- Defective Hydragas units and/or dampers (where fitted) (Chapter 10).

Excessively stiff steering
- Lack of steering gear lubricant (Chapter 10).
- Seized track rod balljoint or suspension balljoint (Chapter 10).
- Incorrect front wheel alignment (Chapter 10).
- Steering rack or column bent or damaged (Chapter 10).

Excessive play in steering
- Worn steering column universal joint(s) or intermediate coupling (Chapter 10).
- Worn steering track rod balljoints (Chapter 10).
- Worn steering gear (Chapter 10).
- Worn steering or suspension joints, bushes or components (Chapter 10).

Tyre wear excessive

Tyres worn on inside or outside edges
- Tyres underinflated (wear on both edges) (Chapter 1).
- Incorrect camber or castor angles (wear on one edge only) (Chapter 10).
- Worn steering or suspension joints, bushes or components (Chapter 10).
- Excessively hard cornering.
- Accident damage.

Tyre treads exhibit feathered edges
- Incorrect toe setting (Chapter 10).

Tyres worn in centre of tread
- Tyres overinflated (Chapter 1).

Tyres worn on inside and outside edges
- Tyres underinflated (Chapter 1).

Tyres worn unevenly
- Tyres out of balance (Chapter 1).
- Excessive wheel or tyre run-out (Chapter 1).
- Defective Hydragas units and/or worn dampers (where fitted) (Chapter 10).
- Faulty tyre (Chapter 1).

9   Electrical system

Note: *For problems associated with the starting system, refer to the faults listed under 'Engine' earlier in this Section*

Battery will not hold a charge for more than a few days
- Battery defective internally (Chapter 12).
- Battery electrolyte level low (Chapter 1).

- Battery terminal connections loose or corroded (Chapter 12).
- Alternator drivebelt worn or incorrectly adjusted (Chapter 1).
- Alternator not charging at correct output (Chapter 12).
- Alternator or voltage regulator faulty (Chapter 12).
- Short-circuit causing continual battery drain (Chapter 12).

Ignition warning light remains illuminated with engine running
- Alternator drivebelt broken, worn, or incorrectly adjusted (Chapter 1).
- Alternator brushes worn, sticking, or dirty (Chapter 12).
- Alternator brush springs weak or broken (Chapter 12).
- Internal fault in alternator or voltage regulator (Chapter 12).
- Broken, disconnected, or loose wiring in charging circuit (Chapter 12).

Ignition warning light fails to come on
- Warning light bulb blown (Chapter 12).
- Broken, disconnected, or loose wiring in warning light circuit (Chapter 12) .
- Alternator faulty (Chapter 12).

Lights inoperative
- Bulb blown (Chapter 12).
- Corrosion of bulb or bulbholder contacts (Chapter 12).
- Blown fuse (Chapter 12).
- Faulty relay (Chapter 12).
- Broken, loose, or disconnected wiring (Chapter 12).
- Faulty switch (Chapter 12).

Instrument readings inaccurate or erratic

Instrument readings increase with engine speed
- Faulty voltage regulator (Chapter 12).

Fuel or temperature gauge give no reading
- Faulty gauge sender unit (Chapters 3 or 4).
- Wiring open circuit (Chapter 12).
- Faulty gauge (Chapter 12).

Fuel or temperature gauges give continuous maximum reading
- Faulty gauge sender unit (Chapters 3 or 4).
- Wiring short-circuit (Chapter 12).
- Faulty gauge (Chapter 12).

Horn inoperative or unsatisfactory in operation

Horn operates all the time
- Horn push either earthed or stuck down (Chapter 12).
- Horn cable to horn push earthed (Chapter 12).

Horn fails to operate
- Blown fuse (Chapter 12).
- Cable or cable connections loose, broken or disconnected (Chapter 12).
- Faulty horn (Chapter 12).

Horn emits intermittent or unsatisfactory sound
- Cable connections loose (Chapter 12).
- Horn mountings loose (Chapter 12).
- Faulty horn (Chapter 12).

Windscreen/tailgate wipers inoperative or unsatisfactory in operation

Wipers fail to operate or operate very slowly
- Wiper blades stuck to screen, or linkage seized or binding (Chapter 12).
- Blown fuse (Chapter 12).
- Cable or cable connections loose, broken or disconnected (Chapter 12).
- Faulty relay (Chapter 12).
- Faulty wiper motor (Chapter 12).

Wiper blades sweep over too large or too small an area of the glass
- Wiper arms incorrectly positioned on spindles (Chapter 1).

- Excessive wear of wiper linkage (Chapter 1).
- Wiper motor or linkage mountings loose or insecure (Chapter 12).

Wiper blades fail to clean the glass effectively
- Wiper blade rubbers worn or perished (Chapter 1).
- Wiper arm tension springs broken or arm pivots seized (Chapter 1).
- Insufficient windscreen washer additive to adequately remove road dirt film (Chapter 1).

Windscreen/tailgate washers inoperative or unsatisfactory in operation

One or more washer jets inoperative
- Blocked washer jet (Chapter 12).
- Disconnected, kinked or restricted fluid hose (Chapter 12).
- Insufficient fluid in washer reservoir (Chapter 1).

Washer pump fails to operate
- Broken or disconnected wiring or connections (Chapter 12).
- Blown fuse (Chapter 12).
- Faulty washer switch (Chapter 12).
- Faulty washer pump (Chapter 12).

Washer pump runs for some time before fluid is emitted from jets
- Faulty one-way valve in fluid supply hose (Chapter 12).

Electric windows inoperative or unsatisfactory in operation

Window glass will only move in one direction
- Faulty switch (Chapter 12).

Window glass slow to move
- Incorrectly adjusted door glass guide channels (Chapter 11).
- Regulator seized or damaged, or in need of lubrication (Chapter 11).
- Door internal components or trim fouling regulator (Chapter 11).
- Faulty motor (Chapter 12).

Window glass fails to move
- Incorrectly adjusted door glass guide channels (Chapter 11).
- Blown fuse (Chapter 12).
- Faulty relay (Chapter 12).
- Broken or disconnected wiring or connections (Chapter 12).
- Faulty motor (Chapter 12).

Central locking system inoperative or unsatisfactory in operation

Complete system failure
- Blown fuse (Chapter 12).
- Faulty relay (Chapter 12).
- Broken or disconnected wiring or connections (Chapter 12).

Latch locks but will not unlock, or unlocks but will not lock
- Faulty master switch (Chapter 12).
- Broken or disconnected latch operating rods or levers (Chapter 11).
- Faulty relay (Chapter 12).

One motor fails to operate
- Broken or disconnected wiring or connections (Chapter 12).
- Faulty motor (Chapter 12).
- Broken, binding or disconnected latch operating rods or levers (Chapter 11) .
- Fault in door latch (Chapter 11).

MOT test checks

Introduction

Motor vehicle testing has been compulsory in Great Britain since 1960 when the Motor Vehicle (Tests) Regulations were first introduced. At that time testing was only applicable to vehicles ten years old or older, and the test itself only covered lighting equipment, braking systems and steering gear. Current vehicle testing is far more extensive and, in the case of private cars, is now an annual inspection commencing three years after the date of first registration.

This section is intended as a guide to getting your car through the MOT test. It lists all the relevant testable items, how to check them yourself, and what is likely to cause the vehicle to fail. Obviously it will not be possible to examine the vehicle to the same standard as the professional MOT tester who will be highly experienced in this work and will have all the necessary equipment available. However, working through the following checks will provide a good indication as to the condition of the vehicle and will enable you to identify any problem areas before submitting the vehicle for the test. Where a component is found to need repair or renewal, a cross reference is given to the relevant Chapter in the manual where further information and the appropriate repair procedures will be found.

The following checks have been sub-divided into three categories as follows.

(a) Checks carried out from the driver's seat.
(b) Checks carried out with the car on the ground.
(c) Checks carried out with the car raised and with the wheels free to rotate.

In most cases the help of an assistant will be necessary to carry out these checks thoroughly.

Checks carried out from the driver's seat

Handbrake (Chapters 1 and 9)

Test the operation of the handbrake by pulling on the lever until the handbrake is in the normal fully-applied position. Ensure that the travel of the lever (the number of clicks of the ratchet) is not excessive before full resistance of the braking mechanism is felt. If so, this indicates incorrect adjustment of the rear brakes or incorrectly adjusted handbrake cables. With the handbrake fully applied, tap the lever sideways and make sure that it does not release, indicating wear in the ratchet and pawl. Release the handbrake and move the lever from side to side to check for excessive wear in the pivot bearing. Check the security of the lever mountings and make sure that there is no corrosion of any part of the body structure within 30 cm (12 in) of the lever mounting. If the lever mountings cannot be readily seen from inside the vehicle, carry out this check later when working underneath.

Footbrake (Chapters 1 and 9)

Check that the brake pedal is sound without visible defects such as excessive wear of the pivot bushes or a broken or damaged pedal pad. Check also for signs of fluid leaks on the pedal, floor or carpets, indicating failed seals in the brake master cylinder. Depress the brake pedal slowly at first, then rapidly until sustained pressure can be held. Maintain this pressure and check that the pedal does not creep down to the floor, indicating problems with the master cylinder. Release the pedal, wait a few seconds then depress it once until firm resistance is felt. Check that this resistance occurs near the top of the pedal travel. If the pedal travels nearly to the floor before firm resistance is felt, this indicates incorrect brake adjustment resulting in 'insufficient reserve travel' of the footbrake. If firm resistance cannot be felt, ie the pedal feels spongy, this indicates the presence of air in the hydraulic system, which will necessitate complete bleeding of the system. Check that the servo unit is operating correctly by depressing the brake pedal several times to exhaust the vacuum. Keep the pedal depressed and start the engine. As soon as the engine starts, the brake pedal resistance will be felt to alter. If this is not the case, there may be a leak from the brake servo vacuum hose, or the servo unit itself may be faulty.

Steering wheel and column (Chapter 10)

Examine the steering wheel for fractures or looseness of the hub, spokes or rim. Move the steering wheel from side to side and then up and down, in relation to the steering column. Check that the steering wheel is not loose on the column, indicating wear in the column splines or a loose steering wheel retaining nut. Continue moving the steering wheel as before, but also turn it slightly from left to right. Check that there is no abnormal movement of the steering wheel, indicating excessive wear in the column upper support bearing, universal joint(s) or flexible coupling.

Electrical equipment (Chapter 12)

Switch on the ignition and operate the horn. The horn must operate and produce a clear sound audible to other road users. Note that a gong, siren or two-tone horn fitted as an alternative to the manufacturer's original equipment is not acceptable.

Check the operation of the windscreen washers and wipers. The washers must operate with adequate flow and pressure and with the jets adjusted so that the liquid strikes the windscreen near the top of the glass.

Operate the windscreen wipers in conjunction with the washers and check that the blades cover their designed sweep of the windscreen without smearing. The blades must effectively clean the glass so that the driver has an adequate view of the road ahead and to the front nearside and offside of the vehicle. If the screen smears or does not clean adequately, it is advisable to renew the wiper blades before the MOT test.

Depress the footbrake with the ignition switched on and have your assistant check that both rear stop lights operate, and are extinguished when the footbrake is released. If one stop light fails to operate it is likely that a bulb has blown or there is a poor electrical contact at, or near the bulbholder. If both stop lights fail to operate, check for a blown fuse, faulty stop light switch or possibly two blown bulbs. If the lights stay on when the brake pedal is released, it is possible that the switch is at fault.

Seat belts (Chapters 1 and 11)

Note: *The following checks are applicable to the seat belts provided for the driver's seat and front passenger's seat. Both seat belts must be of a type that will restrain the upper part of the body; lap belts are not acceptable*

Check the security of all seat belt mountings

Check the flexible brake hoses for cracks or deterioration

Examine the steering rack rubber gaiters for condition and security

Check all rubber suspension mounting bushes (arrow) for damage or deterioration

Shake the roadwheel vigorously to check for excess play in the wheel bearings and suspension components

Check the condition of the shock absorber mountings and bushes (arrow)

Carefully examine the seat belt webbing for cuts or any signs of serious fraying or deterioration. If the seat belt is of the retractable type, pull the belt all the way out and examine the full extent of the webbing.

Fasten and unfasten the belt ensuring that the locking mechanism holds securely and releases properly when intended. If the belt is of the retractable type, check also that the retracting mechanism operates correctly when the belt is released.

Check the security of all seat belt mountings and attachments which are accessible, without removing any trim or other components, from inside the car (photo). Any serious corrosion, fracture or distortion of the body structure within 30 cm (12 in) of any mounting point will cause the vehicle to fail. Certain anchorages will not be accessible, or even visible from inside the car and in this instance further checks should be carried out later, when working underneath. If any part of the seat belt mechanism is attached to the front seat, then the seat mountings are treated as anchorages and must also comply as above.

Checks carried out with the car on the ground

Electrical equipment (Chapter 12)

Switch on the side lights and check that both front and rear side lights are illuminated and that the lenses and reflectors are secure and undamaged. This is particularly important at the rear where a cracked or damaged lens would allow a white light to show to the rear, which is unacceptable. It is also worth noting that any lens that is excessively dirty, either inside or out, such that the light intensity is reduced, could also constitute a fail.

Switch on the headlamps and check that both dipped beam and main beam units are operating correctly and at the same light intensity. If either headlamp shows signs of dimness, this is usually attributable to a poor earth connection or severely corroded internal reflector. Inspect the headlamp lenses for cracks or stone damage. Any damage to the headlamp lens will normally constitute a fail, but this is very much down to the tester's discretion. Bear in mind that with all light units they must operate correctly when first switched on – it is not acceptable to tap a light unit to make it operate.

The headlamps must be aligned so as not to dazzle other road users when switched to dipped beam. This can only be accurately checked using optical beam setting equipment so if you have any doubts about the headlamp alignment, it is advisable to have this professionally checked and if necessary reset, before the MOT test.

With the ignition switched on, operate the direction indicators and check that they show a white or amber light to the front and red or amber light to the rear, that they flash at the rate of between one and two flashes per second and that the 'tell-tale' on the instrument panel also functions. Examine the lenses for cracks or damage as described previously.

Footbrake (Chapters 1 and 9)

From within the engine compartment examine the brake pipes for signs of leaks, corrosion, insecurity, chafing or other damage and check the master cylinder and servo unit for leaks, security of their mountings or excessive corrosion in the vicinity of the mountings.

Turn the steering as necessary so that the right-hand front brake flexible hose can be examined. Inspect the hose carefully for any sign of cracks or deterioration of the rubber. This will be most noticeable if the hose is bent in half and is particularly common where the rubber portion enters the metal end fitting (photo). Turn the steering onto full left then full right lock and ensure that the hose does not contact the wheel, tyre, or any part of the steering or suspension mechanism. While your assistant depresses the brake pedal firmly, check the hose for any bulges or fluid leaks under pressure. Now repeat these checks on the left-hand front hose. Should any damage or deterioration be noticed, renew the hose.

Steering mechanism and suspension (Chapters 1 and 10)

Have your assistant turn the steering wheel from side to side slightly, up to the point where the steering gear just begins to transmit this movement to the roadwheels. Check for excessive free play between the steering wheel and the steering gear, indicating wear in the steering column joints, wear or insecurity of the steering column to steering gear coupling, or insecurity, incorrect adjustment, or wear in the steering gear itself. Generally speaking, free play greater than 1.3 cm (0.5 in) should be considered excessive.

Have your assistant turn the steering wheel more vigorously in each direction up to the point where the roadwheels just begin to turn. As this is done, carry out a complete examination of all steering joints, linkages, fittings and attachments. Any component that shows signs of wear, damage, distortion, or insecurity should be renewed or attended to accordingly. Additional checks can be carried out later with the vehicle raised when there will be greater working clearance underneath.

Check that the vehicle is standing level and at approximately the correct ride height. Ensure that there is sufficient clearance between the suspension components and the bump stops to allow full suspension travel over bumps.

Hydragas units and dampers (Chapter 10)

Depress each corner of the car in turn and then release it. If the suspension components are in good condition the corner of the car will rise and then settle in its normal position. If there is no noticeable damping effect and the car continues to rise and fall, then the suspension is defective.

Exhaust system (Chapter 1)

Start the engine and with your assistant holding a rag over the tailpipe, check the entire system for leaks which will appear as a rhythmic fluffing or hissing sound at the source of the leak. Check the effectiveness of the silencer by ensuring that the noise produced is of a level to be expected from a vehicle of similar type. Providing that the system is structurally sound, it is acceptable to cure a leak using a proprietary exhaust system repair kit or similar method.

Checks carried out with the car raised and with the wheels free to rotate

Jack up the front and rear of the car and securely support it on axle stands positioned at suitable load bearing points under the vehicle structure. Position the stands clear of the suspension assemblies and ensure that the wheels are clear of the ground and that the steering can be turned onto full right and left lock.

Inspect the constant velocity joint gaiters for splits or damage

Chech the handbrake mechanism for signs of frayed or broken cables or insecurity of the linkage

Check the condition of the exhaust system paying particular attention to the mountings

Steering mechanism (Chapter 10)

Examine the steering rack rubber gaiters for signs of splits, lubricant leakage or insecurity of the retaining clips (photo). Also check for excessive stiffness or binding of the steering, a missing split pin or locking device or any severe corrosion of the body structure within 30 cm (12 in) of any steering component attachment point.

Have your assistant turn the steering onto full left then full right lock. Check that the steering turns smoothly without undue tightness or roughness and that no part of the steering mechanism, including a wheel or tyre, fouls any brake flexible or rigid hose or pipe, or any part of the body structure.

Front and rear suspension and wheel bearings (Chapter 10)

Starting at the front right-hand side of the vehicle, grasp the roadwheel at the 3 o'clock and 9 o'clock positions and shake it vigorously. Check for any free play at the wheel bearings, suspension ball joints, or suspension mountings, pivots and attachments. Check also for any serious deterioration of the rubber or metal casing of any mounting bushes, or any distortion, deformation or severe corrosion of any components (photo). Look for missing split pins, tab washers or other locking devices on any mounting or attachment, or any severe corrosion of the vehicle structure within 30 cm (12 in) of any suspension component attachment point. If any excess free play is suspected at a component pivot point, this can be confirmed by using a large screwdriver or similar tool and levering between the mounting and the component attachment. This will confirm whether the wear is in the pivot bush, its retaining bolt or in the mounting itself (note that the bolt holes can often become elongated). Now grasp the wheel at the 12 o'clock and 6 o'clock positions, shake it vigorously and repeat the previous inspection (photo). Rotate the wheel and check for roughness or tightness of the front wheel bearing such that imminent failure of the bearing is indicated. Carry out all the above checks at the other front wheel and then at both rear wheels. Note, however, that the condition of the rear wheel bearings is not actually part of the MOT test, but if they are at all suspect, it is likely that this will be brought to the owner's attention at the time of the test.

Roadsprings and shock absorbers (Chapter 10)

On vehicles with strut type suspension units, examine the strut assembly for signs of fluid leakage, corrosion or severe pitting of the piston rod or damage to the casing. Check also for security of the mounting points.

If coil springs are fitted check that the spring ends locate correctly in their spring seats, that there is no severe corrosion of the spring and that it is not cracked, broken or in any way damaged.

If the vehicle is fitted with leaf springs, check that all leaves are intact, that the axle is securely attached to each spring and that there is no wear or deterioration of the spring eye mountings, bushes, and shackles.

The same general checks apply to vehicles fitted with other suspension types, such as torsion bars, Hydragas units etc. In all cases ensure that all mountings and attachments are secure, that there are no signs of excessive wear, corrosion, cracking, deformation or damage to any component or bush, and that there are no fluid leaks or damaged hoses or pipes (hydraulic types).

Inspect the dampers (where fitted) for signs of fluid leakage, excessive wear of the mounting bushes or attachments or damage to the body of the unit (photo).

Driveshafts (Chapter 8)

With the steering turned onto full lock, rotate each front wheel in turn and inspect the constant velocity joint gaiters for splits or damage (photo). Also check the gaiter is securely attached to its respective housings by clips or other methods of retention.

Continue turning the wheel and check that each driveshaft is straight with no sign of damage.

Braking system (Chapters 1 and 9)

If possible, without dismantling, check for wear of the brake pads and the condition of the discs. Ensure that the friction lining material has not worn excessively and that the discs are not fractured, pitted, scored or worn excessively.

Carefully examine all the rigid brake pipes underneath the car and the flexible hoses at the rear. Look for signs of excessive corrosion, chafing or insecurity of the pipes and for signs of bulging under pressure, chafing, splits or deterioration of the flexible hoses.

Look for signs of hydraulic fluid leaks at the brake calipers or on the brake backplates, indicating failed hydraulic seals in the components concerned.

Slowly spin each wheel while your assistant depresses the footbrake then releases it. Ensure that each brake is operating and that the wheel is free to rotate when the pedal is released.

Examine the handbrake mechanism and check for signs of frayed or broken cables, excessive corrosion or wear or insecurity of the linkage (photo). Have your assistant operate the handbrake while you check that the mechanism works on each relevant wheel and releases fully without binding.

Exhaust system (Chapter 1)

Starting at the front, examine the exhaust system over its entire length checking for any damaged, broken or missing mountings, security of the pipe retaining clamps and condition of the system with regard to rust and corrosion (photo).

Wheels and tyres (Chapter 1)

Carefully examine each tyre in turn on both the inner and outer walls and over the whole of the tread area and check for signs of cuts, tears, lumps, bulges, separation of the tread and exposure of the ply or cord due to wear or other damage. Check also that the tyre bead is correctly seated on the wheel rim and that the tyre valve is sound and properly seated. Spin the wheel and check that it is not excessively distorted or damaged particularly at the bead rim. Check that the tyres are of the correct size for the car and that they are of the same size and type on each axle. They should also be inflated to the specified pressures.

Using a suitable gauge check the tyre tread depth. The current legal requirement states that the tread pattern must be visible over the whole tread area and must be of a minimum depth of 1.6 mm over at least three-quarters of the tread width. It is acceptable for some wear of the inside or outside edges of the tyre to be apparent but this wear must be in one even circumferential band and the tread must be visible. Any excessive wear of this nature may indicate incorrect front wheel alignment which should be checked before the tyre becomes excessively worn. See Chapters 1 and 10 for further information on tyre wear patterns and front wheel alignment.

Body corrosion

Check the condition of the entire vehicle structure for signs of corrosion in any load bearing areas. For the purpose of the MOT test all chassis box sections, side sills, subframes, crossmembers, pillars, suspension, steering, braking system and seat belt mountings and anchorages should all be considered as load bearing areas. As a general guide, any corrosion which has seriously reduced the metal thickness of a load bearing area to weaken it, is likely to cause the vehicle to fail. Should corrosion of this nature be encountered, professional repairs are likely to be needed.

Chapter 1 Routine maintenance and servicing

Contents

Specifications

Engine
Oil filter type .... Champion B104

Cooling system
Antifreeze properties – 50% antifreeze (by volume):
    Commences freezing.. $-36°C$
    Frozen solid .... $-48°C$

Fuel system
Air cleaner filter element:
    Carburettor engines .... Champion W218
    Fuel-injected engines.. Champion W221
Idle speed:
    Carburettor engines .... 850 ± 50 rpm
    Fuel-injected engines.. See text
CO level at idle speed – engine at normal operating temperature:
    Carburettor engines – without catalytic converter – at exhaust
    tailpipe... 2.0 to 3.0%
    Carburettor engines – with catalytic converter – at gas-sampling
    pipe... 1.0 to 3.0%
    Fuel-injected engines.. See text
Recommended fuel:
    Cars without catalytic converter....................................... 95 RON unleaded (ie unleaded Premium) or 97 RON leaded
    (ie 4-star)
    Cars with catalytic converter .... 95 RON unleaded (ie unleaded Premium) **only**

Ignition system

Firing order	1–3–4–2 (No 1 cylinder at timing belt end)
Direction of crankshaft rotation	Clockwise (viewed from right-hand side of car)
Direction of distributor rotor arm rotation	Anti-clockwise (viewed from left-hand side of car)

Ignition timing – carburettor engines – @ 1500 rpm (vacuum pipe disconnected):

1.1 models – with carburettor number MAC 10003 or MAC 10010	8° ± 1° BTDC
1.1 models – with carburettor number MAC 10043	10° ± 1° BTDC
1.4 models	9° ± 1° BTDC
Ignition timing – fuel-injected engines	See text

Spark plugs:

Type	Champion RC9YCC
Electrode gap	0.8 mm

Spark plug (HT) leads:

Resistance	25 K ohms per lead, maximum

Braking system

Front brake pad friction material minimum thickness	3.0 mm
Rear brake shoe friction material minimum thickness	1.5 mm

Handbrake adjustment:

Roadwheels bind at:

Up to VIN 661301	2 to 3 notches
VIN 661301 on	1 notch

Roadwheels lock at:

Up to VIN 661301	3 to 4 notches
VIN 661301 on	1 to 2 notches

Tyre pressures – tyres cold

	Front	Rear
1.1C, 1.1L, 1.1S, 1.4SL, 1.4GS:		
Up to and including four persons	2.1 bar (31 lbf/in^2)	2.1 bar (31 lbf/in^2)
Four persons up to maximum permissible gross vehicle weight	2.1 bar (31 lbf/in^2)	2.2 bar (32 lbf/in^2)
GTa, GTi 16v:		
All loads – up to 100 mph	2.0 bar (29 lbf/in^2)	2.0 bar (29 lbf/in^2)
All loads – over 100 mph	2.3 bar (33 lbf/in^2)	2.3 bar (33 lbf/in^2)

Electrical system

Alternator drivebelt deflection	6 to 8 mm @ 10 kg pressure
Wiper blades – front and rear	Champion X-4103

Torque wrench settings

	Nm	lbf ft
Air intake duct-to-cylinder head support bracket screws – K16 engine	8	6
Spark plug cover screws – K16 engine	2	1.5
Spark plugs	25	18.5
Timing belt cover fasteners:		
Upper right-hand/outer cover	4	3
Lower and upper left-hand inner covers	9	6.5
Distributor cap screws	2	1.5
Distributor rotor arm (hex-head) screw – fuel-injected engines	10	7.5
Distributor mounting bolts – carburettor engines	25	18.5
Alternator pivot and clamp bolts:		
10 mm	45	33
8 mm	25	18.5
Engine oil drain plug	42	31
Transmission oil filler/level and drain plugs	25	18.5
Fuel system pressure release bolt – at fuel filter	12	9
Fuel filter inlet union	40	29.5
Fuel filter outlet union	35	26
Front brake caliper guide pin bolts	30	22
Rear brake drum securing screws	7	5
Roadwheel nuts	70	51.5
Seatbelt top mounting bolt	25	19

Lubricants, fluids and capacities

K8 ENGINE (1)   (1) K16 ENGINE

Lubricants and fluids

Component or system	Lubricant type/specification	Duckhams recommendation
1 Engine	SAE 10W/40 multigrade engine oil meeting specifications API-SG or SG/CD, CCMC G4, or RES.22.OL.G4	Duckhams QXR or 10W/40 Motor Oil
2 Transmission	Special gearbox oil – refer to your Rover dealer	Duckhams Hypoid PT 75W/80 Gear Oil – for topping-up only
3 Cooling system	Ethylene glycol-based antifreeze with non-phosphate corrosion inhibitors, suitable for mixed-metal engines, containing no methanol and meeting specifications BS6580 and BS5117	Duckhams Universal Antifreeze and Summer Coolant
4 Braking system	Hydraulic fluid meeting specification SAE J1703 or DOT 4	Duckhams Universal Brake and Clutch Fluid
5 General greasing	Multi-purpose lithium-based grease, NLGI consistency No. 2	Duckhams LB10 Grease

Capacities

Engine oil
Total capacity (including filter)... 4.5 litres
Difference between dipstick MAX and MIN marks................................... 0.5 litre (approx)

Cooling system .... 4.5 litres

Fuel tank... 35.4 litres

Transmission .... 2.0 litres

Washer system reservoir .... 2.6 litres

Maintenance schedule

Introduction

This Chapter is designed to help the DIY owner maintain the Rover Metro with the goals of maximum economy, safety, reliability and performance in mind.

On the following pages is a master maintenance schedule, listing the servicing requirements, and the intervals at which they should be carried out as recommended by the manufacturers. The operations are listed in the order in which the work can be most conveniently undertaken. For example, all the operations that are performed from within the engine compartment are grouped together, as are all those that require the car to be raised and supported for access to the suspension and underbody. Alongside each operation in the schedule is a reference which directs the reader to the Sections in this Chapter covering maintenance procedures or to other Chapters in the Manual, where the operations are described and illustrated in greater detail. Specifications for all the maintenance operations, together with a list of lubricants, fluids and capacities are provided at the beginning of this Chapter. Refer to the accompanying photographs of the engine compartment and the underbody of the car for the locations of the various components.

Servicing your car in accordance with the mileage/time maintenance schedule and step-by-step procedures will result in a planned maintenance programme that should give a long and reliable service life. Bear in mind that it is a comprehensive plan, so maintaining some items but not others at the specified intervals will not produce the same results.

The first step in this maintenance program is to prepare yourself before the actual work begins. Read through all the procedures to be undertaken then obtain all the parts, lubricants and any additional tools needed.

Daily

Operations internal and external

Check the operation of the horn, all lamps, the direction indicators and the wipers and washers (Section 11)
Check the operation of the seat belts (Section 10)
Check the operation of the brakes (Section 8)
Check under the car for signs of fluid leaks on the ground

Every 250 miles (400 km) or weekly

Operations internal and external

Visually examine the tyres for tread depth and wear or damage (Section 9)
Check, and if necessary adjust, the tyre pressures (Section 9)

Operations in the engine compartment

Check the engine oil level (Section 1)
Check the washer system reservoir fluid level (Section 11)

Every 1000 miles (1500 km) or monthly – whichever comes first

Carry out the daily and weekly checks, then check the following:

Operations internal and external

Check the operation of all locks, hinges and latch mechanisms (Section 10)

Operations in the engine compartment

Check the coolant level (Section 2)
Check the brake fluid level (Section 8)

Every 6000 miles (10 000 km) or 6 months – whichever comes first

In addition to all the items listed above, carry out the following:

Operations internal and external

Renew the engine oil and filter (Section 1)

Note: *The manufacturer has recently (approx mid-1991) extended the service schedule so that this task need no longer be carried out at this interval, except for the First Lubrication Service, carried out when the car is new. Owners of high-mileage cars, or those who do a lot of stop-start driving, may prefer to adhere to the original recommendation, changing the oil and filter in-between the major services described below*

Every 12 000 miles (20 000 km) or 12 months – whichever comes first

In addition to the items listed under the daily, weekly and monthly checks, carry out the following:

Operations internal and external

Renew the engine oil and filter (Section 1)
Check the operation of the clutch (Section 5)
Check the transmission oil level (Section 6)
Check the tightness of the roadwheel nuts (Section 9)
Check the exterior paintwork, the body panels and the underbody sealer (Section 10)
Check and lubricate all locks, hinges, latch mechanisms and the sunroof (Section 10)

Operations with the car raised and supported

Check the fuel tank hoses, pipes and connections (Section 3)
Check the exhaust system (Section 3)
Check the driveshaft gaiters and CV joints (Section 7)
Check the front brake pads, calipers and discs (Section 8)*
Check and adjust the rear brake shoes, check the wheel cylinders and drums (Section 8)*
Check the braking system master cylinder, flexible hoses and metal pipes (Section 8)*
Adjust and lubricate the handbrake (Section 8)
Check the front suspension and grease the upper arm pivot bearings (Section 9)
Check the steering gear, the rubber gaiters and the track rod balljoints (Section 9)
Check the rear suspension and grease the trailing arm pivot bearings (Section 9)

Every 60 000 miles/100 000 km or every THREE years – whichever comes first – the braking system master cylinder, the front brake calipers and the rear brake wheel cylinders must be overhauled and their seals renewed as a matter of course (Chapter 9)

Operations in the engine compartment

Check the cooling system hoses and connections (Section 2)
Check the operation of the radiator electric cooling fan (Section 2)
Drain, flush and refill the cooling system, renewing the antifreeze (Section 2)*
Top up the carburettor piston damper (Section 3)
Check, where possible, the idle speed and mixture (Section 3)

Check the operation of the lambda sensor – where fitted (Chapter 4 and Section 3)
Check the distributor cap, ignition HT coil and the spark plug (HT) leads (Section 4)
Check the battery connections and electrolyte level (Section 11)
Check and adjust the alternator drivebelt (Section 11)

If Rover-recommended antifreeze is used, this task need only be carried out after the first three years of the car's life and every two years thereafter

Road test
Check that the engine starts and warms up properly, that the oil pressure and ignition/battery charging warning lamps go out, that the throttle pedal movement is correct and that the engine responds correctly to the throttle. When driving, check the operation of the clutch, gearchange and brakes and listen for noises, roughness or other faults from the engine and transmission, the steering and the suspension.

Every 24 000 miles (40 000 km) or 2 years – whichever comes first

In addition to all the items listed under the 12 000 mile service heading, carry out the following:

Operations with the car raised and supported
Renew the braking system hydraulic fluid (Section 8)

Operations in the engine compartment
Renew the air cleaner filter element (Section 3)
Renew the fuel filter (Section 3)
Check the crankcase breather hoses (Section 1)
Renew the spark plugs (Section 4)
Check and adjust the ignition timing – where possible (Section 4)

Every 48 000 miles (80 000 km) or 4 years – whichever comes first

In addition to all the items listed under the 24 000 mile service heading, carry out the following:

Operations in the engine compartment
Check the timing belt (Section 1)

Every 60 000 miles (100 000 km) or 5 years – whichever comes first

In addition to all the items listed under the 12 000 mile service heading, carry out the following:

Operations in the engine compartment
Check the components of the evaporative emission control system – where fitted (Chapter 4 and Section 3)

Every 96 000 miles (160 000 km) or 8 years – whichever comes first

In addition to all the items listed under the 24 000 mile service heading, carry out the following:

Operations in the engine compartment
Renew the timing belt (Section 1)

Engine compartment component locations – K8 carburettor engine

1   Engine oil level dipstick
2   Engine oil filler cap
3   Cooling system expansion
    tank and filler cap
4   Braking system fluid
    reservoir filler cap
5   Air cleaner assembly

6   Battery
7   Fusible link box
8   Distributor
9   VIN plate
10 Washer system reservoir
11 Alternator
12 Spark plug (HT) leads

13 Intake air temperature
    control valve
14 Cold air intake duct
15 Fuel pump
16 Vacuum capsule
17 Amplifier module

18 Vehicle identification
    number
19 Battery positive terminal
20 Battery negative terminal
21 Coolant hose – heater feed
22 Starter relay
23 Inlet manifold heater relay

Engine compartment component locations – K16 fuel-injected engine

1 Engine oil level dipstick	6 Battery	13 Intake air temperature	18 Vehicle identification
2 Engine oil filler cap	7 Fusible link box	control valve	number
3 Cooling system expansion	8 Distributor	14 Cold air intake duct	19 Battery positive terminal
tank and filler cap	9 VIN plate	15 Fuel injection/ignition	20 Battery negative terminal
4 Braking system fluid	10 Washer system reservoir	system ECU	21 Coolant hose – heater feed
reservoir filler cap	11 Alternator	16 Relay module	22 Fuel filter
5 Air cleaner assembly	12 Spark plug (HT) leads	17 Fuel cut-off inertia switch	23 Fuel system pressure
			release bolt

Front underbody view

1   Engine oil drain plug
2   Oil filter
3   Transmission oil drain plug
4   Transmission oil filler/level plug
5   Left-hand driveshaft inboard constant
    velocity joint

6   Right-hand driveshaft inboard constant
    velocity joint
7   Starter motor
8   Front suspension subframe front
    mountings
9   Front suspension subframe rear
    mountings
10 Anti-roll bar

11 Hydragas suspension system
    connecting pipe
12 Fuel feed and return pipes
13 Brake pipes
14 Gearchange linkage
15 Front suspension lower arms
16 Steering gear track rods
17 Front towing eyes

Rear underbody view

1   Fuel tank
2   Rear suspension subframe
3   Rear suspension Hydragas
    units
4   Hydragas suspension
    system ride height
    adjustment valves
5   Handbrake cable
6   Rear towing eye
7   Anti-roll bar
8   Rear suspension trailing
    arms
9   Exhaust system rubber
    mounting

Maintenance procedures

1 Engine

Engine oil level check

1 The engine oil level is checked with a dipstick that extends through a tube and into the sump at the bottom of the engine. The dipstick is located at the rear right-hand end of the engine, between the air cleaner assembly and the cooling system expansion tank.

2 The oil level should be checked with the car standing on level ground and before it is driven, or at least 5 minutes after the engine has been switched off. If the oil is checked immediately after driving the car, some of the oil will remain in the engine upper components and oil galleries, resulting in an inaccurate dipstick reading.

3 Withdraw the dipstick from the tube and wipe all the oil from its end with a clean rag or paper towel. Insert the clean dipstick back into the tube as far as it will go, then withdraw it once more. Note the oil level on the end of the dipstick. Add oil as necessary until the level is between the upper (MAX) and lower (MIN) marks on the dipstick (photo). Note that 1 litre of oil will be required to raise the level from the lower mark to the upper mark.

4 Always maintain the level between the two dipstick marks. If the level is allowed to fall below the lower mark, oil starvation may result which could lead to severe engine damage. If the engine is overfilled by adding too much oil, this may result in oil-fouled spark plugs, oil leaks or oil seal failures.

5 Oil is added to the engine after removing the filler cap (rotate it through a quarter-turn anti-clockwise and withdraw it) in the cylinder head cover (photo). An oil can spout or funnel may help to reduce spillage. Always use the correct grade and type of oil as shown in *'Lubricants, fluids and capacities'*.

Engine oil and filter renewal

6 Frequent oil and filter changes are the most important preventative maintenance procedures that can be undertaken by the DIY owner. As engine oil ages, it becomes diluted and contaminated, which leads to premature engine wear.

7 Before starting this procedure, gather together all the necessary tools and materials (photo). Also make sure that you have plenty of clean rags and newspapers handy to mop up any spills. Ideally, the engine oil should be warm as it will drain better and more built-up sludge will be removed with it. Take care however, not to touch the exhaust or any other hot parts of the engine when working under the car. To avoid any possibility of scalding and to protect yourself from possible skin irritants and other harmful contaminants in used engine oils, it is advisable to wear gloves when carrying out this work.

8 The engine oil drain plug is located on the front of the sump and can be reached easily, without having to raise the car. Remove the oil filler cap and use a spanner, or preferably a suitable socket and bar, to slacken the drain plug about half a turn (photo). Position the draining container under the drain plug, then remove the plug completely. If possible, try to keep the plug pressed into the sump while unscrewing it by hand the last couple of turns. As the plug releases from the threads, move it away sharply so the stream of oil issuing from the sump runs into the container, not up your sleeve!

9 Allow some time for the old oil to drain, noting that it may be necessary to reposition the container as the flow of oil slows to a trickle; work can be speeded-up by removing the oil filter, as described below, while the oil is draining.

10 After all the oil has drained, wipe off the drain plug with a clean rag and renew its sealing washer. Clean the area around the drain plug opening and refit the plug. Tighten the plug securely, preferably to the

1.3 Engine oil dipstick MAX (A) and MIN (B) marks

1.5 Use only good quality oil of specified type when topping up engine – note location of dipstick (arrow)

1.7 Requirements for engine oil and filter renewal

1.8 Unscrewing engine oil drain plug

1.12 Using an oil filter removal tool to slacken filter

1.14 Applying a light coating of clean oil to the sealing ring before fitting the new filter

specified torque using a torque wrench.

11   Move the container into position under the oil filter, which is located next to the drain plug on the front of the engine.

12   Using an oil filter removal tool, slacken the filter initially then unscrew it by hand the rest of the way (photo). Empty the oil in the old filter into the container and allow any residual oil to drain out of the engine.

13   Use a clean rag to remove all oil, dirt and sludge from the filter sealing area on the engine. Check the old filter to make sure that the rubber sealing ring has not stuck to the engine. If it has, carefully remove it.

14   Apply a light coating of clean engine oil to the new filter's sealing ring and screw the filter into position on the engine until it seats, then tighten it through a further half-turn **only**; tighten the filter by hand only, do not use any tools (photo).

15   Remove the old oil and all tools from under the car.

16   Refill the engine with fresh oil, using the correct grade and type of oil, as described earlier in this Section. Pour in half the specified quantity of oil first, then wait a few minutes for the oil to fall to the sump. Continue adding oil a small quantity at a time until the level is up to the lower mark on the dipstick. Adding a further 1.0 litre will bring the level up to the upper mark on the dipstick.

17   Start the engine and run it for a few minutes while checking for leaks around the oil filter seal and the sump drain plug.

18   Switch off the engine and wait a few minutes for the oil to settle in the sump once more. With the new oil circulated and the filter now completely full, recheck the level on the dipstick and add more oil as necessary.

19   Dispose of the used engine oil safely with reference to 'Tools and working facilities' in the preliminary Sections of this Manual.

Timing belt check

20   Working as described in Chapter 2, Section 6, remove the timing belt upper right-hand (outer) cover.

21   Apply the handbrake and ensure that the transmission is in neutral, then jack up the front right-hand side of the car and support it on an axle stand.

22   Remove the roadwheel and the underwing shield to expose the alternator drive pulley, so that the crankshaft can be rotated using a spanner applied to the alternator drive pulley bolt.

23   Rotating the crankshaft so that the full length of the timing belt is checked, examine the belt carefully for any signs of uneven wear, splitting or oil contamination and renew it if there is the slightest doubt about its condition (see below).

24   Note that Rover state that there is no need to adjust the belt's tension once it has been installed. If, however, the belt is thought to be incorrectly tensioned, especially if it has been disturbed for other servicing/repair work, the tensioner can be reset following the procedure outlined in Chapter 2, Section 7 (under 'Adjustment – general').

25   Refit all removed components and lower the car to the ground once the check is complete.

Timing belt renewal

26   The timing belt **must** be renewed as a matter of course at the specified interval, following the procedure given in Section 7 of Chapter 2. If the belt is not renewed as directed, it may break while the engine is running, which will result in serious and expensive engine damage.

General engine checks

Valve clearances – general

27   It is necessary for a clearance to exist between the tip of each valve stem and the valve operating mechanism, to allow for the expansion of the various engine components as the engine reaches normal operating temperature.

28   On most older engine designs, this meant that the valve clearances (also known as 'tappet' clearances) had to be checked and adjusted regularly. If the clearances were too slack, the engine would be very noisy, its power output would suffer and its fuel consumption would increase; conversely, if the clearances were too tight, the engine's power output would be reduced and the valves and their seats could be severely damaged.

29   The engines covered in this Manual, however, employ hydraulic

tappets which use the lubricating system's oil pressure automatically to take up the clearance between each camshaft lobe and its respective valve stem. Therefore there is no need for regular checking and inspection of the valve clearances, but it is essential that **only** good quality oil of the recommended viscosity and specification is used in the engine and that this oil is scrupulously changed at the recommended intervals. If this advice is not followed, the oilways and tappets may become clogged with particles of dirt or deposits of burnt engine oil (resulting from the use of an inferior oil) so that the system cannot work properly; ultimately one or more of the tappets may fail and expensive repairs may be required.

30   On starting the engine from cold, there will be a slight delay while full oil pressure builds up in all parts of the engine, especially in the tappets; the valve clearances, therefore, may well 'rattle' for about 10 seconds or so and then quieten. This is a normal state of affairs and is nothing to worry about, provided that all tappets quieten quickly and stay quiet.

31   After the car has been standing for several days, the valve clearances may 'rattle' for longer than usual as nearly all the oil will have drained away from the engine's top end components and bearing surfaces; while this is only to be expected, care must be taken not to damage the engine by running it at high speed until all the tappets are refilled with oil and operating normally. With the car stationary, hold the engine at no more than a fast idle speed (maximum 2000 to 2500 rpm)

Fig. 1.1 Coolant hose inspection (Sec 2)

A   Check hose for chafed or burned areas; these may lead to sudden and costly failure

B   A soft hose indicates inside deterioration, leading to contamination of the cooling system and clogging of the radiator

C   A hardened hose can fail at any time; tightening the clamps will not seal the joint or prevent leaks

D   A swollen hose or one with oil-soaked ends indicates contamination from oil or grease. Cracks and breaks can be easily seen by squeezing the hose for 10 to 15 minutes or until the noise ceases. **Do not** run the engine at more than 3000 rpm until the tappets are fully recharged with oil and the noise has ceased.

32   If the valve clearances are thought to be noisy, or if a light rattle persists from the engine's top end after it has reached normal operating temperature, take the car to a Rover dealer for expert advice. Depending on the mileage covered and the usage to which each car has been put, some cars may be noisier than others; only a good mechanic experienced in these engines can tell if the noise level is typical for the car's mileage or if a genuine fault exists. If any tappet's operation is faulty, it must be renewed (Chapter 2, Section 10).

General engine checks

33   Visually inspect the engine joint faces, gaskets and seals for any signs of water or oil leaks. Pay particular attention to the areas around the cylinder head cover, cylinder head, oil filter and sump joint faces. Bear in mind that over a period of time some very slight seepage from these areas is to be expected, but what you are really looking for is any indication of a serious leak. Should a leak be found, renew the offending gasket or oil seal by referring to the appropriate Chapters in this Manual.
34   Also check the security and condition of all the engine related pipes and hoses, particularly the crankcase breather hose(s) from the cylinder head cover. Ensure that all cable ties or securing clips are in place and in good condition. Clips which are broken or missing can lead to chafing of the hoses pipes or wiring which could cause more serious problems in the future.

---

2   Cooling, heating and ventilation systems

Coolant level check

Warning: *DO NOT attempt to remove the expansion tank filler cap when the engine is hot, as there is a very great risk of scalding*

1   All models are equipped with a sealed cooling system. A translucent expansion tank located between the washer system reservoir and the air cleaner assembly is connected by hoses to the cooling system (see Chapter 3) so that a continual flow of coolant passes through it to purge any air from the system.
2   The coolant level in the expansion tank should be checked regularly. The level in the tank varies with the temperature of the engine. When the engine is cold, the coolant level should be between the MAX and MIN marks on the side of the tank (photo); when the engine is hot, the level will be slightly higher.
3   If topping-up is necessary, wait until the engine is cold, then cover the expansion tank with a thick layer of rag and unscrew the filler cap anti-clockwise until a hissing sound is heard; wait until the hissing ceases, indicating that all pressure is released, then slowly unscrew the filler cap until it can be removed. If more hissing sounds are heard, wait until they have stopped before unscrewing the cap completely. At all times keep well away from the filler opening.
4   Add a mixture of water and antifreeze (see below) through the expansion tank filler neck until the coolant is up to the level mark (photo). Refit the cap, tightening it securely.

5   With this type of cooling system, the addition of coolant should only be necessary at very infrequent intervals. If frequent topping-up is required, it is likely there is a leak in the system. Check the radiator, all hoses and joint faces for any sign of staining or actual wetness and rectify as necessary. If no leaks can be found, it is advisable to have the expansion tank filler cap and the entire system pressure-tested by a dealer or suitably-equipped garage as this will often show up a small leak not previously visible.

Coolant draining

Warning: *Wait until the engine is cold before starting this procedure. Do not allow antifreeze to come in contact with your skin or painted surfaces of the car. Rinse off spills immediately with plenty of water. Never leave antifreeze lying around in an open container or in a puddle in the driveway or on the garage floor. Children and pets are attracted by its sweet smell. Antifreeze is fatal if ingested*

6   To drain the system, remove the expansion tank filler cap as described above, then move the heater air temperature control to the maximum heat position.
7   Place a large drain tray under the front of the car and disconnect the radiator bottom hose from the radiator; direct as much of the escaping coolant as possible into the tray (photo).

System flushing

8   With time, the cooling system may gradually lose its efficiency due to the radiator core having become choked with rust, scale deposits from the water and other sediment. To minimise this, as well as using only good quality antifreeze and clean soft water the system should be flushed as follows whenever the coolant is renewed.
9   With the coolant drained, refit the bottom hose and refill the system with fresh water. Refit the expansion tank filler cap, start the engine and warm it up to normal operating temperature, then stop it and (after allowing it to cool down completely) drain the system again. Repeat as necessary until only clean water can be seen to emerge, then refill finally with the specified coolant mixture.
10   If the specified coolant mixture has been used and has been renewed at the specified intervals, the above procedure will be sufficient to keep clean the system for a considerable length of time. If, however, the system has been neglected, a more thorough operation will be required, as follows:
11   First drain the coolant, then disconnect the radiator top hose at the coolant outlet elbow. Insert a garden hose into the top hose and allow water to circulate through the radiator until it runs clean from the bottom outlet.
12   To flush the engine, insert the garden hose into the outlet elbow and allow water to circulate until it runs clear from the bottom hose union. If, after a reasonable period, the water still does not run clear, the radiator should be flushed with a good proprietary cleaning system such as Holts Radflush or Holts Speedflush.
13   In severe cases of contamination, reverse-flushing of the radiator may be necessary. To do this, remove the radiator (Chapter 3), invert it and insert a garden hose into the bottom outlet. Continue flushing until clear water runs from the top hose outlet. A similar procedure can be used to flush the heater matrix.

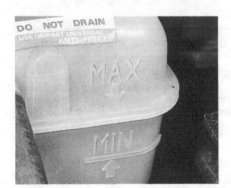

2.2 Coolant level must be maintained between expansion tank MAX and MIN marks

2.4 Use only specified coolant mixture to top up cooling system

2.7 Cooling system must be drained by disconnecting radiator bottom hose

2.17A Cooling system has a bleed plug (arrow) on heater feed hose ...

2.17B ... and a bleed screw (arrow) on the coolant rail to allow trapped air to escape

14   The use of chemical cleaners should be necessary only as a last resort; the regular renewal of the coolant will prevent excessive contamination of the system.

Coolant filling

15   With the cooling system drained and flushed, refit the bottom hose and ensure that all other disturbed hose unions are correctly secured.
16   Prepare a sufficient quantity of the specified coolant mixture (see below); allow for a surplus so as to have a reserve supply for topping-up.
17   Unscrew the bleed plug from the heater feed hose and the bleed screw from the coolant rail underneath the distributor to allow the escape of air trapped during refilling, thus preventing the formation of air-locks (photos).
18   Fill the system slowly through the expansion tank. When coolant can be seen emerging from the bleed screw in a steady stream, tighten the screw. Continue filling until the same happens at the bleed plug; tighten it securely and top the expansion tank up to the correct level, then refit the filler cap.
19   Start the engine and run it at no more than idle speed until it has warmed up to normal operating temperature and the radiator electric cooling fan has cut in; watch the temperature gauge to check for signs of overheating.
20   Stop the engine and allow it to cool down **completely**, then remove the expansion tank filler cap and top up the tank to the correct level. Refit the filler cap and wash off all the spilt coolant from the engine compartment and bodywork.
21   After refilling, always check carefully all components of the system (but especially any unions disturbed during draining and flushing) for signs of coolant leaks; fresh antifreeze has a searching action which will rapidly expose any weak points in the system.
22   **Note:** *If, after draining and refilling the system, symptoms of overheating are found which did not occur previously, then the fault is almost certainly due to trapped air at some point in the system causing an air-lock and restricting the flow of coolant; usually the air is trapped because the system was refilled too quickly. In some cases air-locks can be released by tapping or squeezing the various hoses. If the problem persists, stop the engine and allow it to cool down completely before unscrewing the bleed plug or screw to bleed out the trapped air.*

Antifreeze mixture

23   The antifreeze should always be renewed at the specified intervals. This is necessary not only to maintain the antifreeze properties, but also to prevent corrosion which would otherwise occur as the corrosion inhibitors become progressively less effective.
24   Always use an ethylene glycol-based antifreeze which is suitable for use in mixed-metal cooling systems. The type of antifreeze and levels of protection afforded are indicated in the Specifications. To give the recommended 50 % concentration, 2.25 litres of antifreeze must be mixed with 2.25 litres of clean, soft water; this should provide enough to refill the complete system, but it is best to make up a larger amount so that a supply is available for subsequent topping-up.
25   Before adding antifreeze the cooling system should be completely drained, preferably flushed and all hoses checked for condition and security; fresh antifreeze has a searching action which will rapidly find any weaknesses in the system.
26   After filling with antifreeze, a label should be attached to the radiator or expansion tank stating the type and concentration of antifreeze used and the date installed. Any subsequent topping-up should be made with the same type and concentration of antifreeze.
27   Do not use engine antifreeze in the screen washer system, as it will damage the car's paintwork. A screen wash such as Turtle Wax High Tech Screen Wash should be added to the washer system in the recommended quantities.

General cooling system checks

28   The engine should be cold for the cooling system checks, so perform the following procedure before driving the car or after it has been shut off for at least three hours.
29   Remove the expansion tank filler cap (see above) and clean it thoroughly inside and out with a rag. Also clean the filler neck on the expansion tank. The presence of rust or corrosion in the filler neck indicates that the coolant should be changed. The coolant inside the expansion tank should be relatively clean and transparent. If it is rust-coloured, drain and flush the system and refill with a fresh coolant mixture.
30   Carefully check the radiator hoses and heater hoses along their entire length. Renew any hose which is cracked, swollen or deteriorated. Cracks will show up better if the hose is squeezed. Pay close attention to the hose clips that secure the hoses to the cooling system components. Hose clips can pinch and puncture hoses, resulting in cooling system leaks. If wire type hose clips are used, it may be a good idea to replace them with screw-type clips.
31   Inspect all the cooling system components (hoses, joint faces etc) for leaks. A leak in the cooling system will usually show up as white or rust-coloured deposits on the area adjoining the leak. Where any problems of this nature are found on system components, renew the component or gasket with reference to Chapter 3.
32   Clean the front of the radiator with a soft brush to remove all insects, leaves etc imbedded in the radiator fins. Be extremely careful not to damage the radiator fins or cut your fingers on them.

---

3   Fuel, exhaust and emission control systems

Warning: *Certain procedures in this Section require the removal of fuel lines and connections which may result in some fuel spillage. Before carrying out any operation on the fuel system refer to the precautions given in Safety first! at the beginning of this Manual and follow them implicitly. Petrol is a highly dangerous and volatile liquid and the precautions necessary when handling it cannot be overstressed*

Air cleaner filter element renewal

1   Release the clips securing the air cleaner assembly cover, then unscrew the retaining screws and carefully unclip the cover from the assembly (photos). If the assembly is dislodged, lift it carefully and check that none of the vacuum pipes, hoses or wiring (as applicable) connected to its underside have been damaged or disconnected.

2 Lift out the air cleaner filter element and discard it. Wipe clean the inside of the assembly and the cover, then check that there is no foreign matter visible either in the air cleaner intake duct or in the inlet tract.
3 Place the new element in the air cleaner assembly, ensure that it is correctly seated and clip the cover back onto the assembly (photo). Refit the retaining screws and the clips to secure the cover.

Fuel filter renewal

4 Access is much improved if the air cleaner assembly is removed first (Chapter 4). Place wads of rag around the fuel filter to catch any spilled fuel.
5 Depressurise the fuel system by removing the black plastic cap and slackening the pressure release bolt (fitted above the fuel filter, in the filter outlet pipe) with a spanner counter-holding the pipe boss (photo). When the pressure is released, retighten the bolt to its specified torque wrench setting; again, use a spanner to counter-hold the pipe boss, to prevent damage to the pipe or filter.
6 Using two spanners to prevent damage to any of the fuel system pipes or components, disconnect the fuel filter inlet and outlet unions and remove the clamp screw to release the filter from its mounting (photo).
7 Fit the new filter with the arrows indicating fuel flow pointing to the right of the car (photo). Tighten the clamp screw, connect the fuel pipes to the filter and tighten their unions securely, to the specified torque wrench settings if possible. Start the engine and check carefully for any signs of fuel leaks from any of the disturbed components.
8 Dispose safely of the old filter; it will be highly inflammable and may explode if thrown on a fire.

Topping-up the carburettor piston damper

9 Unscrew the four screws securing the air cleaner assembly to its mounting bracket and release the quarter-turn fastener securing the intake duct to the cylinder head support bracket. Carefully lift the air cleaner assembly and disconnect the thermac switch vacuum pipes; note that these are colour-coded (yellow to the temperature control valve, red to the inlet manifold) to ensure correct reconnection. Place the

Fig. 1.2 Topping up carburettor piston damper (Sec 3)

1 Piston damper   2 Oil level

assembly to one side, clear of the carburettor.
10 Unscrew the piston damper from the top of the carburettor suction chamber and top up the damper chamber to the top of the damper cylinder (Fig. 1.2) with the specified type and viscosity of engine oil. Note that since the advent of modern low-viscosity multigrade engine oils there is no need to use a special carburettor oil in SU carburettors (photos).
11 Raise and lower the carburettor piston, ensuring that it moves smoothly and without sticking, then refit and tighten (very carefully, but securely) the piston damper.
12 Refit the air cleaner assembly, ensuring that the vacuum pipes are correctly reconnected.

3.1A Release air cleaner assembly cover retaining clips ...

3.1B ... and remove screws (carburettor-type air cleaner screws arrowed), then unclip cover

3.3 Ensure new filter element is correctly seated on reassembly

3.5 Slackening fuel pressure release bolt to depressurise fuel system

3.6 Use two spanners when slackening fuel filter unions – note filter clamp screw (arrowed)

3.7 Fitting a new fuel filter – ensure arrow marks (arrowed) point to the right of the car

Idle speed and mixture adjustment

Carburettor engines

13   Before beginning any form of carburettor adjustment, always check first the following.

(a)   *Check that the ignition timing is accurate (Section 4).*
(b)   *Check that the spark plugs are in good condition and correctly gapped (Section 4).*
(c)   *Check that the throttle and choke cables are correctly adjusted (Chapter 4).*
(d)   *Check that the carburettor idle bypass system is functioning correctly (Chapter 4).*
(e)   *Check that the piston damper is topped-up.*
(f)   *Check that the crankcase breather hose(s), the float chamber vent hose and the full load air bleed hose are clear.*
(g)   *Check that the air cleaner filter element is clean and that the exhaust system is in good condition.*
(h)   *If the engine is running very roughly, check the compression pressures (Chapter 2) and bear in mind the possibility that one of the hydraulic tappets might be faulty, producing an incorrect valve clearance.*

14   Take the car on a journey of sufficient length to warm it up to normal operating temperature. **Note:** *Adjustment should be completed within two minutes of return, without stopping the engine. If this cannot be achieved, or if the radiator electric cooling fan operates, wait for the cooling fan to stop and clear any excess fuel from the inlet manifold by racing the engine two or three times to between 2000 and 3000 rpm, then allow it to idle again.*

15   Ensure all electrical loads are switched off; if the car is not equipped with a tachometer, connect one following its manufacturer's instructions. Note the idle speed, comparing it with that specified.

16   The idle speed adjusting knob is under the air cleaner assembly, on the rear right-hand corner of the carburettor; screw it in or out as necessary to obtain the specified speed (photo).

17   The idle mixture is set at the factory and should require no further adjustment. If, due to a change in engine characteristics (carbon build-up, bore wear etc) or after a major carburettor overhaul, the mixture becomes incorrect it can be reset. Note, however, that an exhaust gas analyser (CO meter) will be required to check the mixture and to set it with the necessary standard of accuracy; if this is not available, the car must be taken to a Rover dealer for the work to be carried out.

18   If an exhaust gas analyser is available, follow its manufacturer's instructions to check the CO level. If adjustment is required, it is made by turning the idle air bypass screw, which is set in a deep recess on the carburettor left-hand side, beneath the breather hose (photo). Using a Torx-type screwdriver, size TX10, turn the screw in very small increments until the level is correct; screwing it in (clockwise) richens the idle mixture and increases the CO level.

19   When adjustments are complete, disconnect any test equipment and refit any components removed for access.

Fuel-injected engines

20   While experienced home mechanics with a considerable amount of skill and equipment (including a good-quality tachometer and a good-quality, carefully-calibrated exhaust gas analyser) may be able to check the exhaust CO level and the idle speed, if these are found to be in need of adjustment the car **must** be taken to a suitably-equipped Rover dealer; adjustments can be made only by re-programming the fuel-injection/ignition system ECU using Rover diagnostic equipment connected to the system by the diagnostic connector (photo). For most owners the best solution will be to carry out those maintenance operations that they feel able to undertake, with the car then being taken to a Rover dealer for expert attention to the remaining items.

Lambda sensor operational check

21   This task (outlined in Chapter 4, Part C) can only be carried out using Rover diagnostic equipment; see the preceding paragraph. Do not neglect to have this check made at the specified intervals, especially as the car's mileage increases, as it is the only means of checking (in

3.10A Unscrew piston damper from carburettor suction chamber ...

3.10B ... to top up carburettor damper chamber with engine oil – note carburettor's metal identification tag (arrowed)

3.16 Turn idle speed adjusting knob to alter engine idle speed

3.18 Adjusting idle mixture – shown with air cleaner removed for clarity

3.20 Fuel-injection/ignition system diagnostic connector

conjunction with a CO level check) whether the catalytic converter's closed-loop control system is working properly or not. Lambda sensors are delicate components working under arduous conditions and do not last for ever; if the sensor is no longer effective, it must be renewed.

General fuel system checks

22 The fuel system is most easily checked with the car raised on a hoist or suitably supported on axle stands so the components underneath are readily visible and accessible.

23 If the smell of petrol is noticed while driving or after the car has been parked in the sun, the system should be thoroughly inspected immediately.

24 Remove the petrol tank filler cap and check for damage, corrosion and an unbroken sealing imprint on the gasket. Renew the cap if necessary.

25 With the car raised, inspect the petrol tank and filler neck for punctures, cracks and other damage. The connection between the filler neck and tank is especially critical. Sometimes a rubber filler neck or connecting hose will leak due to loose retaining clamps or deteriorated rubber.

26 Carefully check all rubber hoses and metal fuel lines leading away from the petrol tank. Check for loose connections, deteriorated hoses, crimped lines and other damage. Pay particular attention to the vent pipes and hoses which often loop up around the filler neck and can become blocked or crimped. Follow the lines to the front of the car carefully inspecting them all the way. Renew damaged sections as necessary.

27 From within the engine compartment, check the security of all fuel hose attachments and inspect the fuel hoses and vacuum hoses for kinks, chafing and deterioration. Where an evaporative emission control system is fitted, check its hoses and the security of the purge control valve wiring as well as checking the physical condition of the charcoal canister.

28 Check the operation of the throttle linkage and lubricate the linkage components with a few drops of light oil.

Exhaust system check

29 With the engine cold (or at least an hour after the car has been driven), check the complete exhaust system from the engine to the end of the tailpipe. Ideally the inspection should be carried out with the car on a hoist to permit unrestricted access. If a hoist is not available, raise and support the car on axle stands.

30 Check the exhaust pipes and connections for evidence of leaks, severe corrosion and damage. Make sure that all brackets and mountings are in good condition and tight. Leakage at any of the joints or in other parts of the system will usually show up as a black sooty stain in the vicinity of the leak. Holts Flexiwrap and Holts Gun Gum exhaust repair systems can be used for effective repairs to exhaust pipes and silencer boxes, including ends and bends. Holts Flexiwrap is an MOT approved permanent exhaust repair. Holts Firegum is suitable for the assembly of all exhaust system joints.

31 Rattles and other noises can often be traced to the exhaust system, especially the brackets and mountings. Try to move the pipes and silencers. If the components can come into contact with the body or suspension parts, secure the system with new mountings or if possible, separate the joints and twist the pipes as necessary to provide additional clearance.

4 Ignition system

Warning: *Voltages produced by an electronic ignition system are considerably higher than those produced by conventional ignition systems. Extreme care must be taken when working on the system with the ignition switched on. Persons with surgically-implanted cardiac pacemaker devices should keep well clear of the ignition circuits, components and test equipment*

Ignition timing check and adjustment

Carburettor engines

1 Access to the alternator drive pulley and the ignition timing marks is only possible with the front of the car raised and supported on axle stands (see *'Jacking, towing and wheel changing'*) so that the steering can be turned to full right lock (or the roadwheel removed) and the right-hand underwing shield can be removed (Chapter 11).

2 Before the ignition timing can be checked, the timing marks must be clarified. When looking at a brand-new pulley, the only obvious timing mark is the straight line (emphasised by the factory with white paint) cut radially in the pulley's outer (right-hand) face; this is, however, an engine assembly mark **only** which when aligned with the single, separate mark (at the 12 o'clock position) on the timing belt lower cover sets the crankshaft to 90° BTDC. The **ignition** timing mark is a tiny notch cut in the rim of the pulley's inner (left-hand) rim at approximately 100° anticlockwise from the engine assembly mark; it is virtually invisible and care is required to identify it.

3 Rotate the pulley so that the engine assembly mark points vertically downwards, whereupon the ignition timing mark can be seen clearly enough to scribe a line squarely across the pulley rims. A hacksaw can then be used to enlarge the mark in the pulley outer (right-hand) rim and white paint can be used to highlight it (photos).

4 Start the engine and warm it up to normal operating temperature, then stop the engine and connect a timing light, according to the manufacturer's instructions; if the car is not equipped with a tachometer connect one, following its manufacturer's instructions. Disconnect the vacuum pipe from the distributor and plug it temporarily.

5 Start the engine and have an assistant increase engine speed to the specified amount, then aim the timing light at the timing marks; the highlighted mark should stand out clearly. Check that the pulley mark aligns with the correct cover reference mark, or within the specified tolerance (see Specifications). The carburettor number (where necessary) is given on the metal identification tag attached to one of the suction chamber screws (see photo 3.10B).

6 If adjustment is required, slacken the distributor mounting bolts until the distributor body is just able to rotate, then turn the body clockwise (viewed from the car's left-hand side) to advance the ignition timing, or anti-clockwise to retard it. Tighten the bolts to their specified torque wrench setting when the correct position is found, then recheck the ignition timing to ensure that it has not altered.

7 Increase engine speed and check that the pulley mark advances to beyond the beginning of the cover reference marks, returning to close to the TDC mark when the engine is allowed to idle; this shows that the centrifugal advance mechanism is functioning, but a detailed check must be left to a Rover dealer who has the necessary equipment.

8 Unplug and reconnect the vacuum pipe; the ignition timing should

4.3A Ignition timing reference marks are on timing belt lower cover

4.3B Alternator drive pulley engine assembly mark 'A', factory ignition timing mark 'B', home-made ignition timing mark 'C'

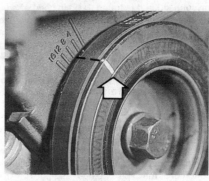

4.3C Ignition timing marks on pulley (arrow) must be clarified as described before timing can be checked

4.11 Tools required for removing, refitting and adjusting spark plugs

4.12A Spark plugs are easily accessible on K8 engines

4.12B On K16 engines remove air cleaner intake duct and spark plug cover ...

4.12C ... unclip spark plug (HT) leads from clip plate – note identifying numbers ...

4.12D ... and remove spark plugs as described in text

advance as the pipe is reconnected, retarding again when it is disconnected. If the ignition timing does not alter, check that the pipe is clear of blockages or kinks and that it is not leaking. Suck on the carburettor end of the pipe; if there is no effect on the ignition timing, then the vacuum capsule is faulty and must be renewed unless the car is fitted with a catalytic converter, in which case the thermostatically-operated vacuum switch may be at fault (Chapter 5). This can be eliminated by connecting a vacuum pipe directly from the carburettor to the distributor; if the vacuum advance is then restored to normal the switch is faulty and must be renewed. Again, more detailed tests must be left to a Rover dealer.

9   When the ignition timing is correct, stop the engine and disconnect the timing light and tachometer, then reconnect the vacuum pipe. Refit the underwing shield and the roadwheel.

Fuel-injected engines

10   While home mechanics with a timing light and a good-quality tachometer may be able to check the ignition timing (the procedure being as described in paragraphs 1 to 5 above, except that the check should be made at idle speed and there is no vacuum pipe to disconnect), if it is found to be in need of adjustment the car **must** be taken to a suitably-equipped Rover dealer; adjustments can be made only by re-programming the fuel-injection/ignition system ECU using Rover diagnostic equipment connected to the system by the diagnostic connector. Note also that the timing and idle speed are under ECU control and may, therefore, vary significantly from the nominal values given in Chapters 4 and 5; without full equipment, any check is therefore nothing more than a rough guide.

Spark plug renewal

11   The correct functioning of the spark plugs is vital for the correct running and efficiency of the engine. It is essential that the plugs fitted are appropriate for the engine (the suitable type is specified at the beginning of this Chapter). If this type is used and the engine is in good condition, the spark plugs should not need attention between scheduled replacement intervals. Spark plug cleaning is rarely necessary and should not be attempted unless specialised equipment is available as damage can easily be caused to the firing ends (photo).

12   To remove the plugs, first open the bonnet. On K8 engines the plugs are easily reached along the front of the engine. On K16 engines disconnect the vacuum pipe from the air temperature control valve, then undo the single screw securing the intake duct to its support bracket and unfasten the rubber strap. Release the two clips securing the air intake duct to the air cleaner assembly and place the duct to one side, taking care not to lose the hot air intake connector hose. Undo the retaining screws and remove the spark plug cover (photos).

13   If the marks on the original-equipment spark plug (HT) leads cannot be seen, mark the leads one to four to correspond to the cylinder the lead serves (number one cylinder is at the timing belt end of the engine). Pull the leads from the plugs by gripping the end fitting, not the lead, otherwise the lead connection may be fractured.

14   It is advisable to remove the dirt from the spark plug recesses using a clean brush, vacuum cleaner or compressed air before removing the plugs, to prevent dirt dropping into the cylinders.

15   Unscrew the plugs using a spark plug spanner, suitable box spanner or a deep socket and extension bar. Keep the socket aligned with the spark plug, otherwise if it is forcibly moved to one side, the ceramic insulator may be broken off. As each plug is removed, examine it as follows.

16   Examination of the spark plugs will give a good indication of the condition of the engine. If the insulator nose of the spark plug is clean and white, with no deposits, this is indicative of a weak mixture or too hot a plug (a hot plug transfers heat away from the electrode slowly, a cold plug transfers heat away quickly).

17   If the tip and insulator nose are covered with hard black-looking deposits, then this is indicative that the mixture is too rich. Should the plug be black and oily, then it is likely that the engine is fairly worn, as well as the mixture being too rich.

18   If the insulator nose is covered with light tan to greyish brown deposits, then the mixture is correct and it is likely that the engine is in good condition.

19   The spark plug electrode gap is of considerable importance as, if it is too large or too small, the size of the spark and its efficiency will be seriously impaired. The gap should be set to the value given in the Specifications at the beginning of this Chapter.

20   To set it, measure the gap with a feeler gauge and then bend open,

or closed, the outer plug electrode until the correct gap is achieved (photos). The centre electrode should never be bent, as this may crack the insulator and cause plug failure, if nothing worse.

21 Special spark plug electrode gap adjusting tools are available from most motor accessory shops (photo).

22 Before fitting the spark plugs check that the threaded connector sleeves are tight and that the plug exterior surfaces and threads are clean.

23 Screw in the spark plugs by hand where possible, then tighten them to the specified torque (photo). Take extra care to enter the plug threads correctly as the cylinder head is of aluminium alloy.

24 Reconnect the spark plug (HT) leads in their correct order and refit all components removed for access.

Spark plug (HT) leads, distributor cap and rotor arm check and renewal

25 The spark plug (HT) leads should be checked whenever new spark plugs are installed in the engine.

26 Ensure that the leads are numbered before removing them, to avoid confusion when refitting. Pull the leads from the plugs by gripping the end fitting, not the lead, otherwise the lead connection may be fractured.

27 Check inside the end fitting for signs of corrosion, which will look like a white crusty powder. Push the end fitting back onto the spark plug ensuring that it is a tight fit on the plug. If not, remove the lead again and use pliers to carefully crimp the metal connector inside the end fitting until it fits securely on the end of the spark plug.

28 Using a clean rag, wipe the entire length of the lead to remove any built-up dirt and grease. Once the lead is clean, check for burns, cracks and other damage. Do not bend the lead excessively or pull the lead lengthwise – the conductor inside might break.

29 Disconnect the other end of the lead from the distributor cap. Again, pull only on the end fitting. Check for corrosion and a tight fit in the same manner as the spark plug end. If an ohmmeter is available, check the resistance of the lead by connecting the meter between the spark plug end of the lead and the segment inside the distributor cap. Refit the lead securely on completion (photos).

4.20A Measuring the spark plug electrode gap using a feeler gauge

4.20B Measuring the spark plug electrode gap using a wire gauge

4.21 Adjusting the spark plug electrode gap using a special tool

4.23 Using a short length of rubber hose to guide spark plugs into place on refitting

4.29A Disconnecting a spark plug (HT) lead from the distributor cap

4.29B Checking the resistance of the spark plug (HT) leads using a digital ohmmeter

4.32A Distributor cap is retained by two (offset) screws

4.32B Removing distributor rotor arm screw – fuel-injected engines

30   Check the remaining leads one at a time, in the same way.

31   If new spark plug (HT) leads are required, purchase a set for your specific car and engine. A suitable type is given in the Specifications at the beginning of this Chapter.

32   Unscrew its two screws and remove the distributor cap, wipe it clean and carefully inspect it inside and out for signs of cracks, carbon tracks (tracking) and worn, burned or loose contacts; check that the cap's carbon brush is unworn, free to move against spring pressure and making good contact with the rotor arm. Similarly inspect the rotor arm; on fuel-injected engines it is secured by a (hex-head) screw – if checking components with a meter, note that the rotor arm has an in-built resistor. Renew these components if any defects are found. It is common practice to renew the cap and rotor arm whenever new spark plug (HT) leads are fitted. When fitting a new cap, remove the leads from the old cap one at a time and fit them to the new cap in the exact same location – do not simultaneously remove all the leads from the old cap or firing order confusion may occur – note that the screw locations are offset so that the cap may be refitted only one way; tighten the screws to their specified torque wrench settings (photos).

33   Even with the ignition system in first class condition, some engines may still occasionally experience poor starting attributable to damp ignition components. To disperse moisture Holts Wet Start can be very effective. Holts Damp Start should be used for providing a sealing coat to exclude moisture from the ignition system, and in extreme difficulty, Holts Cold Start will help to start a car when only a very poor spark occurs.

5   Clutch

General check

1   Check that the clutch pedal moves smoothly and easily through its full travel and that the clutch itself functions correctly, with no trace of slip or drag. If excessive effort is required to operate the clutch, check first that the cable is correctly routed and undamaged, then remove the pedal to ensure that its pivot is properly greased before suspecting a fault in the cable itself; if the cable is worn or damaged, or if its self-adjusting mechanism is no longer effective, it must be renewed (Chapter 6).

2   No adjustment is possible of the cable or of the clutch release; if any fault develops in the clutch, the transmission must be removed (Chapter 7) so that the clutch can be overhauled (Chapter 6).

6   Transmission

Oil level check

1   Even though this makes access awkward, the oil level must be checked with the car standing on its wheels on level ground. Also, the level must be checked before the car is driven, or at least 5 minutes after the engine has been switched off. If the oil is checked immediately after driving the car, some of the oil will remain distributed around the transmission components, resulting in an inaccurate level reading.

2   Wipe clean the area around the (hex-head) filler/level plug, which is located at the rear of the transmission, next to the left-hand driveshaft inner constant velocity joint, then unscrew the plug and clean it; discard the sealing washer. To avoid rounding-off the corners of the plug hexagon, use only good quality, close-fitting, single-hexagon or surface drive spanners or sockets.

3   The oil level should reach the lower edge of the filler/level hole. A certain amount of oil will have gathered behind the filler/level plug and will trickle out when it is removed; this does **not** necessarily indicate that the level is correct. To ensure that a true level is established, wait until the initial trickle has stopped, then add oil as necessary until a trickle of new oil can be seen emerging. The level will be correct when the flow ceases; use only good quality oil of the specified type (photo).

4   **Note:** *Refilling the transmission is an extremely awkward operation; above all, allow plenty of time for the oil level to settle properly before checking it. If a large amount had to be added to the transmission and a large amount flows out on checking the level, refit the filler/level plug and take the vehicle on a short journey so that the new oil is distributed fully around the transmission components, then recheck the level when it has settled again.*

5   If the transmission has been overfilled so that oil flows out as soon as the filler/level plug is removed, check that the car is completely level (front-to-rear and side-to-side) and allow the surplus to drain off into a suitable container.

6   When the level is correct, fit a new sealing washer and refit the filler/level plug, tightening it to the specified torque wrench setting. Wash off any spilt oil.

Oil renewal

7   The manufacturer specifies that, provided only the recommended oils are used (see a Rover dealer for details) the transmission is filled for life and the oil does not require regular changes; this operation does not, therefore, appear in the manufacturer's service schedule.

8   If the transmission oil is to be drained and refilled for any other reason, the operation is described in Chapter 7, Section 2.

7   Driveshafts

Driveshaft rubber gaiter and CV joint check

1   With the car raised and securely supported on axle stands, turn the steering onto full lock then slowly rotate the roadwheel. Inspect the condition of the outer constant velocity (CV) joint rubber gaiters while

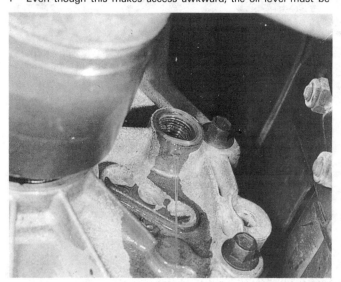

6.3 Transmission oil level is correct when oil has just stopped trickling from filler/level plug hole

7.1 Checking driveshaft outer CV joint rubber gaiter

squeezing the gaiters to open out the folds (photo). Check for signs of cracking, splits or deterioration of the rubber which may allow the grease to escape and lead to the entry of water and grit into the joint. Also check the security and condition of the retaining clips. Repeat these checks on the inner CV joints. If any damage or deterioration is found, the gaiters should be renewed (Chapter 8).

2   At the same time check the general condition of the CV joints themselves by first holding the driveshaft and attempting to rotate the roadwheel. Repeat this check by holding the inner joint and attempting to rotate the driveshaft. Any appreciable movement indicates wear in the joints, in the driveshaft splines, or a loose driveshaft nut.

8 Braking system

Hydraulic fluid level check

1   The brake master cylinder and fluid reservoir is mounted on top of the vacuum servo unit in the engine compartment. The MAX and MIN level marks are indicated on the side of the reservoir and the fluid level should be maintained between these marks at all times.

2   If topping-up is necessary, first wipe the area around the filler cap with a clean rag before removing the cap; hold the cap's centre terminal block stationary to prevent damage to the electrical connections. When adding fluid, pour it carefully into the reservoir to avoid spilling it on surrounding painted surfaces. Be sure to use only the specified brake hydraulic fluid since mixing different types of fluid can cause damage to the system (photo). See 'Lubricants, fluids and capacities' at the beginning of this Chapter. **Warning:** *Brake hydraulic fluid can harm your eyes and damage painted surfaces, so use extreme caution when handling and pouring it. Do not use fluid that has been standing open for some time as it absorbs moisture from the air. Excess moisture can cause a dangerous loss of braking effectiveness.*

3   When adding fluid it is a good idea to inspect the reservoir for contamination. The system should be drained and refilled if deposits, dirt particles or contamination are seen in the fluid.

4   After filling the reservoir to the proper level, make sure that the cap is refitted securely to avoid leaks and the entry of foreign matter.

5   The fluid level in the master cylinder reservoir will drop slightly as the brake pads and shoes wear down during normal operation. If the reservoir requires repeated topping-up to maintain the proper level, this is an indication of an hydraulic leak somewhere in the system which should be investigated immediately.

Hydraulic fluid renewal

6   The procedure is similar to that for the bleeding of the hydraulic system as described in Chapter 9, except that the brake fluid reservoir should be emptied by syphoning, using a clean poultry baster or similar before starting, and allowance should be made for the old fluid to be expelled when bleeding a section of the circuit.

7   Working as described in Chapter 9, open the first bleed nipple in the sequence and pump the brake pedal gently until nearly all the old fluid has been emptied from the master cylinder reservoir. Top up to the 'Max' level with new fluid and continue pumping until only the new fluid

remains in the reservoir and new fluid can be seen emerging from the bleed nipple. Tighten the nipple and top the reservoir level up to the 'Max' level line.

8   Old hydraulic fluid is invariably much darker in colour than the new, making it easy to distinguish the two.

9   Work through all the remaining nipples in the sequence until new fluid can be seen at all of them. Be careful to keep the master cylinder reservoir topped up to above the 'Min' level at all times or air may enter the system and greatly increase the length of the task.

10   When the operation is complete, check that all nipples are securely tightened and that their dust caps are refitted. Wash off all traces of spilt fluid and recheck the master cylinder reservoir fluid level.

11   Check the operation of the brakes before taking the car on the road.

General system check

12   Check that the brake pedal pivot is properly greased and that the pedal moves smoothly and easily through its full travel. When the engine is switched off, the pedal should have a small amount of free play, then firm resistance. If the pedal feels spongy or if it has a long travel, the system should be checked further, as described in Chapter 9.

13   The brake hydraulic system consists of a number of metal hydraulic pipes which run from the master cylinder around the engine compartment to the front brakes and pressure regulating valves and along the underbody to the rear brakes. Flexible hoses are fitted at front and rear to cater for steering and suspension movement.

14   When checking the system, first look for signs of leakage at the pipe or hose unions, then examine the flexible hoses for signs of cracking, chafing or deterioration of the rubber. Bend them sharply between the fingers (but do not actually bend them double or the casing may be damaged) and check that this does not reveal previously hidden cracks, cuts or splits (photo). Check that all pipes and hoses are securely fastened in their clips.

15   Carefully work along the length of the metal hydraulic pipes looking for dents, kinks, damage of any sort or corrosion. Corrosion should be polished off; if the depth of pitting is significant the pipe must be renewed.

Front brake pad, caliper and disc check

16   Jack up the front of the car and support it securely on axle stands, then remove the roadwheel (see 'Jacking, towing and wheel changing').

17   For a quick check, the thickness of friction material remaining on each brake pad can be measured through the slot in the caliper body (photo). If any pad's friction material is worn to the specified thickness or less, all four pads must be renewed.

18   For a comprehensive check, the brake pads should be removed and cleaned. This will permit the operation of the caliper to be checked and the condition of the brake disc itself to be fully examined on both sides (Chapter 9).

Rear brake shoe adjustment and check, wheel cylinder and drum check

Rear brake shoe adjustment

19   Jack up the rear of the car and support it securely on axle stands (see 'Jacking, towing and wheel changing').

20   Check that the handbrake is fully released and that the roadwheel rotates freely, with no sound of the brake shoes rubbing on the drum.

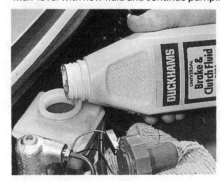

8.2 Use only good quality hydraulic fluid of specified type when topping up brake system fluid reservoir

8.14 Checking a braking system flexible hose

8.17 Front brake pad friction material can be checked through slot in caliper body

8.21 Using a brake-adjusting spanner to adjust rear brake shoes

8.25 Rear brake shoe friction material can be checked by removing grommet in brake backplate

8.32 Adjusting the handbrake

21   Locate the square-headed brake adjuster on the inboard face of the rear brake backplate, at the top. If it is stuck with corrosion, apply a good quantity of penetrating fluid and allow time for it to 'work' before attempting adjustment. Using a brake-adjusting spanner, rotate the adjuster clockwise (looking at it outwards from the car's centre-line) until the roadwheel locks (photo). Do not apply excessive force to the adjuster, but note that it has four 'tight spots' per revolution; ensure that the roadwheel is locked when the adjuster is backed off from the last (tightest) of these tight spots.

22   Now rotate the adjuster anti-clockwise until the roadwheel is just free to rotate with no sound of rubbing; again, ensure that the final setting is between the tight spots.

23   Apply a smear of grease to the exposed adjuster threads to prevent corrosion, then repeat the operation on the opposite side of the car. Finally, check the handbrake adjustment.

Rear brake shoe, wheel cylinder and drum check

24   Jack up the rear of the car and support it securely on axle stands (see *'Jacking, towing and wheel changing'*).

25   For a quick check, the thickness of friction material remaining on one of the brake shoes can be measured through the slot in the brake backplate that is exposed by prising out its sealing grommet (photo). If a rod of the same diameter as the specified minimum thickness is placed against the shoe friction material, the amount of wear can quickly be assessed; if any shoe's friction material is worn to the specified thickness or less, all four shoes must be renewed.

26   For a comprehensive check, the brake drums should be removed and cleaned. This will permit the wheel cylinders to be checked and the condition of the brake drum itself to be fully examined (Chapter 9).

Handbrake check and adjustment

27   The handbrake should be capable of holding the parked car stationary, even on steep slopes, when applied with moderate force. The mechanism should be firm and positive in feel with no trace of stiffness or sponginess from the cables, and should release immediately the handbrake lever is released. If the mechanism is faulty in any of these respects it must be checked immediately.

28   To check the setting, apply the handbrake firmly several times to establish correct shoe-to-drum clearance, then release fully the lever. Applying normal, moderate pressure, pull the handbrake lever to the fully-applied position and count the number of notches required to do so; if the number of notches is more or less than that specified, adjustment is required.

29   To adjust the handbrake, first jack up the rear of the car and support it securely on axle stands (see *'Jacking, towing and wheel changing'*).

Condition	Probable cause	Corrective action	Condition	Probable cause	Corrective action
Shoulder wear	• Underinflation (wear on both sides) • Incorrect wheel camber (wear on one side) • Hard cornering	• Check and adjust pressure • Repair or renew suspension parts • Reduce speed	**Feathered edge** **Toe wear**	• Incorrect toe setting	• Adjust front wheel alignment
Centre wear	• Overinflation	• Measure and adjust pressure	**Uneven wear**	• Incorrect camber or castor • Malfunctioning suspension • Unbalanced wheel • Out-of-round brake disc/drum	• Repair or renew suspension parts • Repair or renew suspension parts • Balance tyres • Machine or renew disc/drum

Fig. 1.3 Tyre tread wear patterns and causes (Sec 9)

Are your plugs trying to tell you something?

Normal.
Grey-brown deposits, lightly coated core nose. Plugs ideally suited to engine, and engine in good condition.

Heavy Deposits.
A build up of crusty deposits, light-grey sandy colour in appearance.
Fault: Often caused by worn valve guides, excessive use of upper cylinder lubricant, or idling for long periods.

Lead Glazing.
Plug insulator firing tip appears yellow or green/yellow and shiny in appearance.
Fault: Often caused by incorrect carburation, excessive idling followed by sharp acceleration. Also check ignition timing.

Carbon fouling.
Dry, black, sooty deposits.
Fault: over-rich fuel mixture.
Check: carburettor mixture settings, float level, choke operation, air filter.

Oil fouling.
Wet, oily deposits. Fault: worn bores/piston rings or valve guides; sometimes occurs (temporarily) during running-in period.

Overheating.
Electrodes have glazed appearance, core nose very white – few deposits. Fault: plug overheating. Check: plug value, ignition timing, fuel octane rating (too low) and fuel mixture (too weak).

Electrode damage.
Electrodes burned away; core nose has burned, glazed appearance. Fault: pre-ignition. Check: for correct heat range and as for 'overheating'.

Split core nose.
(May appear initially as a crack). Fault: detonation or wrong gap-setting technique. Check: ignition timing, cooling system, fuel mixture (too weak).

WHY DOUBLE COPPER IS BETTER FOR YOUR ENGINE.

Unique Trapezoidal Copper Cored Earth Electrode — 50% Larger Spark Area

Copper Cored Centre Electrode

Champion Double Copper plugs are the first in the world to have copper core in both centre <u>and</u> earth electrode. This innovative design means that they run cooler by up to 100°C – giving greater efficiency and longer life. These double copper cores transfer heat away from the tip of the plug faster and more efficiently. Therefore, Double Copper runs at cooler temperatures than conventional plugs giving improved acceleration response and high speed performance with no fear of pre-ignition.

Champion Double Copper plugs also feature a unique trapezoidal earth electrode giving a 50% increase in spark area. This, together with the double copper cores, offers greatly reduced electrode wear, so the spark stays stronger for longer.

 FASTER COLD STARTING

 FOR UNLEADED OR LEADED FUEL

 ELECTRODES UP TO 100°C COOLER

 BETTER ACCELERATION RESPONSE

 LOWER EMISSIONS

 50% BIGGER SPARK AREA

 THE LONGER LIFE PLUG

Plug Tips/Hot and Cold.
Spark plugs must operate within well-defined temperature limits to avoid cold fouling at one extreme and overheating at the other.
Champion and the car manufacturers work out the best plugs for an engine to give optimum performance under all conditions, from freezing cold starts to sustained high speed motorway cruising.
Plugs are often referred to as hot or cold. With Champion, the higher the number on its body, the hotter the plug, and the lower the number the cooler the plug. For the correct plug for your car refer to the specifications at the beginning of this chapter.

Plug Cleaning
Modern plug design and materials mean that Champion no longer recommends periodic plug cleaning. Certainly don't clean your plugs with a wire brush as this can cause metal conductive paths across the nose of the insulator so impairing its performance and resulting in loss of acceleration and reduced m.p.g.
However, if plugs are removed, always carefully clean the area where the plug seats in the cylinder head as grit and dirt can sometimes cause gas leakage.
Also wipe any traces of oil or grease from plug leads as this may lead to arcing.

CHAMPION

DOUBLE COPPER

30   Remove the split pin and clevis pin from the left-hand rear brake handbrake lever; **do not** touch the right-hand brake.
31   Rotate the brake adjusters clockwise until the roadwheels lock (see paragraph 21 above), then pump the brake pedal several times to ensure that the shoes are forced firmly into contact with the drums. Check that both rear roadwheels are locked, then rotate both adjusters anti-clockwise through two flats.
32   Working inside the passenger compartment, carefully peel back the carpet between the front seat rear mounting bar and the handbrake lever. Hold the adjuster nut whilst slackening the adjuster locknut (photo).
33   Ensuring that the threaded adjuster itself does not rotate, turn the adjuster nut until the holes line up in the end of the left-hand handbrake cable and the rear brake handbrake lever, then refit the clevis pin and secure it with a new split pin, spreading its ends securely. Tighten the adjuster locknut without disturbing the setting.
34   With the handbrake fully released, check that the roadwheels are free to rotate and that they first bind and then lock at the specified number of notches as the lever is pulled on.
35   If all is well, pull the handbrake to the fully-applied position and then release it. If the left-hand side rear brake still binds, rotate the adjuster anti-clockwise through no more than two flats until the roadwheel rotates freely; **do not** adjust the right-hand brake.
36   When adjustment is correct, lower the car to the ground.

9   Suspension and steering

Front suspension and steering check

1   Raise the front of the car and securely support it on axle stands.
2   Visually inspect the balljoint dust covers and the steering gear rubber gaiters for splits, chafing or deterioration (photo). Any wear of these components will cause loss of lubricant together with dirt and water entry, resulting in rapid deterioration of the balljoints or steering gear.

3   Grasp the roadwheel at the 12 o'clock and 6 o'clock positions and try to rock it (photo). Very slight free play may be felt, but if the movement is appreciable further investigation is necessary to determine the source. Continue rocking the wheel while an assistant depresses the brake pedal. If the movement is now eliminated or significantly reduced, it is likely that the hub bearings are at fault. If the free play is still evident with the brake pedal depressed, then there is wear in the suspension joints or mountings.
4   Now grasp the roadwheel at the 9 o'clock and 3 o'clock positions and try to rock it as before. Any movement felt now may again be caused by wear in the hub bearings, or in the track rod balljoints. If a balljoint is worn the visual movement will be obvious. If the inner joint is suspect it can be felt by placing a hand over the steering gear rubber gaiter and gripping the track rod. If the wheel is now rocked, movement will be felt at the inner joint if wear has taken place.
5   Using a large screwdriver or flat bar check for wear in the suspension mounting bushes by levering between the relevant suspension component and its attachment point (photo). Some movement is to be expected as the mountings are made of rubber, but excessive wear should be obvious. Also check the condition of any visible rubber bushes, looking for splits, cracks or contamination of the rubber.
6   With the car standing on its wheels, have an assistant turn the steering wheel back and forth about an eighth of a turn each way. There should be very little, if any, lost movement between the steering wheel and the roadwheels. If this is not the case, closely observe the joints and mountings previously described, but in addition check for wear of the steering column universal joint and the steering gear itself.
7   Check the Hydragas system components, looking for signs of fluid leaks from the units and connecting pipes as well as for signs of corrosion or other damage; if any is found, it should be repaired as soon as possible. The manufacturer does not specify a regular check of the ride heights, but these should be checked with reasonable frequency to ensure that the steering and suspension are functioning properly; refer to the relevant Sections of Chapter 10.

Damper check

8   Where additional dampers are fitted, check for any signs of fluid

9.2 Checking one of the steering gear rubber gaiters

9.3 Rocking the roadwheel to check steering/suspension wear

9.5 Using a lever to check for wear in anti-roll bar mountings

9.15 Greasing the front suspension upper arm pivot bearings

9.19A Using a lever to check for wear in rear suspension trailing arm pivot bearings

9.19B Using a lever to check for wear in rear suspension subframe (front) mountings

leakage around the damper body or from the piston rod. Should any fluid be noticed the damper is defective internally and should be renewed. **Note:** *Dampers should always be renewed in pairs on the same axle.*

9   The efficiency of the damper may be checked by bouncing the car at each corner. Generally speaking, the body should return to its normal position and stop after being depressed. If it rises and returns on a rebound, the damper is probably suspect. Examine also the damper upper and lower mountings for any signs of wear.

Front suspension upper arm pivot bearings – greasing

10   Metros are unusual for modern cars in that they are still fitted with grease nipples. This is so that highly-stressed bearings can be lubricated regularly using a grease gun instead of having to dismantle them, clean them and repack them with grease on reassembly.

11   It is essential that the suspension pivots are greased regularly in accordance with the maintenance schedule or their bearings will wear out very quickly indeed, causing poor handling, a poor ride and instability, poor braking and greatly increased tyre wear, as well as the considerable expense of time and money in effecting repairs. Worn suspension pivot bearings are also a well-known MOT failure point for Metros, so the slight effort spent in greasing the pivots regularly will be well repaid in terms of long bearing life.

12   If you do not already possess one, obtain a grease gun which will fit the grease nipples (one with a long, flexible spout would be best) and follow its manufacturer's instructions to fill it with the specified type of grease – see *'Lubricants, fluids and capacities'*. This is always a filthy job, so have plenty of clean rag available and make sure the hand cleaner is within easy reach for afterwards!

13   When the grease gun is filled, force a little grease out of the nozzle to eject any dirt and check that any air bubbles are removed using the bleed screw. Wipe clean the nozzle.

14   If you don't mind getting dirty, the grease nipple can be reached by turning the steering to the appropriate full lock and working behind the roadwheel; if more than one task is to be carried out, however, it is best to jack up the car and to remove the roadwheel. If the roadwheel is not to be removed, take the weight of the car off the pivot by jacking it up until the roadwheel is just clear of the ground and supporting the car on an axle stand.

15   A grease nipple is screwed into the front end of each front suspension upper arm pivot (photo); wipe the nipple clean and press the gun's nozzle firmly and squarely over it. Operate the gun until **clean** grease can be seen exuding from **both** ends of the pivot, then remove the gun, wipe clean the nipple and wipe off the excess grease from the pivot. It is essential that as much as possible of the old grease within the pivot is pushed out and replaced by clean grease; if your grease gun has a small capacity, you may have to refill it more than once before the pivot is full.

16   If, on operating the gun, grease just escapes from between the nozzle and the nipple, first reseat the nozzle and try again. If grease still escapes it is probable that the nipple is clogged; this can happen if the suspension has not been greased for some time as the grease can harden in the nipple. To clear the nipple, unscrew it and force grease through it with the gun; if the nipple is still clogged it must be renewed, although it is always worth trying the effect of immersing it first in boiling water to melt the grease.

17   When the pivot is properly greased, repeat the operation on the other side of the car.

Rear suspension check

18   Raise the rear of the car and support it securely on axle stands.

19   Working as described above for the front suspension, check the rear hub bearings and the trailing arm pivot bearings for wear, check the security of all component mountings and use a lever to check the condition of the subframe (front) and other mountings (photos).

Rear suspension trailing arm pivot bearings – greasing

20   All the general comments made previously about greasing the front suspension upper arm pivot bearings apply equally to the rear suspension trailing arm pivot bearings. However, it is even more important that the trailing arm pivot bearings are regularly greased as the pivots are directly exposed to the road dirt, water and salt thrown up by the rear wheels; this makes the bearings much more vulnerable and even more prone to wearing out if not regularly greased.

21   The actual greasing procedure is exactly the same as that described previously; read through that procedure before starting work.

22   A grease nipple is screwed into the outboard end of each rear suspension trailing arm pivot (photo); although access is easy, do not forget first to take the weight of the car off the pivot by jacking it up until the roadwheel is just clear of the ground. There is no need to use axle stands if you are not intending to work under the car, but take care while the car is supported only on the jack.

23   When **clean** grease can be seen exuding from **both** ends of the pivot, remove the gun and wipe clean the nipple, then wipe off as much excess grease as possible from the pivot and repeat the operation on the other side of the car.

Wheel and tyre maintenance and tyre pressure checks

24   Periodically remove the wheels and clean any dirt or mud from their inside and outside surfaces. Examine the wheel rims for signs of rusting, corrosion or other damage. Light alloy wheels are easily damaged by 'kerbing' whilst parking, and similarly steel wheels may become dented or buckled. Renewal of the wheel is very often the only course of remedial action possible.

25   To check that the roadwheel nuts are securely fastened, remove the roadwheel trim (where fitted), then slacken each nut in turn through one-quarter of a turn and tighten it to the specified torque wrench setting. Refit the trim, where applicable.

26   The tyres originally fitted are equipped with tread wear indicators which will appear flush with the surface of the tread, thus producing the effect of a continuous band of rubber across the width of the tyre when the tread depth is reduced to approximately 1.6 mm (0.063 in); **at this point, the tyre must be renewed immediately**. Tread wear can be monitored with a simple inexpensive device, known as a tread depth indicator gauge (photo).

27   Note any abnormal tread wear with reference to Fig. 1.3. Tread pattern irregularities such as feathering, flat spots and more wear on one side than the other are indications of front wheel alignment and/or balance problems. If any of these conditions are noted, they should be rectified as soon as possible.

9.22 Greasing the rear suspension trailing arm pivot bearings

9.26 Checking tyre tread depth with a depth gauge

9.31 Checking the tyre pressures with a tyre pressure gauge

28   General tyre wear is influenced to a large degree by driving style – harsh braking and acceleration or fast cornering will all produce more rapid tyre wear. Interchanging of tyres may result in more even wear, however it is worth bearing in mind that if this is completely effective, the added expense is incurred of replacing simultaneously a complete set of tyres, which may prove financially restrictive for many owners.

29   Front tyres may wear unevenly as a result of wheel misalignment. The front wheels should always be correctly aligned according to the settings specified (Chapter 10).

30   Regularly check the tyres for damage in the form of cuts or bulges, especially in the sidewalls. Remove any nails or stones embedded in the tread before they penetrate the tyre to cause deflation. If removal of a nail does reveal that the tyre has been punctured, refit the nail so that its point of penetration is marked, then immediately change the wheel and have the tyre repaired by a tyre dealer. Do not drive on a tyre in such a condition. In many cases a puncture can be simply repaired by the use of an inner tube of the correct size and type. If in any doubt as to the possible consequences of any damage found, consult your local tyre dealer for advice.

31   Ensure that tyre pressures are checked regularly and maintained correctly. Checking should be carried out with the tyres cold and not immediately after the car has been in use (photo). If the pressures are checked with the tyres hot, an apparently high reading will be obtained owing to heat expansion. Under no circumstances should an attempt be made to reduce the pressures to the quoted cold reading in this instance, or effective underinflation will result.

32   Underinflation will cause overheating of the tyre owing to excessive flexing of the casing, and the tread will not sit correctly on the road surface. This will cause a consequent loss of adhesion and excessive wear, not to mention the danger of sudden tyre failure due to heat build-up.

33   Overinflation will cause rapid wear of the centre part of the tyre tread coupled with reduced adhesion, harsher ride, and the danger of shock damage occurring in the tyre casing.

34   The balance of each wheel and tyre assembly should be maintained to avoid excessive wear, not only to the tyres but also to the steering and suspension components. Wheel imbalance is normally signified by vibration through the car's bodyshell, although in many cases it is particularly noticeable through the steering wheel. Conversely, it should be noted that wear or damage in suspension or steering components may cause excessive tyre wear. Out-of-round or out-of-true tyres, damaged wheels and wheel bearing wear also fall into this category. Balancing will not usually cure vibration caused by such wear.

35   Wheel balancing may be carried out with the wheel either on or off the car. If balanced on the car, ensure that the wheel-to-hub relationship is marked in some way prior to subsequent wheel removal so that it may be refitted in its original position.

36   Legal restrictions apply to many aspects of tyre fitting and usage and in the UK this information is contained in the Motor Vehicle Construction and Use Regulations. It is suggested that a copy of these regulations is obtained from your local police if in doubt as to current legal requirements with regard to tyre type and condition, minimum tread depth, etc.

10   Bodywork and fittings

Cleaning the car's exterior

1   The general condition of a car's bodywork is the one thing that significantly affects its value. Maintenance is easy but needs to be regular. Neglect, particularly after minor damage, can lead quickly to further deterioration and costly repair bills. It is important also to keep watch on those parts of the car not immediately visible, for instance the underbody, inside all the wheel arches and the lower part of the engine compartment.

2   The basic maintenance routine for the bodywork is washing – preferably with a lot of water, from a hose. This will remove all the loose solids which may have stuck to the car. It is important to flush these off in such a way as to prevent grit from scratching the finish. The wheel arches and underbody need washing in the same way to remove any accumulated mud which will retain moisture and tend to encourage rust, particularly in winter when it is essential that any salt (from that put

down on the roads) is washed off. Paradoxically enough, the best time to clean the underbody and wheel arches is in wet weather when the mud is thoroughly wet and soft. In very wet weather the underbody is usually cleaned automatically of large accumulations; this is therefore a good time for inspection.

3   If the car is very dirty, especially underneath or in the engine compartment, it is tempting to use one of the pressure washers or steam cleaners available on garage forecourts; while these are quick and effective, especially for the removal of the accumulation of oily grime which sometimes is allowed to become thick in certain areas, their usage does have some disadvantages. If caked-on dirt is simply blasted off the paintwork, its finish soon becomes scratched and dull and the pressure can allow water to penetrate door and window seals and the lock mechanisms; if the full force of such a jet is directed at the car's underbody the wax-based protective coating can easily be damaged and water (with whatever cleaning solvent is used) could be forced into crevices or components that it would not normally reach. Similarly, if such equipment is used to clean the engine compartment water can be forced into the components of the fuel and electrical systems and the protective coating can be removed that is applied to many small components during manufacture; this may therefore actually promote corrosion (especially inside electrical connectors) and initiate engine problems or other electrical faults. Also, if the jet is pointed directly at any of the oil seals, water can be forced past the seal lips and into the engine or transmission. Great care is required, therefore, if such equipment is used and, in general, regular cleaning by such methods should be avoided.

4   A much better solution in the long term is just to flush away as much loose dirt as possible using a hose alone, even if this leaves the engine compartment looking 'dirty'. If an oil leak has developed, or if any other accumulation of oil or grease is to be removed, there are one or two excellent grease solvents available, such as Holts Engine Cleaner or Holts Foambrite, which can be brush applied. The dirt can then be simply hosed off. Take care to replace the wax-based protective coat, if this was affected by the solvent.

5   Normal washing of the car's bodywork is best carried out using cold or warm water with a proprietary car shampoo such as Holts Turtle Wax Zipwax or Turtle Extra Car Wash and Wax. Remove dead insects with products such as Holts Fly Squash Remover; tar spots can be removed either by using white spirit, followed by soapy water to remove all traces of spirit, or by using Holts Body + Plus Tar Remover. Try to keep water out of the bonnet air intakes and check afterwards that the heater air inlet box drain tube is clear so that any water has drained out of the box.

6   After washing the paintwork, wipe off with a chamois leather to give an unspotted clear finish. A coat of clear protective wax polish, such as one of the many excellent Turtle Wax polishes, will give added protection against chemical pollutants in the air. If the paintwork sheen has dulled or oxidised, use a cleaner/polisher combination such as Turtle Extra to restore the brilliance of the shine. This requires a little effort, but such dulling is usually caused because regular washing has been neglected. Care needs to be taken with metallic paintwork, as special non-abrasive cleaner/polisher is required to avoid damage to the finish.

7   Brightwork should be treated in the same way as paintwork.

8   Windscreens and windows can be kept clear of the smeary film which often appears, by the use of proprietary glass cleaner like Holts Mixra. Never use any form of wax or other body or chromium polish on glass.

Exterior paintwork and body panels check

9   Once the car has been washed and all tar spots and other surface blemishes have been cleaned off, check carefully all paintwork, looking closely for chips or scratches; check with particular care vulnerable areas such as the front (bonnet and spoiler) and around the wheel arches. Any damage to the paintwork must be rectified as soon as possible to comply with the terms of the manufacturer's cosmetic and anti-corrosion warranties; check with a Rover dealer for details.

10   If a chip or (light) scratch is found that is recent and still free from rust, it can be touched-up using the appropriate touch-up pencil; these can be obtained from Rover dealers or from the Holts Dupli-Color Touch range. Any more serious damage, or rusted stone chips, can be repaired as described in the relevant sub-section of Chapter 11, Section 2, but if damage or corrosion is so severe that a panel must be renewed, seek professional advice as soon as possible.

11   Always check that the door and ventilator opening drain holes and pipes are completely clear so that water can be drained out.

Underbody sealer check

12   The wax-based underbody protective coating should be inspected annually, preferably just prior to winter, when the underbody should be washed down as thoroughly but gently as possible (see paragraph 3 above concerning steam cleaners, etc) and any damage to the coating repaired using Holts Undershield; if any of the body panels are disturbed for repair or renewed, do not forget to replace the coating and to inject wax into door panels, sills, box sections etc, to maintain the level of protection provided by the car's manufacturer.

13   Check carefully that the wheel arch liners and underwing shields are in place and securely fastened and that there is no sign of underbody damage or of developing corrosion; if any is found, seek immediate professional advice.

Hinge and lock check and lubrication

14   Lubricate the hinges of the bonnet, doors and tailgate with a light machine oil (Duckhams Home Oil).

15   Lightly lubricate the bonnet release mechanism and cable with the specified type of grease.

16   The door and tailgate latches, strikers and locks must be lubricated using only the special Rover Door Lock and Latch Lubricant supplied in 25 gram sachets under Part Number VWN 10075; inject 1 gram into each lock and wipe off any surplus, then apply a thin film to the latches and strikers. Do not lubricate the steering lock mechanism with oil or any other lubricant which might foul the ignition switch contacts; if the lock is stiff, try to introduce a graphite-based powder into the mechanism.

17   Check carefully the security and operation of all hinges, latches and locks, adjusting them where required. Check the operation of the central locking system (if fitted).

18   Check the condition and operation of the tailgate struts, renewing them if either is leaking or no longer able to support the tailgate securely when raised.

19   If a sunroof is fitted, lubricate very sparingly the seal lip with Rover's Non-Staining Grease (Corning No. 7) available under Part Number BAU 5812.

Seat belt check

20   All models are fitted with three-point lap and diagonal inertia reel seat belts at both front and the rear outer seats. The rear centre seat has a two-point lap-type belt which is fixed (ie not inertia reel).

21   Each front seat belt has two threaded holes provided in the door pillar to permit the top anchorage to be positioned (as closely as possible) so that the belt crosses the mid-point of the wearer's shoulder, rather than rest on his/her neck; if this adjustment is made, ensure that the mounting bolt is tightened to the specified torque wrench setting and that the blanking plug is refitted in the unused hole.

22   Belt maintenance is limited to regular inspection. Check the webbing for signs of fraying, cuts or other damage, pulling the belt out to its full extent to check its entire length. Check the operation of the buckles by fitting the belt tongue plate and pulling hard to ensure that it remains locked, then check the retractor mechanism (inertia reel only) by pulling out the belt to the halfway point and jerking hard; the mechanism must lock immediately to prevent any further unreeling, but must allow free movement during normal driving. Finally, ensure that all mounting bolts are securely tightened. Note that the bolts are shouldered so that the belt anchor points are free to rotate.

23   If there is any sign of damage, or any doubt about a belt's condition, it must be renewed. If the car has been involved in a collision any belts in use at the time must be renewed as a matter of course and all other belts should be checked carefully.

24   Use only warm water and non-detergent soap to clean the belts. Never use any chemical cleaners, strong detergents, dyes or bleaches. Keep the belts fully extended until they have dried naturally; do not apply heat to dry them.

Cleaning the car's interior

25   Mats and carpets should be brushed or vacuum cleaned regularly to keep them free of grit. If they are badly stained remove them from the car for scrubbing or sponging and make quite sure they are dry before refitting.

26   Where leather upholstery is fitted it should be cleaned only if necessary, using either a mild soap (such as saddle soap) or a proprietary leather cleaner; do not use strong soaps, detergents or chemical cleaners. If the leather is very stained, seek the advice of a Rover dealer. Fabric-trimmed seats and interior trim panels can be kept clean by wiping with a damp cloth and Turtle Wax Carisma. If they do become stained (which can be more apparent on light coloured upholstery) use a little liquid detergent and a soft nail brush to scour the grime out of the grain of the material. Do not forget to keep the headlining clean in the same way as the (fabric) upholstery.

27   When using liquid cleaners of any sort inside the car do not over-wet the surfaces being cleaned. Excessive damp could get into the seams and padded interior causing stains, offensive odours or even rot. If the inside of the car gets wet accidentally it is worthwhile taking some trouble to dry it out properly, particularly where carpets are involved. Do not leave oil or electric heaters inside the car for this purpose.

11   Electrical system

Battery check and maintenance

Caution: Before carrying out any work on the car battery, read through the precautions given in Safety first! at the beginning of this manual

1   A 'maintenance-free' (sealed for life) battery is standard equipment on all cars covered by this manual. Although this type of battery has many advantages over the older re-fillable type and should never require the addition of distilled water, it should still be routinely checked according to the following procedure.

2   The battery is located on the left-hand side of the engine compartment. The exterior of the battery should be inspected periodically for damage such as a cracked case or cover and should be kept clean and dry.

3   The electrolyte level can be seen through the battery's translucent case; although it should not alter in normal use, if the level has lowered (for example, due to electrolyte having boiled away as a result of overcharging) it is permissible to gently prise up the cell cover(s) and to top up the level as described in paragraphs 10 and 11 below.

4   If regular topping-up becomes necessary and the battery case is not fractured, the battery is being over-charged and the voltage regulator will have to be checked (Chapter 12).

5   Check the tightness of the battery terminal clamps to ensure good electrical connections and check the entire length of each cable for cracks and frayed conductors. Remove the fusible link box cover and check the security of the link connections, then refit the cover.

6   If corrosion (visible as white, fluffy deposits) is evident, remove the cables from the battery terminals, clean them with a small wire brush then refit them. Corrosion can be kept to a minimum by applying a layer of petroleum jelly to the clamps and terminals after they are reconnected.

7   Make sure that the battery tray is in good condition and the retaining clamp is tight.

8   Corrosion on the retaining clamp and the battery itself can be removed with a solution of water and baking soda. Thoroughly rinse all cleaned areas with plain water.

9   Any metal parts of the car damaged by corrosion due to contact with battery electrolyte should be treated with a water/baking soda solution or with household ammonia to neutralise the acid. The area should then be flushed with plain water, dried thoroughly and coated with a zinc-based primer before repainting.

10   If a conventional battery has been fitted as a replacement, the electrolyte level of each cell should be checked every month and, if necessary, topped up until the separators are just covered. On some batteries the case is translucent and incorporates minimum and maximum level marks. The check should be made more often if the car is operated in high ambient temperature conditions.

11   If necessary, top up the level with distilled or de-ionized water after removing the cell plug(s) or cover(s) from the top of the casing, although it should be noted that this should not be necessary often under normal operating conditions.

12   Further information on the battery, charging and jump starting can be found in Chapter 12 and in the preliminary sections of this manual.

Alternator drivebelt check, adjustment and renewal
General

13   The alternator drivebelt is located in the front right-hand corner of the engine compartment, next to the engine oil filter. Due to the belt's

11.17 To check alternator drivebelt tension, measure amount of belt deflection when specified force is applied

11.18 Alternator clamp bolt 'A', adjuster bolt 'B'

Renewal

21   Unscrew the adjuster bolt to fully slacken the drivebelt tension (see above), until the belt can be slipped off the pulleys and withdrawn.

22   Clean the belt pulleys carefully, removing all traces of oil or grease and checking that the grooves are clear, then fit the new belt to the pulleys and tighten the adjuster bolt until the tension is approximately correct, then check and adjust the tension as described above.

Lamps, horn and direction indicators operational check

23   Check the operation of all the electrical equipment, ie lamps, direction indicators, horn etc. Refer to the appropriate Sections of Chapter 12 for details if any of the circuits are found to be inoperative.

24   Note that stop-lamp switch adjustment is described in Chapter 9.

25   Visually check all accessible wiring connectors, harnesses and retaining clips for security and for signs of chafing or damage. Rectify any faults found.

Windscreen and rear window washer/wiper system check

Washer system reservoir top-up

26   The reservoir for the windscreen and rear window (where fitted) washer systems is located on the left-hand side of the engine compartment.

27   Check, and if necessary top up, the washer fluid level in the reservoir. When topping-up the reservoir, a screenwash such as Turtle Wax High Tech Screen Wash should be added in the recommended quantities. It is permissible to use only clean water in summer, though this is best mixed with a screenwash additive of the type recommended. In winter mix the water either with methylated spirit or with a combined screenwash additive and antifreeze. Follow the manufacturer's instructions for the mixing ratio.

28   **Never** use strong detergents (washing-up liquids etc) or engine antifreeze in the washer fluid. Not only can they cause smearing of the glass, but they can also damage the car's paintwork.

29   Check the security of the pump wires and the washer tubing; if any of the jets is blocked, clear the obstruction using a thin wire probe.

Washer jet adjustment

30   Check the operation of the windscreen and rear window washers. Adjust the nozzles using a pin if necessary, aiming the spray to a point slightly above the centre of the swept area.

Wiper blade check and renewal

31   Check the condition of the wiper blades; if they are cracked or show any signs of deterioration, or if the glass swept area is smeared, renew them. For maximum clarity of vision wiper blades should be renewed annually, as a matter of course.

32   To remove a wiper blade, pull the arm fully away from the glass until it locks. Swivel the blade through 90°, press the locking tab with a finger nail and slide the blade out of the arm's hooked end. On refitting, ensure that the blade locks securely into the arm.

Fig. 1.4 Check the multi-ribbed alternator drivebelt for signs of wear like these – if the belt looks worn, renew it (Sec 11)

function and construction it is subject to wear and will cause poor battery charging, or may even break, if not checked and adjusted at regular intervals.

14   Access to the drivebelt and related components is possible from under the car, but is much improved if the front of the car is raised and supported on axle stands (see *'Jacking, towing and wheel changing'*) so that the steering can be turned to full right lock and the right-hand underwing shield removed (Chapter 11).

Check and adjustment

15   Remove components as required to gain access to the belt (see above).

16   Check the drivebelt for cracks, splitting, fraying or damage, rotating the crankshaft so that the entire length of the belt is examined. Check also for signs of glazing (shiny patches) and for separation of the belt plies. Renew the belt if worn or damaged.

17   The drivebelt's tension is checked by measuring the amount of deflection that takes place when a pressure of 10 kgf is applied (using a spring balance, or similar) midway between the pulleys on the belt's top run (photo). If the deflection measured is any more or less than that specified, the drivebelt must be adjusted as follows.

18   Slacken the two pivot bolts securing the top of the alternator to its mounting bracket on the front of the engine, then slacken the adjuster clamp bolt and screw the adjuster bolt in or out as necessary to obtain the correct tension (photo).

19   When the correct tension is achieved, tighten the clamp and pivot bolts to their specified torque wrench settings and rotate the crankshaft several times to settle the drivebelt. Recheck the setting, repeating the adjustment if necessary.

20   Refit any components removed and lower the car to the ground.

Chapter 2 Engine

Contents

Specifications

Engine (general)

Type..	Four-cylinder in-line, four-stroke, liquid-cooled
Designation:	
1.1 and 1.4 8-valve sohc...	K8
1.4 16-valve dohc..	K16
Bore..	75.00 mm
Stroke:	
1.1 – K8	63.25 mm
1.4 – K8, K16	79.00 mm
Capacity:	
1.1 – K8	1118 cc
1.4 – K8, K16	1397 cc
Firing order..	1–3–4–2 (No 1 cylinder at timing belt end)
Direction of crankshaft rotation	Clockwise (seen from right-hand side of car)
Compression ratio:	
K8	9.75 : 1
K16	9.50 : 1
Minimum compression pressure	10.3 bar
Maximum compression pressure difference between cylinders..............	1.4 bar
Maximum power (EEC):	
1.1 – K8..	60 ps (44 kW) @ 6000 rpm
1.1 – K8 (with catalytic converter)	60 ps (44 kW) @ 5900 rpm
1.4 – K8..	76 ps (56 kW) @ 5700 rpm
1.4 – K8 (with catalytic converter)	75 ps (55 kW) @ 5500 rpm
1.4 – K16..	95 ps (70 kW) @ 6250 rpm
1.4 – K16 (with catalytic converter)...	90 ps (55 kW) @ 6250 rpm

Maximum torque (EEC):
1.1 – K8	90 Nm (66 lbf ft) @ 3500 rpm
1.4 – K8	117 Nm (86 lbf ft) @ 3500 rpm
1.4 – K16	124 Nm (91 lbf ft) @ 4000 rpm
1.4 – K16 (with catalytic converter)	120 Nm (89 lbf ft) @ rpm

Cylinder block/crankcase
Material	Aluminium alloy
Cylinder liner bore diameter – 60 mm from top of bore:	
Standard – grade A (Red)	74.975 to 74.985 mm
Standard – grade B (Blue)	74.986 to 74.995 mm
Service limit	75.045 mm

Note: *Service liners are Grade B*

Crankshaft
Number of main bearings	5
Main bearing journal diameter	47.979 to 48.000 mm
Main bearing journal size grades:	
Grade A	47.993 to 48.000 mm
Grade B	47.986 to 47.993 mm
Grade C	47.979 to 47.986 mm
Crankpin journal diameter	42.986 to 43.007 mm
Crankpin journal size grades:	
Grade A	43.000 to 43.007 mm
Grade B	42.993 to 43.000 mm
Grade C	42.986 to 42.993 mm
Main bearing and crankpin journal maximum ovality	0.010 mm
Main bearing and big-end bearing running clearance	0.021 to 0.049 mm
Crankshaft endfloat:	
Standard	0.10 to 0.30 mm
Service limit	0.50 mm
Thrustwasher thickness	2.61 to 2.65 mm

Pistons and piston rings
Piston diameter – K8:	
Grade A	74.940 to 74.955 mm
Grade B	74.956 to 74.970 mm
Piston diameter – K16:	
Grade A	74.945 to 74.960 mm
Grade B	74.960 to 74.975 mm

Note: *Service pistons are Grade B*

Piston-to-bore clearance:	
K8 – standard	0.015 to 0.045 mm
K16 – standard	0.010 to 0.040 mm
Service limit – all	0.080 mm
Piston ring end gaps (fitted 20 mm from top of bore):	
Top compression ring:	
K8	0.25 to 0.45 mm
K16	0.30 to 0.50 mm
Second compression ring – all models	0.30 to 0.50 mm
Oil control ring:	
K8 – standard	0.25 to 1.00 mm
K16 – standard	0.25 to 0.50 mm
K16 – service limit	0.60 mm
Piston ring-to-groove clearance:	
Top compression ring – K8	0.04 to 0.09 mm
Top compression ring – K16	0.04 to 0.07 mm
Second compression ring – K8	0.04 to 0.08 mm
Second compression ring – K16	0.04 to 0.07 mm
Oil control ring – all models	0.02 to 0.06 mm

Gudgeon pins
Diameter	18 mm
Fit in connecting rod	Interference

Connecting rods
Length between centres	131.5 mm

Cylinder head
Material	Aluminium alloy
Height	118.95 to 119.05 mm
Reface limit	0.20 mm
Maximum acceptable gasket face distortion	0.05 mm
Valve seat angle	45°

Cylinder head (continued)

Valve seat width	1.5 mm
Seat cutter correction angle:	
Upper	30°
Lower	60°
Valve stem installed height:	
K8 – new	38.95 to 40.81 mm
K8 – service limit	41.06 mm
K16 – new	38.93 to 39.84 mm
K16 – service limit	40.10 mm

Camshaft

Drive	Toothed belt
Number of bearings	6
Bearing journal running clearance:	
Standard	0.060 to 0.094 mm
Service limit	0.150 mm
Camshaft endfloat:	
Standard	0.060 to 0.190 mm
Service limit	0.500 mm
Valve lift:	
1.1 K8	7.9 mm
1.4 K8	9.0 mm
1.4 K16	8.2 mm
Hydraulic tappet outside diameter	32.959 to 32.975 mm

Valves

Seat angle:	
Inlet	45°
Exhaust	44° 30′
Head diameter:	
Inlet – K8	34 mm
Inlet – K16	28 mm
Exhaust – K8	31 mm
Exhaust – K16	24 mm
Stem outside diameter:	
Inlet – K8	6.967 to 6.975 mm
Inlet – K16	5.952 to 5.967 mm
Exhaust – K8	6.952 to 6.967 mm
Exhaust – K16	5.947 to 5.962 mm
Guide inside diameter:	
K8	7.000 to 7.025 mm
K16	6.000 to 6.025 mm
Stem-to-guide clearance:	
Inlet – standard	0.03 to 0.04 mm
Inlet – service limit	0.07 mm
Exhaust – standard	0.07 to 0.08 mm
Exhaust – service limit	0.11 mm
Valve timing – 1.1 K8:	
Inlet opens	3° BTDC
Inlet closes	37° ABDC
Exhaust opens	35° BBDC
Exhaust closes	5° ATDC
Valve timing – 1.4 K8:	
Inlet opens	13° BTDC
Inlet closes	47° ABDC
Exhaust opens	53° BBDC
Exhaust closes	7° ATDC
Valve timing – 1.4 K16:	
Inlet opens	15° BTDC
Inlet closes	45° ABDC
Exhaust opens	55° BBDC
Exhaust closes	5° ATDC
Valve spring free length:	
K8	46.2 mm
K16	50.0 mm
Valve guide fitted height	6.0 mm

Lubrication system

System pressure – @ idle speed	1.0 bar
Oil pump type	Trochoidal, eccentric-rotor

Lubrication system (continued)

Oil pump clearances:

Rotor endfloat	0.02 to 0.06 mm
Outer rotor-to-body clearance	0.28 to 0.36 mm
Rotor lobe clearance	0.05 to 0.13 mm
Pressure relief valve operating pressure	4.1 bar
Oil pressure warning lamp lights at	Below 0.3 to 0.5 bar

Torque wrench settings

	Nm	lbf ft
Spark plug (HT) lead clip screws – K8	9	7
Air intake duct support bracket-to-cylinder head screws – K16	4	3
Spark plug cover screws – K16	2	1.5
Cylinder head cover bolts	9	7
Camshaft bearing cap/carrier-to-cylinder head bolts	9	7
Cylinder head bolts:		
1st stage	20	15
2nd stage	Tighten through 180°	Tighten through 180°
3rd stage	Tighten through (a further) 180°	Tighten through (a further) 180°
Timing belt cover fasteners:		
Upper right-hand (outer) cover	4	3
Lower and upper left-hand (inner) covers	9	7
Timing belt tensioner pulley Allen screw	45	33
Camshaft toothed pulley bolt	33	24
Alternator drive pulley bolt	160	118
Oil pump-to-cylinder block/crankcase bolt and screws	9	7
Alternator mounting bracket-to-cylinder block/crankcase bolts	45	33
Dipstick tube-to-cylinder block/crankcase bolts	9	7
Flywheel bolts	85	63
Transmission-to-engine bolts	85	63
Flywheel cover plate screws	9	7
Flywheel rear cover plate bolt and nut	38	28
Big-end bearing cap bolts:		
1st stage	20	15
2nd stage	Tighten through 45°	Tighten through 45°
Main bearing ladder-to-cylinder block/crankcase bolts	10	8
Oil rail-to-main bearing ladder nuts	9	7
Oil pump pick-up/strainer pipe screws	9	7
Sump screws	10	8
Engine oil drain plug	42	31
Engine/transmission right-hand mounting:		
Bracket-to-cylinder block/crankcase bolts	45	33
Mounting-to-bracket nuts	100	74
Mounting-to-body through-bolt and nut	85	63
Engine/transmission left-hand mounting:		
Support member-to-subframe bolts	45	33
Mounting-to-support member bolts	45	33
Mounting-to-bracket bolts	45	33
Bracket-to-transmission bolts	80	59
Engine/transmission rear mounting:		
Mounting bracket-to-transmission 12 mm bolt(s)	85	63
Mounting bracket-to-transmission 10 mm bolt(s)	45	33
Mounting bracket-to-tie-rod through-bolt	85	63
Tie-rod-to-body bolt and nut	45	33

Part A: In-car engine repair procedures

1 General information

How to use this Chapter

This Part of Chapter 2 describes those repair procedures that can reasonably be carried out on the engine while it remains in the car. If the engine has been removed from the car and is being dismantled as described in Part B, any preliminary dismantling procedures can be ignored.

Note that while it may be possible physically to overhaul items such as the piston/connecting rod assemblies while the engine is in the car, such tasks are not usually carried out as separate operations and usually require the execution of several additional procedures (not to mention the cleaning of components and of oilways); for this reason all such tasks are classed as major overhaul procedures and are described in Part B of this Chapter.

Part B describes the removal of the engine/transmission unit from the car and the full overhaul procedures that can then be carried out.

For ease of reference, all specifications are given in the one Specifications Section at the beginning of the Chapter.

Engine description

The engine is of four-cylinder, in-line type, mounted transversely at the front of the car with the clutch and transmission on its left-hand end. Variations in capacity are achieved by altering the stroke dimensions.

Apart from the pressed steel sump, the plastic timing belt covers and the aluminium alloy cylinder head cover, the engine is constructed from three major castings (the cylinder head, the cylinder block/crankcase and the crankshaft main bearing ladder); there is also an oil rail underneath the main bearing ladder and the camshaft carrier/bearing caps (see below). All these castings are of aluminium alloy, the three major ones being clamped together by ten long through-bolts which perform the dual role of cylinder head bolts and crankshaft main bearing fasteners. Since these bolts pass through the cylinder block/crankcase and the main bearing ladder, the oil rail is secured also to the main bearing ladder (by two nuts) and the main bearing ladder is secured also to the cylinder block/crankcase (by ten smaller bolts) so that the cylinder head can be removed without disturbing the rest of the engine. The passages provided for the bolts in the major castings are used as breather passages or as returns for the oil to the sump.

Note: *A side-effect of this design is that the crankshaft cannot be rotated once the through-bolts have been slackened. During any servicing or overhaul work the crankshaft always must be rotated to the desired position before the bolts are disturbed.*

The crankshaft runs in five main bearings. Thrustwashers are fitted to the centre main bearing (upper half) to control crankshaft endfloat.

The connecting rods rotate on horizontally-split bearing shells at their big-ends. The pistons are attached to the connecting rods by gudgeon pins which are an interference fit in the connecting rod small-end eyes. The aluminium alloy pistons are fitted with three piston rings, comprising two compression rings and an oil control ring.

The cylinder bores are formed by replaceable wet liners that are located from their top ends; two sealing O-rings are fitted at the base of each liner to prevent the escape of coolant into the sump.

The inlet and exhaust valves are each closed by coil springs and operate in guides pressed into the cylinder head; the valve seat inserts are pressed into the cylinder head and can be renewed separately if worn.

On the K8 engine, the camshaft is driven by a toothed timing belt and operates the eight valves via self-adjusting hydraulic tappets, thus eliminating the need for routine checking and adjustment of the valve clearances. The camshaft rotates in six bearings that are line-bored direct in the cylinder head and the (bolted-on) bearing caps; this means that the bearing caps are not available separately from the cylinder head and must not be interchanged with others from another engine. Apart from the fact that it has two camshafts, one inlet and one exhaust, each

controlling eight valves and both retained by a single camshaft carrier, the same applies to the K16 engine.

On the K8 engine, the distributor and (on carburettor engines only) the mechanical fuel pump are driven from the camshaft left-hand end; on the K16 engine the distributor is driven from the inlet camshaft left-hand end.

On both engine types, the water pump is driven by the timing belt.

Lubrication is by means of an eccentric-rotor trochoidal pump mounted on the crankshaft right-hand end. It draws oil through a strainer located in the sump and then forces it through an externally-mounted full-flow cartridge-type filter into galleries in the oil rail and cylinder block/crankcase, from where it is distributed to the crankshaft (main bearings) and camshaft(s). The big-end bearings are supplied with oil via internal drillings in the crankshaft, while the camshaft bearings and the hydraulic tappets receive a pressurised supply. The camshaft lobes and valves are lubricated by splash, as are all other engine components.

Repair operations possible with the engine in the car

The following work can be carried out with the engine in the car.

(a) Compression pressure – testing.
(b) Cylinder head cover – removal and refitting.
(c) Alternator drive pulley – removal and refitting.
(d) Timing belt covers – removal and refitting.
(e) Timing belt – removal, refitting and adjustment.
(f) Timing belt tensioner and toothed pulleys – removal and refitting.
(g) Camshaft oil seal(s) – renewal.
(h) Camshaft(s) and hydraulic tappets – removal, inspection and refitting.
(i) Cylinder head – removal and refitting.
(j) Cylinder head and pistons – decarbonising.
(k) Sump – removal and refitting.
(l) Oil pump – removal, overhaul and refitting.
(m) Crankshaft oil seals – renewal.
(n) Engine/transmission mountings – inspection and renewal.
(o) Flywheel – removal, inspection and refitting.

2 Compression test – description and interpretation

1   When engine performance is down, or if misfiring occurs which cannot be attributed to the ignition or fuel systems, a compression test can provide diagnostic clues as to the engine's condition. If the test is performed regularly it can give warning of trouble before any other symptoms become apparent.

2   The engine must be fully warmed up to normal operating temperature, the battery must be fully charged and the spark plugs must be removed (see Chapter 1). The aid of an assistant will be required also.

3   Disable the ignition system by disconnecting the ignition HT coil lead from the distributor cap and earthing it on the cylinder block. Use a jumper lead or similar wire to make a good connection.

4   Fit a compression tester to the number 1 cylinder spark plug hole – the type of tester which screws into the plug thread is to be preferred (photo).

5   Have the assistant hold the throttle wide open and crank the engine on the starter motor; after one or two revolutions the compression pressure should build up to a maximum figure and then stabilise. Record the highest reading obtained.

6   Repeat the test on the remaining cylinders, recording the pressure in each.

7   All cylinders should produce very similar pressures; any difference greater than that specified indicates the existence of a fault. Note that the compression should build up quickly in a healthy engine; low

Fig. 2.1 Engine lubrication system (Sec 1)

1   Oil pump pick-up/strainer pipe
2   Oil pump
3   Oil pressure relief valve
4   Oil pump intake
5   Oil filter
6   Oil pressure switch
7   Oil rail main gallery
8   Cylinder block/crankcase oilway
9   Cylinder head oilway
10 Camshaft carrier oilways – K16 engine
11 Oil feed tube – K8 engine

2.4 Measuring compression pressure

compression on the first stroke, followed by gradually increasing pressure on successive strokes, indicates worn piston rings. A low compression reading on the first stroke, which does not build up during successive strokes, indicates leaking valves or a blown head gasket (a cracked head could also be the cause). Deposits on the undersides of the valve heads can also cause low compression.

8   If the pressure in any cylinder is reduced to the specified minimum or less, carry out the following test to isolate the cause. Introduce a teaspoonful of clean oil into that cylinder through its spark plug hole and repeat the test.

9   If the addition of oil temporarily improves the compression pressure, this indicates that bore or piston wear is responsible for the pressure loss. No improvement suggests that leaking or burnt valves, or a blown head gasket may be to blame.

10   A low reading from two adjacent cylinders is almost certainly due to the head gasket having blown between them; the presence of coolant in the engine oil will confirm this.

11   If one cylinder is about 20 percent lower than the others and the engine has a slightly rough idle, a worn camshaft lobe could be the cause.

12   If the compression reading is unusually high, the combustion chambers are probably coated with carbon deposits. If this is the case, the cylinder head should be removed and decarbonised.

13   On completion of the test, refit the spark plugs and reconnect the ignition system.

3   Top Dead Centre (TDC) for number one piston – locating

General

Note: *The alternator drive pulley, crankshaft toothed pulley and camshaft toothed pulley(s) are provided by the factory with clear marks which align only at 90° BTDC; this positions the pistons half-way up the bores so that there is no risk of damage as the engine is reassembled. These marks do not indicate TDC; use only the ignition timing marks, as described in this Section, to find TDC*

1   Top dead centre (TDC) is the highest point in its travel up-and-down its cylinder bore that each piston reaches as the crankshaft rotates. While each piston reaches TDC both at the top of the compression stroke and again at the top of the exhaust stroke, for the purpose of timing the engine, TDC refers to the piston position (usually number 1) at the top of its compression stroke.

2   While all engine reassembly procedures use the factory timing marks (90° BTDC), it is useful for several other servicing procedures to be able to position the engine at TDC.

3   Number 1 piston and cylinder is at the right-hand (timing belt) end of the engine. Note that the crankshaft rotates clockwise when viewed from the right-hand side of the car.

Locating TDC

4   Remove all the spark plugs (Chapter 1).

5   Trace number 1 spark plug (HT) lead from the plug back to the distributor cap and use chalk or similar to mark the distributor body or engine casting nearest to the cap's number 1 terminal. Remove the distributor cap (Chapter 1).

6   Disconnect both battery leads (unless the starter motor is to be used to turn the engine).

7   Apply the handbrake and ensure that the transmission is in neutral, then jack up the front right-hand side of the car and support it on axle stands.

8   Remove the roadwheel and the underwing shield to expose the alternator drive pulley and ignition timing marks.

9   It is best to rotate the crankshaft using a spanner applied to the alternator drive pulley bolt. It is, however, possible to use the starter motor (switched on either by an assistant using the ignition key or by using a remote starter switch) to bring the engine close to TDC, then finish with a spanner. If the starter is used, be sure to disconnect the battery leads immediately it is no longer required.

10   Rotate the crankshaft clockwise until the notch on the alternator drive pulley's inboard (left-hand) rim is aligned with the TDC mark on the timing belt lower cover (see Chapter 1, ignition timing check and adjustment, for details of the ignition timing marks).

11   Numbers 1 and 4 cylinders are now at TDC, one of them on the compression stroke. If the distributor rotor arm is pointing at (the previously-marked) number 1 terminal, then number 1 cylinder is correctly positioned; if the rotor arm is pointing at number 4 terminal, rotate the crankshaft one full turn (360°) clockwise until the arm points at the marked terminal. Number 1 cylinder will then be at TDC on the compression stroke.

12   Once number 1 cylinder has been positioned at TDC on the compression stroke, TDC for any of the other cylinders can then be located by rotating the crankshaft clockwise 180° at a time and following the firing order (see Specifications).

13   An alternative method of locating TDC is to remove the cylinder head cover (Sec 4) and to rotate the crankshaft (clockwise, as described in paragraph 9 above) until the inlet valve(s) for the cylinder concerned has opened and just closed again. Insert a length of wooden dowel (approximately 150 mm/6 in long) or similar into the spark plug hole until it rests on the piston crown and slowly further rotate the crankshaft (taking care not to allow the dowel to be trapped in the cylinder) until the dowel stops rising – the piston is now at the top of its compression stroke and the dowel can be removed.

14   There is a 'dead' area around TDC (as the piston stops rising, pauses and then begins to descend) which makes it difficult to locate the exact TDC position by this method; if absolute accuracy is required, establish carefully the exact mid-point of the dead area or refer to the ignition timing marks (paragraph 10 above).

4   Cylinder head cover – removal and refitting

Removal

K8 engines

1   Disconnect the battery negative lead.

2   Referring to Chapters 1 or 4 as necessary for details, remove the screws securing the air cleaner assembly and release the quarter-turn fastener(s) securing the intake duct to its cylinder head bracket(s), then

Fig. 2.2 Cylinder head cover bolt tightening sequence – K8 engine (Sec 4)

4.3 Disconnecting breather hose(s) from cylinder head cover – K8 engines

4.11 Disconnecting breather hoses from cylinder head cover – K16 engines

4.16A Ensure cylinder head cover seal is seated correctly in cover groove ...

4.16B ... refit bolts and apply sealant at locations arrowed – K8 engines

4.24A Fit gasket to cylinder head cover dowels (arrows) so that ...

4.24B ... stamped markings would appear as shown if gasket were placed on camshaft carrier

disconnect the vacuum pipes from the air cleaner assembly and the air temperature control valve. On fuel-injected engines, the fuel trap vacuum hoses need only be disconnected if extra clearance is required. Withdraw the assembly, taking care not to lose the hot air intake connector hose; place the assembly to one side, clear of the cylinder head.

3   Disconnect the breather hose(s) from the cover (photo).

4   Where they prevent access to the cover's retaining bolts or might hinder its removal, unfasten the spark plug (HT) lead clip(s) and air intake duct support bracket(s) from the cylinder head or from the cover, and remove them or move them clear of the working area.

5   Remove the two top (hex-head) retaining screws securing the timing belt upper right-hand/outer cover to the cylinder head cover, then slacken the remaining screws and bolts (Sec 6) as necessary until the timing belt cover can be prised clear of the cylinder head cover without damaging it.

6   Working progressively and in the **reverse** of the sequence shown in Fig. 2.2, unscrew the cylinder head cover retaining bolts.

7   Remove the cover, peel off the rubber seal and check it for cuts, other damage or distortion; renew it if necessary.

K16 engines

8   Disconnect the battery negative lead.

9   Release the two clips securing the air intake duct to the air cleaner assembly and unscrew the bolt securing the duct to its support bracket. Unfasten the rubber strap and disconnect the vacuum pipe from the air temperature control valve.

10   Withdraw the assembly, taking care not to lose the hot air intake connector hose; place the assembly to one side, clear of the cylinder head.

11   Disconnect the breather hoses from the cover (photo).

12   Remove the spark plug cover, disconnect the spark plug (HT) leads from the plugs and withdraw them from the cylinder head with the clip plate and the grommet (Chapter 1).

13   Working progressively and in the **reverse** of the sequence shown in photo 4.26, unscrew the cylinder head cover retaining bolts and withdraw the air intake duct support bracket.

14   Withdraw the cover; take care not to damage the gasket and check

that its sealing path is undamaged and attached to the gasket all around the gasket's periphery. If the sealing path is undamaged the gasket is re-usable and should remain in place on the cover until reassembly, unless its removal is necessary for other servicing work.

Refitting

K8 engines

15   On reassembly, carefully clean the cylinder head mating surfaces and the cover seal's groove and remove all traces of oil.

16   Seat the seal in its groove in the cover and refit the bolts, pushing each through the seal, then apply a smear of silicone-RTV sealant to the seal at the points indicated (photos).

17   Refit the cover and start all bolts finger-tight, ensuring that the seal remains seated in its groove.

18   Working in the sequence shown in Fig. 2.2, tighten the cylinder head cover bolts to the specified torque wrench setting. Check that the seal has not been displaced.

19   Refit the timing belt upper right-hand/outer cover to the cylinder head cover, then tighten the retaining screws and bolts to the specified torque wrench setting.

20   Refit the removed spark plug (HT) lead clip(s) and air intake duct support bracket(s), tightening all fasteners to the appropriate torque wrench settings and routing correctly the spark plug (HT) leads.

21   Connect the breather hose to the cover, then refit the air cleaner assembly (Chapter 1 or 4), ensuring that all vacuum hoses and pipes are correctly routed and secured. Do not forget to refit the hot air intake connector hose.

22   Connect the battery negative lead.

K16 engines

23   On reassembly, clean carefully the mating surfaces, removing all traces of oil.

24   If a new gasket is to be fitted, press it onto the **cover** locating dowels so that if it were laid on the camshaft carrier its stamped markings would be legible; the 'TOP' mark should be nearest the inlet manifold and the 'EXH MAN SIDE' mark should have its arrows pointing to the exhaust manifold (photos).

4.26 Cylinder head cover bolt tightening sequence – K16 engine

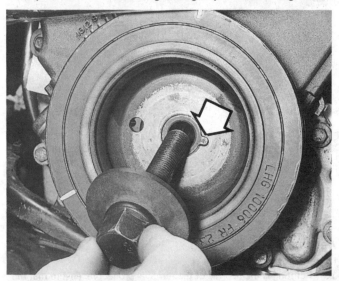

5.7 Notch in alternator drive pulley's centre fits over crankshaft toothed pulley locating lug (arrow)

25   Refit the cover and start the bolts finger-tight, ensuring that the gasket is not damaged or displaced; fit the air intake duct support bracket at the front, in line with number 2 cylinder spark plug.
26   Working in the sequence shown, tighten the cover retaining bolts and pillar bolts to the specified torque wrench setting (photo).
27   Reconnect the spark plug (HT) leads to the spark plugs, routing them using the clip plate and grommet, then refit the spark plug cover (Chapter 1) and reconnect the breather hoses to the cover unions.
28   Ensuring that the hot air intake connector hose is in place, refit the air intake duct to the air cleaner assembly, securing it with its clips and rubber strap. Connect the vacuum pipe to the air temperature control valve and tighten the bolt securing the duct to its support bracket to its specified torque wrench setting.
29   Connect the battery negative lead.

5   Alternator drive pulley – removal and refitting

Removal

1   Raise the front right-hand side of the car and support it on an axle stand (see 'Jacking, towing and wheel changing'). Although roadwheel removal is not strictly necessary, access is greatly improved if this is done; otherwise, turn the steering to full right lock.
2   Remove the underwing shield (Chapter 11).

3   If necessary, rotate the crankshaft until the timing marks align.
4   Slacken the alternator clamp and pivot bolts (Chapter 1), move the alternator as far as possible towards the engine and disengage the drivebelt from the drive pulley.
5   To prevent crankshaft rotation while the pulley bolt is unscrewed, select top gear and have an assistant apply the brakes hard. If the engine has been removed from the car, lock the flywheel using the arrangement shown in photo 34.30C.
6   Unscrew the pulley bolt, noting the special washer behind it, then remove the pulley.

Refitting

7   On refitting, ensure that the notch in the pulley's centre fits over the locating lug on the crankshaft toothed pulley (photo).
8   Lock the crankshaft by the method used on removal and tighten the bolt to the specified torque wrench setting.
9   Refit the alternator drivebelt and adjust it (Chapter 1).
10   Refit, if removed, the underwing shield and roadwheel.

6   Timing belt covers – removal and refitting

Removal
Upper right-hand (outer) cover
1   Slacken the (hex-head) screw at the cover's bottom corner, immediately behind the engine/transmission right-hand mounting bracket.
2   Unscrew the remaining cover retaining (hex-head) screws or bolts and withdraw the cover, noting the rubber seal fitted to its mounting bracket edge. Note that if the cover is not slotted at the bottom corner screw's location, the screw will have to be removed fully; if this is the case the cover can be slotted to ease future removal and refitting (photo).

Lower cover
3   Remove the alternator drive pulley (Sec 5).

Fig. 2.3 Location of K8 engine timing belt upper right-hand (outer) cover fasteners (Sec 6)

1   Slacken screw – cover should be slotted   *2   Remove fasteners*

Fig. 2.4 Timing belt and covers – K8 engine (Sec 6)

1 Timing belt upper right-hand (outer) cover	9 Seal	16 Tensioner pulley Allen screw	23 Camshaft toothed pulley
2 Seal	10 Screw	17 Tensioner backplate screw	24 Bolt
3 Screw	11 Screw	18 Tensioner spring	25 Washer
4 Bolt	12 Alternator drive pulley	19 Sleeve	26 Timing belt upper left-hand (inner) cover
5 Bolt	13 Washer	20 Pillar bolt	27 Screw – cover-to-water pump
6 Shouldered screw	14 Bolt	21 Timing belt	28 Screw
7 Timing belt lower cover	15 Timing belt tensioner pulley assembly	22 Crankshaft toothed pulley	
8 Seal			

4   Remove the cover retaining screws, including the one which also secures the upper cover's bottom front corner and remove the cover, noting the rubber seal fitted to its mounting bracket edge (photo).

Upper left-hand (inner) cover

5   Remove the timing belt (Sec 7).
6   Remove the camshaft toothed pulley(s) and the timing belt tensioner (Sec 8) .
7   Unscrew the bolt securing the cover to the water pump.
8   On K16 engines unbolt the engine/transmission right-hand mounting bracket from the cylinder block/crankcase.
9   Remove the remaining cover retaining bolts (photos) and withdraw the cover.

Refitting

Upper right-hand (outer) cover

10   Refitting is the reverse of the removal procedure; ensure that the seal fits correctly between the cover and the mounting bracket and that the cover edges mate correctly with those of the inner cover and (K8 engines only) cylinder head cover (photo).
11   Tighten the cover fasteners to the specified torque wrench setting.

Lower cover

12   Refitting is the reverse of the removal procedure; ensure that the seal fits correctly between the cover and the mounting bracket and tighten the cover fasteners to the specified torque wrench setting.
13   Refit the alternator drive pulley (Sec 5).

6.2 Location of K16 engine timing belt upper right-hand/outer cover fasteners (arrows) – engine raised for clarity

6.4 Removing timing belt lower cover

6.9A Location of K8 engine timing belt upper left-hand (inner) cover fasteners (arrows)

Fig. 2.5 Timing belt and covers – K16 engine (Sec 6)

1	Timing belt upper right-hand (outer) cover	
2	Screw	
3	Seal	
4	Bolt	
5	Timing belt lower cover	
6	Seal	

7	Screw
8	Screw
9	Alternator drive pulley
10	Washer
11	Bolt
12	Timing belt
13	Camshaft toothed pulleys

14	Bolt
15	Washer
16	Timing belt tensioner pulley assembly
17	Tensioner pulley Allen screw
18	Tensioner spring

19	Sleeve
20	Pillar bolt
21	Tensioner backplate screw
22	Crankshaft toothed pulley
23	Timing belt upper left-hand (inner) cover
24	Screw

Upper left-hand (inner) cover

14   Refitting is the reverse of the removal procedure; tighten all disturbed fasteners to their specified torque wrench settings.

7   Timing belt – removal, refitting and adjustment

Removal

1   Disconnect the battery negative lead.

2   Remove its three retaining screws and move the washer system reservoir clear of the working area; disconnect the pump wiring connector plug(s) if the extra reach is required.
3   Unclip the expansion tank coolant hose from the bonnet lock platform and secure it clear of the working area.
4   Remove the timing belt upper right-hand (outer) cover (Sec 6).
5   Remove the spark plugs and use clean rag to seal the plug holes against the entry of dirt (Chapter 1).
6   Raise the front of the car and support it on axle stands, then remove the front right-hand roadwheel (see *'Jacking, towing and wheel changing'*).
7   Remove the underwing shield (Chapter 11).

6.9B Location of K16 engine timing belt upper left-hand (inner) cover fasteners (arrows) ...

6.9C ... noting that lowermost bolt is accessible only from wheel arch

6.9D Removing K16 engine timing belt upper left-hand (inner) cover

6.10 Ensure timing belt upper right-hand (outer) cover engages correctly with cylinder head cover – K8 engine

7.8 Alternator drive pulley mark aligned with timing belt lower cover mark at 90° BTDC

7.9 Camshaft toothed pulley marks 'A' aligned with timing belt upper left-hand (inner) cover mark 'B' – K16 engine

7.13 Removing engine/transmission right-hand mounting bracket – K8 engine

7.14 Timing belt tensioner pulley Allen screw 'A', tensioner backplate screw 'B'

7.15 If timing belt is to be re-used, mark direction of rotation as shown before removing

8   Rotate the crankshaft clockwise until the long white-painted mark on the alternator drive pulley's outboard (right-hand) face is aligned with the single, separate mark on the timing belt lower cover (photo); see Chapter 1, *Ignition timing check and adjustment*, for details of the pulley/cover marks.
9   Check that the camshaft toothed pulley marks align as described in paragraph 17 below, showing that numbers 1 and 4 cylinders are at 90° BTDC so that there is no risk of the valves contacting the pistons during dismantling and reassembly (photo).
10   On K16 engines use the tool described in Section 8 to lock together the camshaft toothed pulleys so that they cannot move under valve spring pressure when the timing belt is removed.
11   Remove the alternator drive pulley (Sec 5).
12   Remove the timing belt lower cover (Sec 6).
13   Support the weight of the engine/transmission using a trolley jack, with a wooden spacer to prevent damage to the sump, then unscrew the engine/transmission right-hand mounting through-bolt and nut and the mounting-to-bracket nuts. Remove the mounting, noting the two rubber washers; on K8 engines only, unscrew also the retaining bolts and remove the bracket from the cylinder block/crankcase (photo).
14   Slacken through half a turn the timing belt tensioner pulley Allen screw and the tensioner backplate (hex-head) screw, push the pulley assembly down to the (belt) fully-slack position to release tension from the belt, then re-tighten the backplate screw (photo).
15   If the timing belt is to be re-used, use white paint or similar to mark its direction of rotation (photo), then remove it from the toothed pulleys. **Do not** rotate the crankshaft until the timing belt has been refitted.
16   Check the timing belt carefully for any signs of uneven wear, splitting or oil contamination and renew it if there is the slightest doubt about its condition. If the engine is undergoing an overhaul and has covered more than 48 000 miles (80 000 km) since the original belt was fitted, renew the belt as a matter of course, regardless of its apparent condition. If signs of oil contamination are found, trace the source of the oil leak and rectify it, then wash down the engine timing belt area and all related components to remove all traces of oil.

Refitting
17   On reassembly, thoroughly clean the toothed pulleys and check that they are aligned as follows (photos).

(a)   *Camshaft pulley – K8 engine – the 'EX' line and the mark stamped in the pulley's rim must be at the front (looking at the pulley from the right-hand side of the car) and aligned exactly with the cylinder head top surface.*
(b)   *Camshaft pulleys – K16 engine – both 'EXHAUST' arrow marks must point to the rear (looking at the pulleys from the right-hand side of the car) with the 'IN' lines and the pulley rim marks aligned exactly with the line on the timing belt upper left-hand/inner cover (representing the cylinder head top surface); see photo 7.9.*
(c)   *Crankshaft pulley – the two dots must be on each side of the raised rib on the oil pump body.*

It is most important that these marks are aligned exactly as this sets the valve timing, but note that in this position numbers 1 and 4 cylinders are at 90° BTDC so that there is no risk of the valves contacting the pistons during dismantling and reassembly.
18   Fit the timing belt over the crankshaft and camshaft toothed pulleys, ensuring that the belt front run (and, on K16 engines, the top run) is taut ie, all slack is at the tensioner pulley, then over the water pump pulley and tensioner pulley. Do not twist the belt sharply while refitting it, ensure that the belt teeth are correctly seated centrally in the pulleys and that the timing marks remain in alignment. If a used belt is being refitted, ensure that the arrow mark made on removal points in the same direction of rotation as before (photo).
19   Slacken the tensioner backplate screw and check that the tensioner pulley moves to tension the belt; if the tensioner assembly is not free to move under spring tension, rectify the fault or the timing belt will not be correctly tensioned.
20   On K16 engines remove the camshaft toothed pulley locking tool.
21   On K8 engines refit the engine/transmission right-hand mounting

7.17A Camshaft toothed pulley marks 'A' aligned with cylinder head top surface 'B' – K8 engine

7.17B Crankshaft toothed pulley dots 'A' aligned on each side of oil pump raised rib 'B'

7.18 Refitting the timing belt – K16 engine

bracket, tightening its bolts to the specified torque wrench setting.

22   On all engines, refit the timing belt lower cover (Sec 6) and the alternator drive pulley (Sec 5).

23   Rotate the crankshaft two full turns clockwise to settle and tension the belt; check that the timing marks are still aligned exactly.

24   The timing belt will now be tensioned correctly; tighten the tensioner backplate screw, then the tensioner pulley Allen screw to their specified torque wrench settings (where given).

25   Reassemble the engine/transmission right-hand mounting, tightening to their specified torque wrench settings the nuts and bolts and ensuring that the rubber washers are correctly located.

26   Refit the underwing shield (Chapter 11) and the roadwheel, then lower the car to the ground.

27   Refit the timing belt upper right-hand (outer) cover (Sec 6), re-route and secure the coolant hose, refit the spark plugs (Chapter 1) and the washer system reservoir. Re-connect the battery negative lead.

Adjustment – general

28   As the timing belt is a 'fit-and-forget' type, the manufacturer states that tensioning need be carried out only after a new belt has been fitted (although tensioning is obviously required if the existing belt has been disturbed for other servicing/overhaul work); no re-tensioning is recommended once a belt has been fitted and therefore this operation is not included in the manufacturer's maintenance schedule.

29   If the timing belt is thought to be incorrectly tensioned, adjust the tension as described in paragraphs 1 to 9, 19, 23, 24, 26 and 27 above.

30   If the timing belt has been disturbed, adjust its tension following the same procedure, omitting as appropriate the irrelevant preliminary dismantling/reassembly steps.

8   Timing belt tensioner and toothed pulleys – removal, inspection and refitting

Note: *This Section describes as individual operations the removal and refitting of the components concerned – if more than one of them are to be removed at the same time, start by removing the timing belt (Sec 7), then remove the actual component as described below, ignoring the preliminary dismantling steps*

Removal

Camshaft toothed pulley – K8 engine

1   Disconnect the battery negative lead.

2   Remove its three retaining screws and move the washer system reservoir clear of the working area; disconnect the pump wiring connector plug(s) if the extra reach is required.

3   Unclip the expansion tank coolant hose from the bonnet lock platform and secure it clear of the working area.

4   Remove the timing belt upper right-hand (outer) cover (Sec 6).

5   Remove the spark plugs and use clean rag to seal the plug holes against the entry of dirt (Chapter 1).

6   Raise the front right-hand side of the car and support it on an axle stand (see *'Jacking, towing and wheel changing'*), turn the steering to full right lock and remove the underwing shield (Chapter 11).

7   Rotate the crankshaft clockwise until the long white-painted mark on the alternator drive pulley's outboard (right-hand) face is aligned with the single, separate mark on the timing belt lower cover; see Chapter 1, *Ignition timing check and adjustment*, for details of the pulley/cover marks.

8   Check that the camshaft toothed pulley marks align as described in Section 7, paragraph 17.

9   Slacken through half a turn each the timing belt tensioner pulley Allen screw and the tensioner backplate (hex-head) screw, push the pulley assembly down to the (belt) fully-slack position to release tension from the belt, then re-tighten the backplate screw.

10   Remove the belt from the camshaft toothed pulley, taking care not to twist it too sharply; use the fingers only to handle the belt. **Do not** rotate the crankshaft until the timing belt is refitted.

11   Unscrew the toothed pulley bolt and remove it, with its washer. To prevent the camshaft from rotating, use Rover service tool 18G 1521. If this is not available an acceptable substitute can be fabricated from two lengths of steel strip (one long, the other short) and three nuts and bolts; one nut and bolt forming the pivot of a forked tool with the remaining two nuts and bolts at the tips of the 'forks' to engage with the pulley spokes as shown in photo 8.53.

12   Remove the toothed pulley from the camshaft end, noting the locating roll pin (photo).

Camshaft toothed pulleys – K16 engine

13   Disconnect the battery negative lead.

14   Remove its three retaining screws and move the washer system reservoir clear of the working area; disconnect the pump wiring connector plug(s) if the extra reach is required.

15   Unclip the expansion tank coolant hose from the bonnet lock platform and secure it clear of the working area.

16   Remove the timing belt upper right-hand (outer) cover (Sec 6).

17   Remove the spark plugs and use clean rag to seal the plug holes against the entry of dirt (Chapter 1).

18   Raise the front right-hand side of the car and support it on an axle stand (see *'Jacking, towing and wheel changing'*), turn the steering to full right lock and remove the underwing shield (Chapter 11).

19   Rotate the crankshaft clockwise until the long white-painted mark on the alternator drive pulley's outboard (right-hand) face is aligned with the single, separate mark on the timing belt lower cover; see Chapter 1, *Ignition timing check and adjustment*, for details of the pulley/cover marks.

20   Check that the camshaft toothed pulley marks align as described in Section 7, paragraph 17.

21   Slacken through half a turn each the timing belt tensioner pulley Allen screw and the tensioner backplate (hex-head) screw, push the pulley assembly down to the (belt) fully-slack position to release tension from the belt, then re-tighten the backplate screw.

22   Remove the belt from the camshaft toothed pulleys, taking care not to twist it too sharply; use the fingers only to handle the belt. **Do not** rotate the crankshaft until the timing belt is refitted.

23   Unscrew the appropriate toothed pulley bolt and remove it, with its washer. To prevent a camshaft from rotating, lock together both

8.12 Removing camshaft toothed pulley – K8 engine – note roll pin (arrow)

8.24A K16 engine camshaft locking tool cut from steel tube ...

8.24B ... to fit toothed pulley spokes as closely as possible, as shown

8.49 Timing belt tensioner assembly – note spring hooked on pillar bolt

8.53 Use fabricated tool shown to hold pulley while bolt is tightened

8.59 K16 engine camshaft toothed pulleys have two keyways – engage 'EX' keyway with exhaust camshaft roll pin, 'IN' keyway with inlet camshaft roll pin

toothed pulleys using Rover service tool 18G 1570; this is a metal sprag shaped on both sides to fit the pulley teeth and is inserted between the pulleys.

24   If this tool is not available an acceptable substitute can be cut from a length of steel tube or similar to fit as closely as possible around the pulley spokes (photos).

25   Remove the toothed pulley from the camshaft end, noting the locating roll pin. Although the pulleys are identical it is good practice to mark them (inlet or exhaust) so that they can be returned to their original locations on reassembly.

Crankshaft toothed pulley

26   Disconnect the battery negative lead.

27   Remove its three retaining screws and move the washer system reservoir clear of the working area; disconnect the pump wiring connector plug(s) if the extra reach is required.

28   Unclip the expansion tank coolant hose from the bonnet lock platform and secure it clear of the working area.

29   Remove the timing belt upper right-hand (outer) cover (Sec 6).

30   Remove the spark plugs and use clean rag to seal the plug holes (Chapter 1) .

31   Raise the front right-hand side of the car and support it on an axle stand, then remove the front right-hand roadwheel (see 'Jacking, towing and wheel changing') and the underwing shield (Chapter 11).

32   Rotate the crankshaft clockwise until the long white-painted mark on the alternator drive pulley's outboard (right-hand) face is aligned with the single, separate mark on the timing belt lower cover; see Chapter 1, Ignition timing check and adjustment, for details of the pulley/cover marks.

33   Check that the camshaft toothed pulley marks align as described in Section 7, paragraph 17.

34   On K16 engines use the tool described in paragraphs 23 and 24 above to lock together the camshaft toothed pulleys so that they cannot move under valve spring pressure when the timing belt is removed.

35   Remove the alternator drive pulley (Sec 5).

36   Remove the timing belt lower cover (Sec 6).

37   Slacken through half a turn each the timing belt tensioner pulley Allen screw and the tensioner backplate (hex-head) screw, push the pulley assembly down to the (belt) fully-slack position to release tension from the belt, then re-tighten the backplate screw.

38   Work the belt clear of the crankshaft toothed pulley, taking care not to twist it too sharply; use the fingers only to handle the belt. **Do not** rotate the crankshaft until the timing belt is refitted.

39   Remove the pulley.

Tensioner assembly

40   Disconnect the battery negative lead.

41   Remove its three retaining screws and move the washer system reservoir clear of the working area; disconnect the pump wiring connector plug(s) if the extra reach is required.

42   Unclip the expansion tank coolant hose from the bonnet lock platform and secure it clear of the working area.

43   Remove the timing belt upper right-hand (outer) cover (Sec 6).

44   Remove the spark plugs and use clean rag to cover the plug holes (Chapter 1).

45   Raise the front right-hand side of the car and support it on an axle stand (see 'Jacking, towing and wheel changing'), turn the steering to full right lock and remove the underwing shield (Chapter 11).

46   Rotate the crankshaft clockwise until the long white-painted mark on the alternator drive pulley's outboard (right-hand) face is aligned with the single, separate mark on the timing belt lower cover; see Chapter 1, Ignition timing check and adjustment, for details of the pulley/cover marks.

47   Check that the camshaft toothed pulley marks align as described in Section 7, paragraph 17.

48   On K16 engines use the tool described in paragraphs 23 and 24 above to lock together the camshaft toothed pulleys so that they cannot move under valve spring pressure when the timing belt is slackened.

49   Unhook the tensioner spring from its pillar bolt, then unscrew the tensioner pulley Allen screw and the tensioner backplate (hex-head)

8.60 Locking camshafts with fabricated tool while toothed pulley bolt is tightened

screw (photo). Withdraw the tensioner assembly. **Do not** rotate the crankshaft until the timing belt is re-tensioned.

Inspection

50   Clean thoroughly the camshaft/crankshaft pulleys and renew any that show signs of wear, damage or cracks.
51   Clean the tensioner assembly but do not use any strong solvent which may enter the pulley bearing. Check that the pulley rotates freely on the backplate, with no sign of stiffness or of free play. Renew the assembly if there is any doubt about its condition or if there are any obvious signs of wear or damage; the same applies to the tensioner spring, which should be checked with great care as its condition is critical for the correct tensioning of the timing belt.

Refitting

Camshaft toothed pulley – K8 engine

52   On reassembly, refit the pulley so that the timing marks face outwards (to the right) and ensure that the pulley keyway engages with the camshaft roll pin.
53   Refit the pulley bolt and washer, hold the pulley with the tool used on dismantling and tighten the pulley bolt to the specified torque wrench setting (photo). Check that the pulley timing marks align as described in Section 7, paragraph 17.
54   Refit the timing belt, taking care not to twist it too sharply, then slacken the tensioner backplate screw and check that the tensioner pulley moves to tension the belt; if the tensioner assembly is not free to move under spring tension, rectify the fault or the timing belt will not be correctly tensioned.
55   Rotate the crankshaft two full turns clockwise to settle and tension the belt; check that the timing marks are still aligned exactly.
56   The timing belt will now be tensioned correctly; tighten the tensioner backplate screw, followed by the tensioner pulley Allen screw to their specified torque wrench settings (where given).
57   Refit the underwing shield (Chapter 11), then lower the car to the ground.
58   Refit the timing belt upper right-hand (outer) cover (Sec 6), re-route and secure the coolant hose, refit the spark plugs (Chapter 1) and the washer system reservoir. Re-connect the battery negative lead.

Camshaft toothed pulleys – K16 engine

59   On reassembly, refit each pulley so that the timing marks face outwards (to the right) and ensure that the appropriate pulley keyway engages with the camshaft roll pin (ie, if refitting the inlet camshaft toothed pulley, engage its 'IN' keyway with the roll pin and so on) (photo).
60   Refit the pulley bolt and washer, lock the pulleys with the tool used on dismantling and tighten the pulley bolt to the specified torque wrench setting (photo). Check that the pulley timing marks align as

described in Section 7, paragraph 17, then remove the locking tool.
61   Refit the timing belt, taking care not to twist it too sharply, then slacken the tensioner backplate screw and check that the tensioner pulley moves to tension the belt; if the tensioner assembly is not free to move under spring tension, rectify the fault or the timing belt will not be correctly tensioned.
62   Rotate the crankshaft two full turns clockwise to settle and tension the belt; check that the timing marks are still aligned exactly.
63   The timing belt will now be tensioned correctly; tighten the tensioner backplate screw, followed by the tensioner pulley Allen screw to their specified torque wrench settings (where given).
64   Refit the underwing shield (Chapter 11), then lower the car to the ground.
65   Refit the timing belt upper right-hand (outer) cover (Sec 6), re-route and secure the coolant hose, refit the spark plugs (Chapter 1) and the washer system reservoir. Re-connect the battery negative lead.

Crankshaft toothed pulley

66   On reassembly, refit the pulley to the crankshaft so that the pulley locates correctly on the crankshaft's flattened section; the pulley's flange must be inboard so that the two timing marks can be seen from the right-hand side of the car. Check that the pulley timing marks align as described in Section 7, paragraph 17.
67   Refit the timing belt, taking care not to twist it too sharply, then slacken the tensioner backplate screw and check that the tensioner pulley moves to tension the belt; if the tensioner assembly is not free to move under spring tension, rectify the fault or the timing belt will not be correctly tensioned.
68   On K16 engines remove the camshaft toothed pulley locking tool.
69   On all engines, refit the timing belt lower cover (Sec 6) and the alternator drive pulley (Sec 5).
70   Rotate the crankshaft two full turns clockwise to settle and tension the belt; check that the timing marks are still aligned exactly.
71   The timing belt will now be tensioned correctly. Tighten the tensioner backplate screw, followed by the tensioner pulley Allen screw to their specified torque wrench settings (where given).
72   Refit the underwing shield (Chapter 11), then lower the car to the ground.
73   Refit the timing belt upper right-hand (outer) cover (Sec 6), re-route and secure the coolant hose, refit the spark plugs (Chapter 1) and the washer system reservoir. Re-connect the battery negative lead.

Tensioner assembly

74   On reassembly, loosely refit the tensioner assembly, hook the spring to its pillar bolt and tighten the pulley Allen screw and the backplate screw lightly; check that the tensioner is free to move under spring tension and that the pulley bears correctly against the belt.
75   On K16 engines remove the camshaft toothed pulley locking tool.
76   Rotate the crankshaft two full turns clockwise to settle and tension the belt; check that the timing marks are still aligned exactly.
77   The timing belt will now be tensioned correctly; tighten the tensioner backplate screw, followed by the tensioner pulley Allen screw to their specified torque wrench settings.
78   Refit the underwing shield (Chapter 11), then lower the car to the ground.
79   Refit the timing belt upper right-hand (outer) cover (Sec 6), re-route and secure the coolant hose, refit the spark plugs (Chapter 1) and the washer system reservoir. Re-connect the battery negative lead.

9 Camshaft oil seal(s) – renewal

Note: *If an oil seal is renewed with the timing belt still in place, check that the belt is free from oil contamination (renew the belt as a matter of course if signs of oil contamination are found; see Section 7), then cover the belt to protect it from contamination by oil while work is in progress and ensure that all traces of oil are removed from the area before the belt is refitted*

Right-hand seal – K8 engines

1   Remove the camshaft toothed pulley (Sec 8).
2   Punch or drill two small holes opposite each other in the oil seal. Screw a self-tapping screw into each and pull on the screws with pliers to extract the seal.

3   Clean the seal housing and polish off any burrs or raised edges which may have caused the seal to fail in the first place.
4   Lubricate the lips of the new seal with clean engine oil and drive it into position until it seats on its locating shoulder, using a suitable socket or tube. Take care not to damage the seal lips during fitting. Note that the seal lips should face inboard, to the left.
5   Refit the camshaft toothed pulley (Sec 8).

Left-hand seal –   K8 (fuel-injected engine only)

6   Disconnect the battery negative lead.
7   Remove the distributor (Chapter 5).
8   Punch or drill two small holes opposite each other in the seal. Screw a self-tapping screw into each and pull on the screws with pliers to extract the seal.
9   Clean the seal housing and polish off any burrs or raised edges which may have caused the seal to fail in the first place.
10   Lubricate the lips of the new seal with clean engine oil and drive it into position until it seats on its locating shoulder, using a suitable deep socket or tube. Take care not to damage the seal lips during fitting. Note that the seal lips should face inboard, to the right.
11   Refit the distributor (Chapter 5).
12   Connect the battery negative lead.

Right-hand seals –   K16 engines

13   Remove the appropriate camshaft toothed pulley (Sec 8).
14   Punch or drill two small holes opposite each other in the seal. Screw a self-tapping screw into each and pull on the screws with pliers to extract the seal.
15   Clean the seal housing and polish off any burrs or raised edges which may have caused the seal to fail in the first place.
16   Lubricate the lips of the new seal with clean engine oil and drive it into position until it seats on its locating shoulder, using a suitable socket or tube (photo). Take care not to damage the seal lips during fitting. Note that the seal lips should face inboard, to the left.
17   Refit the camshaft toothed pulley (Sec 8).

Left-hand seals –   K16 engines

18   Disconnect the battery negative lead.
19   To reach the inlet camshaft seal, remove the distributor (Chapter 5).
20   To reach the exhaust camshaft seal, unfasten the rubber strap securing the air intake duct to its support bracket, disconnect the vacuum pipe from the air temperature control valve and unclip the pipe from the support bracket, then undo the bracket's retaining (hex-head) screws and remove the bracket from the cylinder head (photo).
21   Punch or drill two small holes opposite each other in the seal. Screw a self-tapping screw into each and pull on the screws with pliers to extract the seal.
22   Clean the seal housing and polish off any burrs or raised edges which may have caused the seal to fail in the first place.
23   Lubricate the lips of the new seal with clean engine oil and drive it into position until it seats on its locating shoulder, using a suitable deep socket or tube. Take care not to damage the seal lips during fitting. Note that the seal lips should face inboard, to the right.
24   On the inlet camshaft, refit the distributor (Chapter 5).
25   On the exhaust camshaft, refit the air intake duct support bracket, tightening its screws to their specified torque wrench setting, then reconnect and secure the air temperature control valve vacuum pipe and refit the rubber strap to secure the air intake duct.
26   Connect the battery negative lead.

10   Camshaft(s) and hydraulic tappets – removal, inspection and refitting

Removal

K8 engine

1   Remove the cylinder head cover (Sec 4).
2   Remove the distributor (Chapter 5).
3   Either remove the timing belt from the camshaft toothed pulley (Section 8, paragraphs 1 to 10) so that the camshaft can be withdrawn complete with the pulley and oil seal, or remove the toothed pulley

9.16 Fitting a new camshaft right-hand oil seal – K16 engine

9.20 Remove air intake duct support bracket to reach exhaust camshaft left-hand oil seal – K16 engine

(Sec 8); the second course of action is preferable as the oil seal should be renewed whenever it is disturbed.
4   Carefully prise up the oil feed tube from the camshaft bearing caps; discard the sealing O-rings, which should be renewed whenever they are disturbed.
5   The camshaft right- and left-hand end bearing caps are noticeably different and cannot be confused; the intermediate bearing caps (which are all similar) are marked by the manufacturer with a number (1, 2, 3, or 4) stamped in the boss next to the oil feed hole. Before unbolting any of the caps, make written notes to ensure that each can be easily identified and refitted in its original location.
6   Working in the **reverse** of the sequence shown in Fig. 2.6, slacken the camshaft bearing cap bolts progressively, and by one turn at a time. Work only as described to release the pressure of the valve springs on the bearing caps gradually and evenly.
7   Withdraw the bearing caps, noting the presence of the locating dowels on the end caps, then remove the camshaft and withdraw the oil seal(s).
8   Obtain eight small, clean plastic containers and number them 1 to 8. Using a rubber sucker, withdraw each hydraulic tappet in turn, invert it to prevent oil loss and place it in its respective container, which should then be filled with clean engine oil. Do not interchange the hydraulic tappets or the rate of wear will be much increased and do not allow them to lose oil or they will take a long time to refill with oil on restarting the engine, resulting in incorrect valve clearances.

Fig. 2.6 Camshaft bearing cap bolt tightening sequence – K8 engine (Sec 10)

Note: *Apply thin bead of sealant to end bearing cap mating surfaces along paths shown by heavy black lines*

Fig. 2.7 Apply thin bead of sealant to camshaft carrier mating surface along paths shown by heavy black lines – K16 engine (Sec 10)

Fig. 2.8 Camshaft carrier bolt tightening sequence – K16 engine (Sec 10)

K16 engine

9   Remove the timing belt upper left-hand (inner) cover (Sec 6). If it is wished not to remove the timing belt, it is possible to remove both toothed pulleys (Sec 8) and to unscrew the inner cover's upper retaining bolts (see Section 6 and photos for details) so that the cover can be pulled away from the cylinder head just far enough for adequate

10.9 Securing partly-removed timing belt upper left-hand (inner) cover clear of cylinder head

working clearance; take care not to distort or damage the cover or the timing belt (photo).
10   Remove the cylinder head cover (Sec 4).
11   Remove the distributor (Chapter 5).
12   Unclip the air temperature control valve vacuum pipe from the air intake duct support bracket, then unbolt the bracket from the cylinder head.
13   Working in the **reverse** of the sequence shown in Fig. 2.8, slacken the camshaft carrier bolts progressively and by one turn at a time. Work only as described to release the pressure of the valve springs on the carrier gradually and evenly.
14   Withdraw the camshaft carrier, noting the presence of the locating dowels, then remove the camshafts and withdraw their oil seals. The inlet camshaft can be identified by the distributor rotor arm drive spindle (or its location); therefore there is no need to mark the camshafts.
15   Obtain sixteen small, clean plastic containers and number them 1 to 16. Using a rubber sucker, withdraw each hydraulic tappet in turn, invert it to prevent oil loss and place it in its respective container, which should then be filled with clean engine oil. Do not interchange the hydraulic tappets or the rate of wear will be much increased and do not allow them to lose oil or they will take a long time to refill with oil on restarting the engine, resulting in incorrect valve clearances.

Inspection

16   Remove the camshaft(s) and tappets for inspection as described in the relevant sub-section above.
17   With the hydraulic tappets removed, check each for signs of obvious wear (scoring, pitting etc) and for ovality; renew if necessary.
18   If the engine's valve clearances have sounded noisy, particularly if the noise persists after initial start-up from cold, there is reason to suspect a faulty hydraulic tappet. Only a good mechanic experienced in these engines can tell whether the noise level is typical, or if renewal is warranted of one or more of the tappets. If faulty tappets are diagnosed and the engine's service history is unknown, it is always worth trying the effect of renewing the engine oil and filter (Chapter 1), using **only** good quality engine oil of the recommended viscosity and specification, before going to the expense of renewing any of the tappets. If any tappet's operation is faulty, it must be renewed.
19   With the camshaft(s) removed, examine the camshaft bearing journals and the cylinder head bearing surfaces for signs of obvious wear or pitting. If any such signs are evident, renew the component concerned.
20   To check the bearing journal running clearance, remove the hydraulic tappets, clean carefully the bearing surfaces and refit the camshaft(s) and carrier/bearing caps with a strand of Plastigage (see Section 34 for instructions on usage) across each journal. Tighten the carrier/bearing cap bolts to the specified torque wrench setting (do not rotate the camshaft), then remove the carrier/bearing caps and use the

scale provided with the Plastigage kit to measure the width of each compressed strand.

21   If the running clearance of any bearing is found to be worn to the specified service limit or beyond, fit a new camshaft and repeat the check; if the clearance is still excessive the cylinder head must be renewed.

22   To check camshaft endfloat, remove the hydraulic tappets, clean carefully the bearing surfaces and refit the camshaft(s) and carrier/bearing caps. Tighten the carrier/bearing cap bolts to the specified torque wrench setting, then measure the endfloat using a DTI (Dial Test Indicator, or dial gauge) mounted on the cylinder head so that its tip bears on the camshaft right-hand end.

23   Tap the camshaft fully towards the gauge, zero the gauge, then tap the camshaft fully away from the gauge and note the gauge reading. If the endfloat measured is found to be worn to the specified service limit or beyond, fit a new camshaft and repeat the check; if the clearance is still excessive the cylinder head must be renewed.

24   The camshaft itself should show no signs of marks, pitting or scoring on the lobe surfaces; if such marks are evident, renew the camshaft.

25   If a camshaft is renewed, extract the roll pin from the old one and fit the pin to the new camshaft with its split towards the camshaft's centre.

Refitting

K8 engine

26   On reassembly, liberally oil the cylinder head hydraulic tappet bores and the tappets. Note that if new tappets are being fitted, they must be charged with clean engine oil before installation. Carefully refit the tappets to the cylinder head, ensuring that each tappet is refitted to its original bore and is the correct way up. Some care will be required to enter the tappets squarely into their bores.

27   Liberally oil the camshaft bearings and lobes then refit the camshaft, rotating it so that number 1 cylinder lobes are pointing away from their valves and the roll pin in the camshaft's right-hand end is in the 4 o'clock position.

28   Ensure that the locating dowels are pressed firmly into their recesses, check that the mating surfaces are completely clean, unmarked and free from oil, then apply a thin bead of suitable RTV sealant to the mating surfaces of the bearing caps at the points shown in Fig. 2.6. Refit the bearing caps, using the notes made on removal to ensure that each is installed correctly and in its original location.

29   Working in the sequence shown in Fig. 2.6 tighten slowly and by one turn at a time the camshaft bearing cap bolts until the caps touch the cylinder head evenly, then go round again, in the same sequence, tightening the bolts to the specified torque wrench setting. Work only as described to impose the pressure of the valve springs gradually and evenly on the bearing caps.

30   Wipe off all surplus sealant so that none is left to find its way into any oilways. Follow the sealant manufacturer's instructions as to the time needed for curing; usually, at least an hour must be allowed between application of the sealant and the starting of the engine.

31   Fit new oil seal(s) as described in Section 9.

32   Squirt clean engine oil into each camshaft bearing cap oil hole. Fitting new sealing O-rings to each of its stubs, refit the oil feed tube to the bearing caps, pressing it firmly into place.

33   Refit the toothed pulley (if removed) as described in Section 8. Rotate the pulley until its timing marks align with the cylinder head top surface (Sec 7, paragraph 17), then refit the timing belt (Sec 8).

34   Refit the distributor (Chapter 5).

35   Refit the cylinder head cover (Sec 4).

K16 engine

36   On reassembly, liberally oil the cylinder head hydraulic tappet bores and the tappets. Note that if new tappets are being fitted, they must be charged with clean engine oil before installation. Carefully refit the tappets to the cylinder head, ensuring that each tappet is refitted to its original bore and is the correct way up. Some care will be required to enter the tappets squarely into their bores.

37   Liberally oil the camshaft bearings and lobes. Ensuring that each camshaft is in its original location, refit the camshafts, rotating each so that the number 1 cylinder lobes are pointing away from their valves; the roll pin in the inlet camshaft's right-hand end must be in the 4 o'clock position, while that in the exhaust camshaft must be in the 8 o'clock position (photo).

38   Ensure that the locating dowels are pressed firmly into their

10.37 K16 engine camshaft roll pin locations at TDC position (for refitting camshaft carrier)

recesses, check that the mating surfaces are completely clean, unmarked and free from oil, then apply a thin bead of suitable RTV sealant to the mating surfaces of the carrier as shown in Fig. 2.7. Refit the carrier.

39   Working in the sequence shown in Fig. 2.8 tighten slowly and by one turn at a time the camshaft carrier bolts until the carrier touches the cylinder head evenly, then go round again, in the same sequence, tightening the bolts to the specified torque wrench setting. Work only as described to impose the pressure of the valve springs gradually and evenly on the carrier.

40   Wipe off all surplus sealant so that none is left to find its way into any oilways. Follow the sealant manufacturer's instructions as to the time needed for curing; usually, at least an hour must be allowed between application of the sealant and the starting of the engine.

41   Fit new oil seals (Sec 9).

42   Refit the cylinder head cover (Sec 4).

43   Refit the distributor (Chapter 5).

44   Refit the air intake duct support bracket, tightening its screws to their specified torque wrench setting, then reconnect and secure the air temperature control valve vacuum pipe and refit the rubber strap to secure the air intake duct.

45   Refit the timing belt upper left-hand (inner) cover (Sec 6).

46   Refit the toothed pulleys (Sec 8), rotate the pulleys until their timing marks align with the inner cover mark (Sec 7, paragraph 17), then refit the timing belt (Sec 8).

11   Cylinder head – removal and refitting

Note: *Due to the design of the engine, it will become very difficult, almost impossible, to turn the crankshaft once the cylinder head bolts have been slackened. The manufacturer accordingly states that the crankshaft will be 'tight' and should not be rotated more than absolutely necessary once the head has been removed; if the crankshaft cannot be rotated, it must be removed for overhaul work to proceed. With this in mind, during any servicing or overhaul work the crankshaft always must be rotated to the desired position before the bolts are disturbed*

Removal

1   Disconnect the battery negative lead.

2   Drain the cooling system (Chapter 1).

3   Remove the camshaft toothed pulley(s) (Sec 8).

4   Unscrew the bolts securing the timing belt upper left-hand (inner) cover to the cylinder head so that the cover can be pulled away from the cylinder head just far enough for adequate working clearance; take care not to distort or damage the cover or the timing belt (see Sec 6 for details).

Fig. 2.9 Top end components – K8 engine (Sec 11)

1 Cylinder head cover
2 Seal
3 Engine oil filler cap
4 Seal
5 Bolt
6 Spark plug (HT) lead clip
7 Screw
8 Plastic insert
9 Plastic insert
10 Spark plug (HT) lead clip
11 Air intake duct support bracket
12 Fastener insert
13 Screw
14 Oil seal
15 Roll pin
16 Camshaft
17 Camshaft right-hand bearing cap*
18 Dowel
19 Bolt
20 Camshaft intermediate bearing cap*
21 Bolt
22 Camshaft left-hand bearing cap*
23 Oil feed tube
24 O-ring
25 Cylinder head bolt
26 Cylinder head
27 Cylinder head gasket
28 Hydraulic tappet
29 Split collets
30 Spring retainer
31 Valve spring
32 Valve stem seal/spring bottom seat
33 Valve guide
34 Inlet valve
35 Valve seat insert
36 Exhaust valve
37 Valve seat insert
38 Gasket
39 Coolant outlet elbow
40 Screw
41 Coolant temperature gauge sender unit
42 Spark plug
43 Rotor arm drive spindle – fuel-injected engines
44 Oil seal – fuel-injected engines

*Note: Camshaft bearing caps shown for reference only – not available separately from cylinder head

5   Remove the cylinder head cover (Sec 4).
6   Disconnect the exhaust system front pipe from the manifold (Chapter 4) and where fitted, disconnect or release the lambda sensor wiring so that it is not strained by the weight of the exhaust.
7   Note that the following text assumes that the cylinder head will be removed with both inlet and exhaust manifolds attached; this is easier, but makes it a bulky and heavy assembly to handle. If it is wished first to remove the manifolds, proceed as described in the relevant Sections of Chapter 4.
8   On carburettor engines, disconnect the following from the carburettor and inlet manifold as described in the relevant sections of Chapter 4.

(a) Fuel pump feed hose (plug both openings to prevent loss of fuel and the entry of dirt into the system).
(b) Carburettor idle bypass solenoid wires.
(c) Throttle cable.

(d) Choke cable.
(e) Vacuum servo unit vacuum hose.
(f) Inlet manifold PTC heater wire.
(g) Inlet manifold heater temperature switch wiring.

9   On fuel-injected engines, carry out the following operations as described in the relevant sections of Chapter 4.

(a) K8 engines – disconnect the fuel trap vacuum hoses from the air cleaner assembly (if not already disconnected).
(b) K16 engines – remove the air cleaner assembly.
(c) Disconnect (where fitted) the charcoal canister purge control valve hose from the throttle body.
(d) Depressurise the fuel system and disconnect the fuel feed and return hoses from the throttle body pipes – plug both openings of each pipe to prevent loss of fuel and the entry of dirt into the system.

**Fig. 2.10 Top end components –
K16 engine (Sec 11)**

1   Spark plug cover
2   Screw
3   Retaining washer
4   Engine oil filler cap
5   Seal
6   Spark plug
7   Pillar bolt
8   Spark plug (HT) lead grommet
9   Spark plug (HT) lead clip plate
10 Bolt
11 Cylinder head cover
12 Gasket
13 Camshaft carrier*
14 Bolt
15 Cylinder head bolt
16 Inlet camshaft
17 Exhaust camshaft
18 Roll pin
19 Rotor arm drive spindle
20 Oil seal
21 Hydraulic tappet
22 Split collets
23 Spring retainer
24 Valve spring
25 Valve stem seal/spring bottom
    seat
26 Cylinder head
27 Dowel
28 Cylinder head gasket
29 Valve guide
30 Inlet valves
31 Valve seat insert
32 Exhaust valves
33 Valve seat insert
34 Air intake duct support bracket
35 Screw
36 Gasket
37 Coolant outlet elbow
38 Screw
39 Coolant temperature gauge
    sender unit

*Note: Camshaft carrier shown for
reference only – not available
separately from cylinder head

(e)   Disconnect the throttle cable.
(f)   Disconnect the three connector plugs from the throttle body.
(g)   Disconnect the vacuum servo unit vacuum hose from the inlet
      manifold; discard the sealing washers.
(h)   Disconnect the inlet manifold PTC heater wire.
(i)   Disconnect the inlet manifold coolant temperature sensor
      connector plug.

10   Working as described in the relevant Sections of Chapter 3,
disconnect the connector plug from the coolant temperature sensor
screwed into the coolant outlet elbow, then disconnect the coolant
hoses from the (three) inlet manifold unions and from the coolant outlet
elbow.
11   Unclip the engine wiring harness from the inlet manifold or its
support stays, slacken the bolts securing the stays to the manifold, then
unbolt the support stays and the carburettor metal overflow pipes from
the cylinder block/crankcase.
12   Remove the distributor cap (Chapter 1) and place it, with the spark
plug HT leads, clear of the working area.
13   Working in the **reverse** of the sequence shown in photo 11.28A
(K8 engines) or 11.28B (K16 engines), slacken progressively and by one

turn at a time the ten cylinder head bolts; a female Torx-type socket
(No. 12 size) will be required. Remove each bolt in turn and store it in its
correct fitted order by pushing it through a clearly-marked cardboard
template.
14   The joint between the cylinder head and gasket and the cylinder
block/crankcase must now be broken without disturbing the wet liners;
although these liners are better located and sealed than some wet liner
engines, there is still a risk of coolant and foreign matter leaking into the
sump if the cylinder head is lifted carelessly. If care is not taken and the
liners are moved, there is also a possibility of the their bottom seals
being disturbed, causing leakage after refitting the head.
15   To break the joint, obtain two L-shaped metal bars which fit into
the cylinder head bolt holes and gently 'rock' the cylinder head free
towards the front of the car; see Fig. 2.11. Do not try to swivel the head
on the cylinder block/crankcase; it is located by dowels as well as by the
tops of the liners.
16   When the joint is broken lift the cylinder head away; use assistance
if possible as it is a heavy assembly, especially if it is complete with the
manifolds. Remove the gasket, noting the two dowels and discard it.
17   Note that further to the warnings given in the note at the beginning
of this Section, **do not** attempt to rotate the crankshaft with the cylinder

11.19 Checking condition of cylinder head bolt threads – cylinder head removed

11.25A Fit new cylinder head gasket on two locating dowels (arrowed) ...

11.25B ... so that 'TOP' mark is upwards and 'FRONT' arrow points to timing belt end

11.26 Refitting the cylinder head

11.28A Cylinder head bolt tightening sequence – K8 engine

11.28B Cylinder head bolt tightening sequence – K16 engine

11.28C Tightening cylinder head bolts – first stage ...

11.28D ... second and third stages use alignment of bolt head radial marks with cylinder head to establish angles (arrows)

head removed, otherwise the wet liners may be displaced. Operations that would normally require the rotation of the crankshaft (eg cleaning the piston crowns), must be carried out with great care to ensure that no particles of dirt or foreign matter are left behind. If cylinder liner clamps are to be used, they must be clamped in place using spacers fitted under the heads of the cylinder head bolts.

18   If the cylinder head is to be dismantled, remove the camshaft(s) as described in Section 10, then refer to the relevant Sections of Part B of this Chapter.

Refitting

19   Check the condition of the cylinder head bolts and particularly their threads whenever they are removed (see also Sec 26). Keeping all the bolts in their correct fitted order, wash them and wipe dry, then check each for any sign of visible wear or damage, renewing any bolt if necessary. Lightly oil the threads of each bolt, carefully enter it into its original hole (**do not drop**) and screw it in, by hand only until finger-tight. Measure the distance from the cylinder block/crankcase gasket surface

to under the bolt's head (photo).

20   If the distance measured is up to 97 mm, the bolt may be re-used. If the distance measured is more than 97 mm, the bolt **must** be renewed. Considering the task these bolts perform and the pressures they must withstand, owners should consider renewing all the bolts as a matched set if more than one of the originals fail inspection or are close to the limit set.

21   The mating faces of the cylinder head and cylinder block/crankcase must be perfectly clean before refitting the head. Use a hard plastic or wood scraper to remove all traces of gasket and carbon; also clean the piston crowns. Take particular care as the soft aluminium alloy is damaged easily. Also, make sure that the carbon is not allowed to enter the oil and water passages – this is particularly important for the lubrication system, as carbon could block the oil supply to any of the engine's components. Using adhesive tape and paper, seal the water, oil and bolt holes in the cylinder block/crankcase. To prevent carbon entering the gap between the pistons and bores, smear a little grease in the gap. After cleaning each piston, use a small brush to remove all traces of grease and carbon from the gap, then wipe away the

Fig. 2.11 Using two cranked bars to break cylinder head-to-cylinder block/crankcase joint by 'rocking' (Sec 11)

Fig. 2.12 Sump screw tightening sequence (Sec 12)

remainder with a clean rag. Clean all the pistons in the same way.

22   Check the mating surfaces of the cylinder block/crankcase and the cylinder head for nicks, deep scratches and other damage. If slight, they may be removed carefully with a file, but if excessive, machining may be the only alternative to renewal.

23   If warpage is suspected of the cylinder head gasket surface, use a straight-edge to check it for distortion. Refer to Part B of this Chapter if necessary.

24   Wipe clean the mating surfaces of the cylinder head and cylinder block/crankcase. Check that the two locating dowels are in position at each end of the cylinder block/crankcase surface.

25   Position a new gasket on the cylinder block/crankcase surface so that the 'TOP' mark is uppermost and the 'FRONT' arrow points to the timing belt end (photos).

26   Refit the cylinder head, locating it on the dowels (photo).

27   Keeping all the cylinder head bolts in their correct fitted order, wash them and wipe dry, then lightly oil under the head and on the threads of each bolt, carefully enter it into its original hole (**do not drop**) and screw it in, by hand only until finger-tight.

28   Working progressively and in the sequence shown in photo 11.28A (K8 engines) or photo 11.28B (K16 engines), use first a torque wrench, then an ordinary socket extension bar to tighten the cylinder head bolts in the stages given in the Specifications Section of this Chapter. To tighten the bolts through the angles specified, simply use a felt-tip pen or similar to mark the position on the cylinder head of each bolt head's radial mark; the second stage then tightens each bolt through half a turn so that the marks face away from each other and the third stage tightens them through another half-turn so that all the bolt-head marks will then align again with their cylinder head counterparts. If any bolt is overtightened past its mark, slacken it through 90°, then re-tighten until the marks align (photos).

29   Refit and tighten the inlet manifold support stay bolts, then secure the engine wiring harness using the clips provided.

30   Connect all coolant hoses (Chapter 3) and refill the cooling system (Chapter 1), then reconnect the coolant temperature sensor wiring.

31   Working as described in the relevant Sections of Chapter 4, connect or refit all disturbed wiring, hoses and control cable(s) to the inlet manifold and fuel system components, refit the air cleaner assembly (where appropriate), then adjust the cable(s) (Chapter 1).

32   Reconnect the exhaust system front pipe to the manifold and (if applicable) reconnect the lambda sensor wiring (Chapter 4).

33   Refit the cylinder head cover (Sec 4).

34   Refit the timing belt upper left-hand (inner) cover (Sec 6) and the toothed pulley(s) (Sec 8).

35   Refit the spark plugs and distributor cap (Chapter 1).

36   Connect the battery negative lead.

12   Sump – removal and refitting

Removal

1   Disconnect the battery negative lead.

2   Drain the engine oil (Chapter 1), then clean and refit the engine oil drain plug, tightening it to the specified torque wrench setting.

3   Although this is not necessary as part of the dismantling procedure, owners are advised to remove and discard the oil filter (Chapter 1) so that it can be renewed with the oil.

4   Raise the front of the car and support it on axle stands (see 'Jacking, towing and wheel changing').

5   Disconnect the exhaust system front pipe from the manifold (Chapter 4); where fitted, disconnect or release the lambda sensor wiring so that it is not strained by the weight of the exhaust.

6   Unscrew its three (hex-head) retaining screws and remove the flywheel lower cover plate (photo).

7   Progressively slacken, then remove the sump (hex-head) retaining screws.

8   Break the joint by striking the sump with the palm of the hand, then lower the sump and withdraw it (photo).

9   While the sump is removed, take the opportunity to unbolt the oil

12.6 Remove flywheel lower cover plate to reach sump screws

12.8 Removing the sump

12.11 Sump gasket pegs must engage with sump mating surface holes

pump pick-up/strainer pipe and clean it – see the relevant Sections of Part B of this Chapter.

Refitting

10   Clean all traces of gasket from the mating surfaces of the cylinder block/crankcase and sump, then use a clean rag to wipe out the sump and the engine's interior. If the oil pump pick-up/strainer pipe was removed, fit a new sealing O-ring to its end and refit the pipe, tightening its retaining (hex-head) screws to the specified torque wrench setting.
11   If the sump gasket is damaged or shows signs of deterioration it must be renewed; otherwise it can be re-used. Fit it to the sump mating surface so that the gasket's 7 locating pegs fit into the sump holes (photo).
12   Offer up the sump to the cylinder block/crankcase and insert the screws, tightening them lightly at first.
13   Working in the sequence shown in Fig. 2.12, tighten the sump screws to the specified torque wrench setting.
14   Refit the flywheel lower cover plate and tighten its screws to the specified torque wrench setting.
15   Reconnect the exhaust system front pipe to the manifold and (if applicable) reconnect the lambda sensor wiring (Chapter 4).
16   Fit a new oil filter (if applicable) and refill the engine with oil (Chapter 1).
17   Connect the battery negative lead.

13   Oil pump – removal and refitting

Note: *The oil pressure relief valve can be dismantled, if required, without removing the oil pump from the car; see Section 14 for details*

Removal

1   Remove the crankshaft toothed pulley (Sec 8) and secure the timing belt clear of the working area so that it cannot be contaminated with oil.
2   Drain the engine oil (Chapter 1).
3   Although this is not necessary as part of the dismantling procedure, owners are advised to remove and discard the oil filter (Chapter 1) so that it can be renewed with the oil.
4   Unscrew the alternator adjuster link retaining nut and unbolt the engine wiring harness guide retaining screws, then move the link and guide clear of the oil pump (photo).
5   Unscrew the oil pump retaining bolt and screws (see photo 13.4) and withdraw the oil pump. Recover and discard the gasket; the crankshaft right-hand oil seal should be renewed whenever it is disturbed (Sec 15); if desired, the pump can be dismantled and inspected (Sec 14).
6   Whenever the oil pump is overhauled or renewed, the pump pick-up/ strainer pipe should be cleaned (see Section 12 and Part B).

Refitting

7   Thoroughly clean the mating faces of the oil pump and cylinder block/crankcase. Use grease to stick a new gasket in place.
8   Note that whether the original pump is refitted or a new pump is installed, it is essential that the pump is primed before installation by injecting oil into it and turning it by hand.
9   Refit the pump, ensuring that its inner gear engages fully on the crankshaft flats, then push the pump into place.
10   Refit the retaining bolt (see photo 13.4) and screws, tightening them to the specified torque wrench setting.
11   Refit the alternator adjuster link and the engine wiring harness guide, then tighten securely the retaining nut and screws.
12   Fit a new crankshaft right-hand oil seal (Sec 15).
13   Wash off any traces of oil, then refit the crankshaft toothed pulley and the timing belt (Sec 8).

14   Oil pump – dismantling, inspection and reassembly

Note: *If oil pump wear is suspected, check the cost and availability of new parts (only available in the form of repair kit LQX 10001) against the cost of a new pump. Examine the pump as described in this Section and then decide whether renewal or repair is the best course of action*

13.4 Alternator link nut 'A', wiring guide screws 'B', oil pump screws 'C', oil pump bolt 'D'

Dismantling

1   Unscrew the Torx screws (size T25) and remove the pump cover plate; discard the sealing O-ring. Note the identification marks on the outer rotor.
2   Withdraw the rotors.
3   The oil pressure relief valve can be dismantled, if required, without disturbing the pump. If this is to be done, carry out the following preliminary dismantling operations to gain access to the valve.

   (a)   Raise the front right-hand side of the car and support it on an axle stand (see 'Jacking, towing and wheel changing'), then remove the roadwheel.
   (b)   Remove the underwing shield (Chapter 11).

4   To dismantle the valve, unscrew the threaded plug and recover the valve spring and plunger (photo) (Fig. 2.13). Discard the plug's sealing washer.

Inspection

5   Inspect the rotors for obvious signs of wear or damage and renew if necessary; if the pump body or cover plate are scored or damaged, the complete oil pump assembly must be renewed.
6   Using feeler gauge blades of the appropriate thickness, measure the clearance between the outer rotor and the pump body and between the tips of the inner and outer rotor lobes ('a' and 'b' respectively, Fig. 2.14).
7   Using feeler gauge blades and a straight-edge placed across the top of the pump body and the rotors, measure rotor endfloat ('c' Fig. 2.14).
8   If any measurement is outside the specified limits, the complete pump assembly must be renewed.
9   If the pressure relief valve plunger is scored, or if it does not slide

Fig. 2.13 Oil pressure relief valve components (Sec 14)

1   Threaded plug
2   Valve spring and plunger

14.4 Unscrewing oil pressure relief valve threaded plug – in car

freely in the pump body bore, it must be renewed, using all the components from the repair kit.

Reassembly

10   Lubricate the rotors with clean engine oil and refit them to the pump body, ensuring that the outer rotor's identification mark faces outwards (Fig. 2.15) .
11   Fitting a new sealing O-ring, refit the cover plate. Apply thread-locking compound to their threads and refit the cover plate Torx screws, tightening them securely.
12   Check that the pump rotates freely, then prime it by injecting oil into its passages and rotating it; if a long time elapses before the pump is refitted to the engine, prime it again before installation.
13   When reassembling the oil pressure relief valve, ensure that the plunger is refitted the correct way up (Fig. 2.13). Fit a new sealing washer and tighten the threaded plug securely.

Fig. 2.14 Checking oil pump rotors for wear – see text for details (Sec 14)

15   Crankshaft oil seals – renewal

Right-hand oil seal

1   Remove the crankshaft toothed pulley (Sec 8) and secure the timing belt clear of the working area so that it cannot be contaminated with oil.
2   Punch or drill two small holes opposite each other in the seal. Screw a self-tapping screw into each and pull on the screws with pliers to extract the seal.
3   Clean the seal housing and polish off any burrs or raised edges which may have caused the seal to fail in the first place.
4   Lubricate the lips of the new seal with clean engine oil and drive it into position until it seats on its locating shoulder, using a suitable socket or tube. Take care not to damage the seal lips during fitting; use either grease or a thin layer of insulating tape to protect the seal lips from the edges of the crankshaft flats, but be careful to remove all traces of tape and to lubricate the seal lips if the second method is used. Note that the seal lips should face inboard, to the left.
5   Wash off any traces of oil, then refit the crankshaft toothed pulley and timing belt (Sec 8).

Left-hand oil seal

6   Remove the flywheel (Sec 16).
7   Taking care not to mark either the crankshaft or any part of the cylinder block/crankcase, lever the seal evenly out of its housing.
8   Clean the seal housing and polish off any burrs or raised edges which may have caused the seal to fail in the first place.
9   Lubricate with grease the lips of the new seal and the crankshaft shoulder, then offer up the seal to the cylinder block/crankcase.
10   Feeding the seal's lips over the crankshaft shoulder by hand only,

Fig. 2.15 Oil pump outer rotor outside face identifying mark – arrow (Sec 14)

press the seal evenly into its housing and use a soft-faced mallet to tap it gently into place until its outer flange seats evenly on the housing lip.
11   Wash off any traces of oil, then refit the flywheel (Sec 16).

16   Flywheel – removal, inspection and refitting

Removal

1   Remove the transmission (Chapter 7).
2   Remove the clutch (Chapter 6).
3   Prevent the flywheel from turning by locking the ring gear teeth (see photo 34.30C), or by bolting a strap between the flywheel and the cylinder block/crankcase.
4   Unscrew the bolts and discard them; they must be renewed whenever they are disturbed.
5   Withdraw the flywheel. Do not drop it, it is very heavy.

Inspection

6   If the flywheel's clutch mating surface is deeply scored, cracked or otherwise damaged, the flywheel must be renewed, unless it is possible to have it surface ground; seek the advice of a Rover dealer or engine reconditioning specialist.

7   If the ring gear is badly worn or has missing teeth it must be renewed, but this job is best left to a Rover dealer or engine reconditioning specialist. The temperature to which the new ring gear must be heated for installation (350°C, shown by an even light blue colour) is critical and, if not done accurately, the hardness of the teeth will be destroyed.

8   If the reluctor ring is damaged, it must be renewed (Chapter 5).

Refitting

9   Clean the mating surfaces of the flywheel and crankshaft. Clean any remaining adhesive from the threads of the crankshaft threaded holes by making two saw cuts at opposite points along the (carefully-cleaned) threads of one of the original flywheel bolts and screwing it into each hole in turn. **Do not** use a tap to clean the threads in this way.

10   Position the flywheel over the crankshaft's locating dowel, press it into place and fit six **new** bolts.

11   Lock the flywheel by the method used on dismantling and tighten the bolts to the specified torque wrench setting.

12   Refit the clutch (Chapter 6), then remove the locking tool.

13   Refit the transmission (Chapter 7).

---

17   Engine/transmission mountings – inspection and renewal

Inspection

1   If improved access is required, raise the front of the car and support it securely on axle stands (see 'Jacking, towing and wheel changing').

2   Check the mounting rubber to see if it is cracked, hardened or separated from the metal at any point; renew the mounting if any such damage or deterioration is evident.

3   Check that all the mounting's fasteners are securely tightened; use a torque wrench to check if possible.

4   Using a large screwdriver or a pry bar, check for wear in the mounting by carefully levering against it to check for free play; where this is not possible, enlist the aid of an assistant to move the engine/transmission unit back and forth or from side to side while you watch the mounting. While some free play is to be expected even from new components, excessive wear should be obvious. If excessive free play is found, check first that the fasteners are correctly secured, then renew any worn components as described below.

Renewal – right-hand mounting

5   Disconnect the battery negative lead.

6   Remove its three retaining screws and move the washer system reservoir clear of the working area; disconnect the pump wiring connector plug(s) if the extra reach is required.

7   Unclip the expansion tank coolant hose from the bonnet lock platform and secure it clear of the working area.

8   Support the weight of the engine/transmission using a trolley jack, with a wooden spacer to prevent damage to the sump, then unscrew the mounting through-bolt and nut and the mounting-to-bracket nuts. Remove the mounting, noting the two rubber washers (photos).

9   Where necessary, unscrew also the retaining bolts and remove the bracket from the cylinder block/crankcase.

10   Check carefully for signs of wear or damage all components and renew them where necessary.

11   On reassembly, refit the bracket to the cylinder block/crankcase and tighten its bolts to the specified torque wrench setting.

12   Locate the rubber washers on the mounting, one on each side of its centre boss, then refit it to the bracket and tighten the retaining nuts finger-tight.

13   Using the trolley jack to obtain the correct height, refit from rear to front the mounting-to-body through-bolt, check that the rubber washers are correctly seated and refit the nut (photo).

14   Tighten to their specified torque wrench settings the

17.8A Use trolley jack (with wooden spacer to prevent damage) to adjust height of engine/transmission while mountings are renewed

17.8B Right-hand mounting through-bolt 'A', mounting-to-bracket nuts 'B', bracket-to-cylinder block/crankcase bolts (two arrowed) 'C'

17.13 Check rubber washers are correctly installed before tightening through-bolt nut

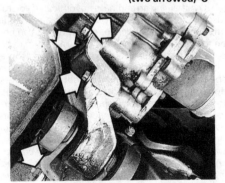

17.30A Remove bolts (arrows) to release ...

17.30B ... complete engine/transmission rear mounting

mounting-to-bracket nuts and the through-bolt retaining nut, then lower and remove the jack.

15   Re-route and secure the coolant hose, refit the washer system reservoir, then connect the battery negative lead.

Renewal – left-hand mounting

16   Disconnect the battery negative lead.
17   Where fitted, remove the charcoal canister (Chapter 4).
18   If the mounting's bracket is to be removed, disconnect the clutch cable (Chapter 6).
19   Unclip the engine wiring harness from the mounting.
20   Support the weight of the engine/transmission using a trolley jack, with a wooden spacer to prevent damage to the transmission casing, then unbolt the mounting from the bracket on the transmission and also from the support member.
21   If required, unbolt the bracket from the transmission.
22   Although the mounting's rubber is secured by two nuts to a metal outer section, the two parts can be renewed only as a complete assembly. Check all components carefully for signs of wear or damage, and renew them where necessary.
23   On reassembly, refit the bracket to the transmission and tighten its bolts to the specified torque wrench setting.
24   Using the trolley jack to obtain the correct height, refit the mounting, tightening its bolts by hand only until finger-tight, then tighten the various fasteners to their specified torque wrench settings.
25   Refit the clutch cable (Chapter 6).
26   Secure the engine wiring harness to the mounting.
27   Refit (if applicable) the charcoal canister (Chapter 4).
28   Connect the battery negative lead.

Renewal – rear mounting

29   Raise the front of the car and support it securely on axle stands (see 'Jacking, towing and wheel changing').
30   Support the weight of the engine/transmission using a trolley jack, with a wooden spacer to prevent damage to the transmission casing, then unbolt the mounting bracket from the transmission and the tie-rod from the underbody bracket and remove the mounting (photos).
31   Unscrew the through-bolt to separate the tie-rod from the bracket and to release (where fitted) the dynamic absorbers. Check carefully for signs of wear or damage all components and renew them where necessary.
32   Reassembly is the reverse of the removal procedure. If the mounting was removed complete and has not been disturbed, tighten all fasteners to their specified torque wrench settings. If the mounting was dismantled, tighten by hand only all fasteners, lower the car to the ground and rock it to settle the weight of the engine/transmission on the mounting, then use a torque wrench to tighten the fasteners to their specified settings.

Part B: Engine removal and general overhaul procedures

18   General information

Included in this part of Chapter 2 are details of removing the engine/transmission unit from the car and general overhaul procedures for the cylinder head, cylinder block/crankcase and all other engine internal components.

The information given ranges from advice concerning preparation for an overhaul and the purchase of replacement parts, to detailed step-by-step procedures covering removal, inspection, renovation and refitting of engine internal components.

After Section 22, all instructions are based on the assumption that the engine has been removed from the car. For information concerning in-car engine repair, as well as the removal and refitting of those external components necessary for full overhaul, refer to Part A of this Chapter and to Section 22. Ignore any preliminary dismantling operations described in Part A that are no longer relevant once the engine has been removed from the car.

All specifications relating to engine overhaul are at the beginning of this Chapter.

19   Engine overhaul – general information

It is not always easy to determine when, or if, an engine should be completely overhauled, as a number of factors must be considered.

High mileage is not necessarily an indication that an overhaul is needed, while low mileage does not preclude the need for an overhaul. Frequency of servicing is probably the most important consideration; an engine which has had regular and frequent oil and filter changes, as well as other required maintenance, should give many thousands of miles of reliable service. Conversely, a neglected engine may require an overhaul very early in its life.

Excessive oil consumption is an indication that piston rings, valve seals and/or valve guides are in need of attention. Make sure that oil leaks are not responsible before deciding that the rings and/or guides are worn. Perform a compression test (Sec 2) to determine the likely cause of the problem.

Check the oil pressure with a gauge fitted in place of the oil pressure switch and compare it with that specified. If it is extremely low, the main and big-end bearings and/or the oil pump are probably worn out.

Loss of power, rough running, knocking or metallic engine noises, excessive valve gear noise and high fuel consumption may also point to the need for an overhaul, especially if they are all present at the same time. If a complete service does not remedy the situation, major mechanical work is the only solution.

An engine overhaul involves restoring all internal parts to the specification of a new engine. During an overhaul, the cylinder liners, the pistons and the piston rings are renewed. New main and big-end bearings are generally fitted and if necessary, the crankshaft may be renewed to restore the journals. The valves are also serviced as well, since they are usually in less than perfect condition at this point. While the engine is being overhauled, other components, such as the distributor, starter and alternator, can be overhauled as well. The end result should be an as-new engine that will give many trouble-free miles. **Note:** *Critical cooling system components such as the hoses, thermostat and water pump should be renewed when an engine is overhauled. The radiator should be checked carefully to ensure that it is not clogged or leaking. Also it is a good idea to renew the oil pump whenever the engine is overhauled.*

Before beginning the engine overhaul, read through the entire procedure to familiarize yourself with the scope and requirements of the job. Overhauling an engine is not difficult if you follow carefully all of the instructions, have the necessary tools and equipment and pay close attention to all specifications; however, it can be time consuming. Plan on the car being off the road for a minimum of two weeks, especially if parts must be taken to an engineering works for repair or reconditioning. Check on the availability of parts and make sure that any necessary special tools and equipment are obtained in advance. Most work can be done with typical hand tools, although a number of precision measuring tools are required for inspecting parts to determine if they must be renewed. Often the engineering works will handle the inspection of parts and offer advice concerning reconditioning and renewal. **Note:** *Always wait until the engine has been completely dismantled and all components, especially the cylinder block/crankcase, the cylinder liners and the crankshaft have been inspected before deciding what service and repair operations must be performed by an engineering works. Since the condition of these components will be the major factor to consider when determining whether to overhaul the original engine or buy a reconditioned unit, do not purchase parts or have overhaul work done on*

Fig. 2.16 Engine bottom end components (Sec 18)

1   Oil pump
2   Gasket
3   Bolt
4   Screw
5   Oil seal
6   Engine oil level dipstick
7   Dipstick tube
8   Bolt
9   Screw
10 Gasket
11 Water pump
12 O-ring
13 Pillar bolt
14 Screw
15 Dowel pin
16 O-ring
17 Thermostat housing
18 Gasket
19 Thermostat
20 Thermostat housing
21 Screw
22 Coolant hose
23 Hose clamp
24 Coolant rail
25 Screw
26 Air bleed screw
27 Sealing washer
28 Liner
29 O-rings
30 Cylinder block/crankcase
31 Dowel
32 Top compression ring
33 Second compression ring
34 Oil control ring
35 Piston
36 Gudgeon pin*
37 Connecting rod
38 Big-end bearing shell
39 Big-end bearing cap
40 Big-end bearing cap bolt
41 Crankshaft
42 Crankshaft thrustwasher
43 Crankshaft main bearing shell
44 Dowel
45 Oil seal
46 Flywheel (with reluctor ring)
47 Bolt
48 Main bearing ladder*
49 Bolt
50 Dowel
51 Stud
52 Oil rail
53 Bolt
54 Nut
55 O-ring
56 Oil pump pick-up/strainer pipe
57 Screw
58 Sump
59 Gasket
60 Screw
61 Engine oil drain plug
62 Sealing washer
63 Oil filter
64 Oil filter adaptor
65 Screw
66 Gasket
67 Oil pressure switch
68 Blanking plate – carburettor engines
69 Screw

*Note: Main bearing ladder is supplied only
with cylinder block/crankcase assembly –
gudgeon pin is supplied only with piston
assembly

21.10 Disconnecting engine wiring harness from main wiring harness – carburettor models

21.12A Removing bolt securing earth lead to body

21.12B Depressing retainer to release battery lead from fusible link box

other components until they have been thoroughly inspected. As a general rule, time is the primary cost of an overhaul, so it does not pay to fit worn or substandard parts.

As a final note, to ensure maximum life and minimum trouble from a reconditioned engine, everything must be assembled with care in a spotlessly clean environment.

20 Engine/transmission removal – methods and precautions

If you have decided that the engine must be removed for overhaul or major repair work, several preliminary steps should be taken.

Locating a suitable place to work is extremely important. Adequate work space, along with storage space for the car, will be needed. If a shop or garage is not available, at the very least a flat, level, clean work surface is required.

Cleaning the engine compartment and engine/transmission before beginning the removal procedure will help keep tools clean and organized.

An engine hoist or A-frame will also be necessary. Make sure the equipment is rated in excess of the combined weight of the engine and transmission (290 lb/130 kg approximately). Safety is of primary importance, considering the potential hazards involved in lifting the engine/transmission out of the car.

If the engine/transmission is being removed by a novice, a helper should be available. Advice and aid from someone more experienced would also be helpful. There are many instances when one person cannot simultaneously perform all of the operations required when lifting the engine out of the car.

Plan the operation ahead of time. Before starting work, arrange for the hire or obtain all of the tools and equipment you will need. Some of the equipment necessary to perform engine/transmission removal and installation safely and with relative ease are (in addition to an engine hoist) a heavy duty trolley jack, a complete sets of spanners and sockets as described in the front of this manual, wooden blocks and plenty of rags and cleaning solvent for mopping up spilled oil, coolant and fuel. If the hoist must be hired, make sure that you arrange for it in advance, and perform all of the operations possible without it beforehand. This will save you money and time.

Plan for the car to be out of use for quite a while. An engineering works will be required to perform some of the work which the do-it-yourselfer cannot accomplish without special equipment. These places often have a busy schedule, so it would be a good idea to consult them before removing the engine in order to accurately estimate the amount of time required to rebuild or repair components that may need work.

Always be extremely careful when removing and refitting the engine/transmission. Serious injury can result from careless actions. Plan ahead, take your time and a job of this nature, although major, can be accomplished successfully.

21 Engine/transmission – removal and refitting

Removal

Note: *The engine can be removed from the car only as a complete unit with the transmission; the two are then separated for overhaul*

1   Park the vehicle on firm, level ground, apply the handbrake and remove the bonnet (Chapter 11).
2   If the engine is to be dismantled, drain its oil and remove the oil filter; clean and refit the drain plug, tightening it to its specified torque wrench setting (Chapter 1).
3   Jack up the front of the car and support it securely on axle stands, then remove the roadwheels (see *'Jacking, towing and wheel changing'*).
4   Drain the transmission oil; clean and refit the drain plug, tightening it to its specified torque wrench setting (Chapter 7).
5   Drain the cooling system (Chapter 1).
6   Remove the battery and its tray (Chapter 12).
7   Remove the complete air cleaner assembly, including the cold air intake duct (Chapter 4).
8   Remove, where fitted, the charcoal canister (Chapter 4).
9   Disconnect the ignition HT coil spark plug (HT) lead from the distributor cap.
10   On carburettor engines, unscrew the bolt securing the relay bracket to the inner wing panel and unplug the connector to disconnect the engine wiring harness from the main wiring harness (photo).
11   On fuel-injected engines, unplug its wiring connector(s) and disconnect the vacuum hose from the ECU, unplug the two connectors from the relay module and the single connector from the inertia switch, release the lambda sensor relay (where fitted) from its bracket, then unplug the connector to disconnect the engine wiring harness from the main wiring harness.
12   On all models, unscrew the bolt securing the earth lead to the body front panel, remove the fusible link box lid and the 30 amp fusible link, then use a small screwdriver gently to depress the retainer so that the battery lead connector can be removed from the fusible link box (photos).
13   Disconnect the remaining wiring from the starter motor and secure all engine/transmission wiring to the unit so that it will not hinder the removal of the engine/transmission from the car.
14   Disconnect the clutch cable and secure it clear of the engine/transmission unit (Chapter 6).
15   Disconnect the speedometer drive upper cable from the lower cable, release the upper cable from any securing clips and secure it clear of the engine/transmission (Chapter 12).
16   Disconnect the washer pump wiring connector plug(s), then remove its three retaining screws and move the washer system reservoir clear of the engine/transmission.
17   Working as described in the relevant Sections of Chapter 3, disconnect the coolant hose from the bottom of the expansion tank, the expansion tank hose from the inlet manifold union, both heater hoses from the heater matrix unions and the radiator top hose from the coolant outlet elbow. Either remove the radiator bottom hose or secure it so that it will not prevent engine/transmission removal.
18   Disconnect the vacuum servo unit vacuum hose from the inlet

21.26 Bolt lifting brackets to cylinder head using tapped holes provided

21.28A Release engine wiring harness from mounting clip and unbolt mounting from bracket (arrows)

21.28B Unscrew mounting/support member-to-front subframe rear bolts ...

21.28C ... and support member-to-front subframe front bolts (arrows) ...

21.28D ... then remove support member with engine/transmission left-hand mounting

21.30 Lifting out engine/transmission unit

manifold; discard the sealing washers (Chapter 4).

19   On carburettor engines, disconnect the fuel pump feed hose – plug both openings to prevent loss of fuel and the entry of dirt into the system (Chapter 4).

20   On fuel-injected engines, depressurise the fuel system and disconnect the fuel feed and return hoses from the throttle body pipes – plug both openings of each pipe to prevent loss of fuel and the entry of dirt into the system (Chapter 4).

21   Disconnect the throttle cable and (on carburettor engines only) the choke cable (Chapter 4).

22   Disconnect and release from the engine/transmission the lambda sensor wiring (where fitted), then disconnect the exhaust system front pipe from the manifold (Chapter 4).

23   Disconnect the gearchange linkage link rods from the transmission upper and lower selector levers (Chapter 7).

24   Either remove the engine/transmission rear mounting (Sec 17) or unbolt the mounting bracket from the transmission and slacken the tie-rod-to-body bolt and nut so that the mounting can be swung down clear of the transmission.

25   Dismantle the front suspension and remove both driveshafts (see Chapter 8 for full details but actually follow the abbreviated procedure given in Chapter 7, Section 6).

26   On K8 engines, the cylinder head has a tapped hole provided at the right-hand rear end (above the dipstick tube) and at the left-hand front end (behind the spark plug lead clips). On K16 engine cylinder heads the right-hand end hole is in the same place, but at the left-hand end the air intake duct support bracket mounting points must be used (photo). Attach lifting brackets to the engine at these points.

27   Take the weight of the engine/transmission using the engine hoist, then unscrew the engine/transmission right-hand mounting's through-bolt and nut.

28   Release the engine wiring harness from the clip on the engine/transmission left-hand mounting, unbolt the mounting bracket from the mounting, then unbolt the support member from the front subframe. Remove the support member (photos).

29   Make a final check that all components have been removed or disconnected that will prevent the removal of the engine/transmission from the car and ensure that components such as the gearchange linkage link rods are secured so that they cannot be damaged on removal.

30   Lift the engine/transmission out of the car, ensuring that nothing is trapped or damaged (photo).

31   Lower the engine/transmission to the ground and remove the starter motor (Chapter 12).

32   Unbolt the flywheel front, lower and rear cover plates, unscrew the four bolts securing the transmission to the engine and gently prise the transmission off the two locating dowels (at the front and rear of the main bearing ladder). Move the transmission squarely away from the engine, ensuring that the clutch components are not damaged (Chapter 7).

33   Remove the clutch (Chapter 6); do not forget to overhaul the clutch components before the engine and transmission are reconnected.

Refitting

34   Refitting is the reverse of removal, following where necessary the instructions given in the other Chapters of this manual. Note the following additional points.

(a)   Overhaul and lubricate the clutch components before refitting (Chapter 6).

(b)   When the transmission, starter motor and flywheel cover plates have been refitted, lift the engine/transmission unit and lower it into the engine compartment so that it is slightly tilted (transmission down); engage both driveshafts then return the unit to the horizontal and refit the engine/transmission mountings.

(c)   Remove the lifting brackets and refit any components removed to enable them to be fitted.

(d)   Tighten all fasteners to their specified torque wrench settings.

(e)   Adjust the control cables (Chapter 4).

(f)   Refill the engine and transmission with oil (Chapters 1 and 7).

(g)   Refill the cooling system (Chapter 1).

23.1A Use a valve-grinding sucker to extract hydraulic tappets ...

23.1B ... and store in clearly-marked containers filled with oil to prevent oil loss

23.3A Using a valve spring compressor to release split collets

23.3B Extracting a valve spring bottom seat/stem seal

23.6 Use a labelled plastic bag to keep together and identify valve components

22 Engine overhaul – dismantling sequence

1   It is much easier to dismantle and work on the engine if it is mounted on a portable engine stand. These stands can often be hired from a tool hire shop. Before the engine is mounted on a stand, the flywheel should be removed (Sec 16) so that the stand bolts can be tightened into the end of the cylinder block/crankcase (**not** the main bearing ladder).

2   If a stand is not available, it is possible to dismantle the engine with it blocked up on a sturdy workbench or on the floor. Be extra careful not to tip or drop the engine when working without a stand.

3   If you are going to obtain a reconditioned engine, all external components must be removed first to be transferred to the replacement engine (just as they will if you are doing a complete engine overhaul yourself). These components include the following.

(a)   Alternator and brackets (Chapter 12).
(b)   Distributor, HT leads and spark plugs (Chapter 5).
(c)   Thermostat and housing, coolant rail, coolant outlet elbow (Chapter 3).
(d)   Dipstick tube.
(e)   Carburettor/fuel-injection system components (Chapter 4).
(f)   All electrical switches and sensors.
(g)   Inlet and exhaust manifolds (Chapter 4).
(h)   Oil filter (Chapter 1).
(i)   Fuel pump (Chapter 4).
(j)   Engine mountings (Sec 17).
(k)   Flywheel (Sec 16).

Note: *When removing the external components from the engine, pay close attention to details that may be helpful or important during refitting. Note the fitted position of gaskets, seals, spacers, pins, washers, bolts and other small items.*

4   If you are obtaining a short motor (which consists of the engine cylinder block/crankcase and main bearing ladder, crankshaft, pistons and connecting rods all assembled), then the cylinder head, sump, oil pump, and timing belt will have to be removed also.

5   If you are planning a complete overhaul, the engine can be dismantled and the internal components removed in the following order.

(a)   Inlet and exhaust manifolds (Chapter 4).
(b)   Timing belt, toothed pulleys, tensioner and timing belt inner cover (Secs 6, 7 and 8).
(c)   Cylinder head (Sec 11).
(d)   Flywheel (Sec 16).
(e)   Sump (Sec 12).
(f)   Oil pump (Sec 13).
(g)   Piston/connecting rod assemblies (Sec 26).
(h)   Crankshaft (Sec 27).

6   Before beginning the dismantling and overhaul procedures, make sure that you have all of the correct tools necessary. Refer to the introductory pages at the beginning of this manual for further information.

23 Cylinder head – dismantling

Note: *New and reconditioned cylinder heads are available from the manufacturer and from engine overhaul specialists. Due to the fact that some specialist tools are required for the dismantling and inspection procedures, and new components may not be readily available, it may be more practical and economical for the home mechanic to purchase a reconditioned head rather than dismantle, inspect and recondition the original head*

1   Remove the camshaft(s) and hydraulic tappets (Sec 10), being careful to store the hydraulic tappets as described (photos).

2   Remove the cylinder head (Sec 11).

3   Using a valve spring compressor, compress each valve spring in turn until the split collets can be removed. Release the compressor and lift off the spring retainer and spring, then use a pair of pliers to extract the spring bottom seat/stem seal (photos).

4   If, when the valve spring compressor is screwed down, the spring retainer refuses to free and expose the split collets, gently tap the top of the tool directly over the retainer with a light hammer. This will free the retainer.
5   Withdraw the valve through the combustion chamber.
6   It is essential that each valve is stored together with its collets, retainer and spring, and that all valves are in their correct sequence unless they are so badly worn that they are to be renewed. If they are going to be kept and used again, place each valve assembly in a labelled polythene bag or similar small container (photo). Note that No 1 valve is nearest to the timing belt end of the engine.

Fig. 2.17 Check the cylinder head gasket surface for warpage along the paths shown (Sec 24)

A   K16 engine   B   K8 engine

24   Cylinder head and valves – cleaning and inspection

1   Thorough cleaning of the cylinder head and valve components, followed by a detailed inspection, will enable you to decide how much valve service work must be carried out during the engine overhaul. **Note:** *If the engine has been severely overheated, it is best to assume that the cylinder head is warped and to check carefully for signs of this*

Cleaning

2   Scrape away all traces of old gasket material and sealing compound from the cylinder head; see Section 11 for details.
3   Scrape away the carbon from the combustion chambers and ports, then wash the cylinder head thoroughly with paraffin or a suitable solvent.
4   Scrape off any heavy carbon deposits that may have formed on the valves, then use a power-operated wire brush to remove deposits from the valve heads and stems.

Inspection

Note: *Be sure to perform all the following inspection procedures before concluding that the services of a machine shop or engine overhaul specialist are required. Make a list of all items that require attention*

Cylinder head

5   Inspect the head very carefully for cracks, evidence of coolant leakage and other damage. If cracks are found, a new cylinder head should be obtained.
6   Use a straight-edge (placed as shown in Fig. 2.17) and feeler gauge blade to check that the cylinder head surface is not distorted (photo). If it is, it may be possible to resurface it, provided that the specified reface limit is not exceeded in so doing, or that the cylinder head is not reduced to less than the specified height.
7   Examine the valve seats in each of the combustion chambers. If they are severely pitted, cracked or burned then they will need to be renewed or re-cut by an engine overhaul specialist. If they are only slightly pitted, this can be removed by grinding-in the valve heads and seats with fine valve-grinding compound as described below. To check whether they are excessively worn, refit the valve and measure the installed height of its stem tip above the cylinder head upper surface (Fig. 2.18); if the measurement is above the specified limit, repeat the test using a new valve. If the measurement is still excessive, renew the seat insert.
8   If the valve guides are worn, indicated by a side-to-side motion of the valve, new guides must be fitted. Measure the diameter of the existing valve stems (see below) and the bore of the guides, then calculate the clearance and compare the result with the specified value; if the clearance is excessive, renew the valves or guides as necessary.
9   The renewal of valve guides is best carried out by an engine overhaul specialist. If the work is to be carried out at home, however, use a stepped, double-diameter drift to drive out the worn guide towards the combustion chamber. On fitting the new guide, place it first in a deep-freeze for one hour, then drive it into its cylinder head bore from the camshaft side until it projects the specified amount above the spring bottom seat/stem seal surface.
10   If the valve seats are to be re-cut, this must be done **only after** the guides have been renewed.

Valves

11   Examine the head of each valve for pitting, burning, cracks and general wear and check the valve stem for scoring and wear ridges. Rotate the valve and check for any obvious indication that it is bent. Look for pits and excessive wear on the tip of each valve stem. Renew any valve that shows any such signs of wear or damage.
12   If the valve appears satisfactory at this stage, measure the valve stem diameter at several points using a micrometer (photo). Any significant difference in the readings obtained indicates wear of the valve stem. Should any of these conditions be apparent, the valve(s) must be renewed.
13   If the valves are in satisfactory condition they should be ground (lapped) into their respective seats to ensure a smooth gas-tight seal. If the seat is only lightly pitted, or if it has been re-cut, fine grinding compound **only** should be used to produce the required finish. Coarse valve-grinding compound should **not** be used unless a seat is badly burned or deeply pitted; if this is the case the cylinder head and valves should be inspected by an expert to decide whether seat re-cutting or even the renewal of the valve or seat insert is required.

Fig. 2.18 Check valve seat wear by measuring valve stem installed height 'A' (Sec 24)

24.6 Checking a cylinder head gasket surface for warpage

24.12 Measuring valve stem diameter

24.15 Grinding-in a valve seat

24.19 Measuring valve spring free length

wipe off the used compound and repeat the process with fine compound. When a smooth unbroken ring of light grey matt finish is produced on both the valve and seat, the grinding operation is complete. **Do not** grind in the valves any further than absolutely necessary, or the seat will be prematurely sunk into the cylinder head.

17   To check that the seat has not been over-ground, measure the valve stem installed height, as described in paragraph 7 above.

18   When all the valves have been ground-in, carefully wash off **all** traces of grinding compound using paraffin or a suitable solvent before reassembly of the cylinder head.

Valve components

19   Examine the valve springs for signs of damage and discoloration and also measure their free length using vernier calipers (photo) or by comparing the existing spring with a new component.

20   Stand each spring on a flat surface and check it for squareness. If any of the springs are damaged, distorted or have lost their tension, obtain a complete new set of springs.

21   Check the hydraulic tappets as described in Section 10.

25 Cylinder head – reassembly

1   Lubricate the stems of the valves and insert them into their original locations. If new valves are being fitted, insert them into the locations to which they have been ground.

2   Working on the first valve, dip the spring bottom seat/stem seal in fresh engine oil then carefully locate it over the valve and onto the guide. Take care not to damage the seal as it is passed over the valve stem. Use a suitable socket or metal tube to press the seal firmly onto the guide (photo).

3   Locate the spring on the seat, followed by the spring retainer.

4   Compress the valve spring and locate the split collets in the recess in the valve stem. Use a little grease to hold the collets in place (photo).

14   Valve grinding is carried out as follows. Place the cylinder head upside down on a bench.

15   Smear a trace of (the appropriate grade of) valve-grinding compound on the seat face and press a suction grinding tool onto the valve head. With a semi-rotary action, grind the valve head to its seat, lifting the valve occasionally to redistribute the grinding compound (photo). A light spring placed under the valve head will greatly ease this operation.

16   If coarse grinding compound is being used, work only until a dull, matt even surface is produced on both the valve seat and the valve, then

25.2 Using a socket to install a valve stem seal

25.4 Use a little grease to hold the collets in place

25.6 Lubricate the hydraulic tappets thoroughly and refit the correct way up

25.7A Apply sealant (arrows) to camshaft bearing caps as directed in Fig. 2.9 – K8 engines

25.7B Fill oil holes with clean oil – note cap stamped identifying number

25.7C Renew O-rings (arrows) before refitting oil feed tube

25.7D K8 engine camshaft roll pin location at TDC position (for refitting camshaft bearing caps)

25.7E Fitting a new camshaft right-hand oil seal – K8 engine

Release the compressor, then repeat the procedure on the remaining valves.

5   With all the valves installed, place the cylinder head flat on the bench and, using a hammer and interposed block of wood, tap the end of each valve stem to settle the components.

6   Refit the hydraulic tappets as described in Section 10 (photo).

7   Refit the camshaft(s) as described in Section 10 (photos).

26   Piston/connecting rod assembly – removal

Note: *Due to the design of the engine, it will become very difficult, almost impossible, to turn the crankshaft once the cylinder head bolts have been slackened. The manufacturer accordingly states that the crankshaft will be 'tight' and should not be rotated more than absolutely necessary once the head has been removed; if the crankshaft cannot be rotated, it must be removed for overhaul work to proceed. With this in mind, during any servicing or overhaul work the crankshaft must always be rotated to the desired position before the bolts are disturbed*

Removal –   without removing crankshaft

1   Remove the timing belt, the camshaft toothed pulley(s) and tensioner, and the timing belt inner cover (Secs 6, 7 and 8).

2   Remove the camshaft(s) and hydraulic tappets (Sec 10), being careful to store the hydraulic tappets as described.

3   If the flywheel has been removed, temporarily refit the alternator drive pulley (Sec 5) and apply a spanner to its bolt to rotate the crankshaft.

4   Rotate the crankshaft until numbers 2 and 3 cylinder pistons are at the bottom of their stroke.

5   Remove the cylinder head (Sec 11); the crankshaft cannot now be rotated.

6   Unbolt the dipstick tube from the cylinder block/crankcase (photo).

7   Remove the sump (Sec 12) and unbolt the oil pump pick-up/strainer pipe from the oil rail; discard its sealing O-ring (photo).

8   Unscrew the two retaining nuts and remove the oil rail (photo).

9   Using a hammer and centre punch, paint or similar, mark each connecting rod big-end bearing cap with its respective cylinder number on the flat, machined surface provided (photo); if the engine has been dismantled before, note carefully any identifying marks made previously. Note that number 1 cylinder is at the timing belt end of the engine.

10   Unscrew and remove the big-end bearing cap bolts and withdraw the cap, complete with bearing shell, from the connecting rod. If only the bearing shells are being attended to, push the connecting rod up and off the crankpin, ensuring that the connecting rod big-ends do not mark the cylinder bore walls, then remove the upper bearing shell. Keep the cap, bolts and (if they are to be refitted) the bearing shells together in their correct sequence.

11   With numbers 2 and 3 cylinder big-ends disconnected, repeat the procedure (exercising great care to prevent damage to any of the components) to remove numbers 1 and 4 cylinder bearing caps.

12   Push each piston/connecting rod assembly up and remove it from the top of the bore. Remove the ridge of carbon from the top of each cylinder bore and ensure that the connecting rod big-ends do not mark the cylinder bore walls. Immediately refit its bearing cap, shells and bolts to each piston/connecting rod assembly so that they are all kept together as a matched set.

13   Note that the number stamped by you on each bearing cap should match the cylinder number stamped on the front (alternator bracket side) of each connecting rod; if any connecting rod number does not match its correct cylinder, mark or label it immediately so that each piston/connecting rod assembly can be refitted to its original bore. Keep each assembly together with its cap, bolts and bearing shells at all times.

Removal –   alternative methods

14   If the engine is being completely dismantled and the cylinder head has been removed, either unbolt the main bearing ladder (Sec 27) so that the crankshaft can be rotated with care, or remove the crankshaft completely and then remove the connecting rods and pistons.

26.6 Dipstick tube mounting bolts (arrows)

26.7 Removing oil pump pick-up/strainer pipe from oil rail – always renew sealing O-ring (arrowed)

26.8 Oil rail must be removed to reach connecting rod big-end bearings

26.9 Always mark big-end bearing caps before removal (see text) – number 4 cylinder cap shown

26.16 Checking condition of cylinder head bolt threads – cylinder head and oil rail removed

Checking the condition of the cylinder head bolts

15   Check the condition of the cylinder head bolts and particularly their threads whenever they are removed. If the cylinder head only is removed, check as described in Section 11, but if the cylinder head and the oil rail are removed, check as follows.

16   Keeping all the bolts in their correct fitted order, wash them and wipe dry, then check each for any sign of visible wear or damage, renewing any bolt if necessary. Lightly oil the threads of each bolt, carefully enter it into its original hole and screw it in, by hand only until finger-tight. If the full length of thread is engaged, the bolt may be re-used. If the full length of thread is not engaged, measure the distance from the oil rail gasket surface to under the bolt's head (photo).

17   If the distance measured is up to 378 mm, the bolt may be re-used. If the distance measured is more than 378 mm, the bolt **must** be renewed. Considering the task these bolts perform and the pressures they must withstand, owners should consider renewing all the bolts as a matched set if more than one of the originals fail inspection or are close to the limit set.

18   Note that if any of the cylinder head bolt threads in the oil rail are found to be damaged, the oil rail must be renewed; thread inserts (eg Helicoils) are not an acceptable repair in this instance.

27   Crankshaft – removal

Note: *The following procedure assumes that the crankshaft alone is being removed and therefore uses a slightly different sequence of operations to that given in Section 26; depending on the reason for dismantling, either sequence may be adapted as necessary. If the crankshaft endfloat is to be checked (Sec 30), this must be done when the crankshaft is free to move; if a dial gauge is to be used, check after paragraph 1 below, but if feeler gauges are to be used, check after paragraph 9*

1   Remove the timing belt, the toothed pulley(s) and tensioner, and the timing belt inner cover (Secs 6, 7 and 8).

Fig. 2.19 Crankshaft main bearing ladder bolt slackening sequence (Sec 27)

A   Bolts hidden in ladder   B   Location of single longer
     flanges   bolt

2   Unbolt the dipstick tube from the cylinder block/crankcase.
3   Remove the cylinder head (Sec 11); the crankshaft cannot now be rotated.
4   Remove the oil pump (Sec 13).
5   Remove the crankshaft left-hand oil seal (Sec 15).
6   Remove the sump and unbolt the oil pump pick-up/strainer pipe from the oil rail; discard its sealing O-ring (Sec 12).
7   Unscrew the two retaining nuts and remove the oil rail.
8   Working progressively and in the sequence shown in Fig. 2.19,

27.8 Removing main bearing ladder – note two locating dowels (arrowed)

27.9 Removing (number 1 cylinder) big-end bearing cap and lower bearing shell

27.10 Removing the crankshaft

unscrew by a turn at a time the main bearing ladder retaining bolts, then withdraw the ladder (photo); note the two locating dowels and the main bearing shells, which should be removed from the ladder and stored in their correct fitted order.

9   Mark the big-end bearing caps (Section 26, paragraph 9), then unscrew and remove the big-end bearing cap bolts and withdraw the cap, complete with the lower bearing shell, from each of the four connecting rods (photo). Push the connecting rods up and off their crankpins, then remove the upper bearing shell. Keep the cap, bolts and (if they are to be refitted) the bearing shells together in their correct sequence.

10   Remove the crankshaft (photo); withdraw the two thrustwashers from the number 3 main bearing upper location. Noting the position of the grooved shells, remove the upper main bearing shells, which must be kept with their correct respective partners from the main bearing ladder so that all shells can be identified and (if necessary) refitted in their original locations.

11   Check the condition of the cylinder head bolts (Sec 26, paragraphs 15 to 18).

28   Cylinder block/crankcase – cleaning and inspection

Cleaning

1   For complete cleaning, remove the liners (see below), all external components and electrical switches/sensors.

2   Scrape all traces of gasket from the cylinder block/crankcase, bearing ladder and oil rail, taking care not to damage the gasket/sealing surfaces.

3   Remove all oil gallery plugs (where fitted). The plugs are usually very tight – they may have to be drilled out and the holes re-tapped. Use new plugs when the engine is reassembled.

4   If any of the castings are extremely dirty, all should be steam cleaned.

5   After the castings are returned, clean all oil holes and oil galleries one more time. Flush all internal passages with warm water until the water runs clear, then dry thoroughly and apply a light film of oil to all liner surfaces to prevent rusting. If you have access to compressed air, use it to speed up the drying process and to blow out all the oil holes and galleries. **Warning:** *Wear eye protection when using compressed air!*

6   If the castings are not very dirty, you can do an adequate cleaning job with hot (as hot as you can stand!), soapy water and a stiff brush. Take plenty of time and do a thorough job. Regardless of the cleaning method used, be sure to clean all oil holes and galleries very thoroughly and to dry all components well; protect the liners as described above to prevent rusting.

7   All threaded holes must be clean to ensure accurate torque readings during reassembly. Run the proper size tap into each of the holes to remove rust, corrosion, thread sealant or sludge and to restore damaged threads. If possible, use compressed air to clear the holes of debris produced by this operation; a good alternative is to inject aerosol-applied water-dispersant lubricant into each hole, using the

long spout usually supplied. **Warning:** *Wear eye protection when cleaning out these holes in this way!* Now is a good time to check the condition of the cylinder head bolts, using the method described in Section 26.

8   Apply suitable sealant to the new oil gallery plugs and insert them into the holes in the block. Tighten them securely.

9   If the engine is not going to be reassembled right away, cover it with a large plastic bag to keep it clean; protect the liners as described above to prevent rusting.

Inspection

10   Visually check the castings for cracks and corrosion. Look for stripped threads in the threaded holes. If there has been any history of internal water leakage, it may be worthwhile having an engine overhaul specialist check the cylinder block/crankcase with special equipment. If defects are found have them repaired, if possible, or renew the assembly.

11   Check the bore of each cylinder liner for scuffing and scoring.

12   Measure the diameter of each cylinder liner bore 60 mm from the top of the bore, both parallel to the crankshaft axis and at right angles to it.

13   Compare the results with the Specifications at the beginning of this Chapter; if any measurement exceeds the service limit specified the liner must be renewed.

14   Measure the piston diameter at right angles to the gudgeon pin axis, 16 mm up from the bottom of the skirt; compare the results with the Specifications at the beginning of this Chapter.

15   To measure the piston-to-bore clearance, either measure the bore and piston skirt as described above and subtract the skirt diameter from the bore measurement, or insert each piston into its original bore, select a feeler gauge blade and slip it into the bore along with the piston. The piston must be aligned exactly in its normal attitude and the feeler gauge blade must be between the piston and bore on one of the thrust faces, 20 mm up from the bottom of the bore.

16   If the clearance is excessive a new piston will be required. If the piston binds at the lower end of the bore and is loose towards the top, the bore is tapered. If tight spots are encountered as the piston/feeler gauge blade is rotated in the bore, the bore is out-of-round.

17   Repeat this procedure for the remaining pistons and cylinder liners.

18   If the cylinder liner walls are badly scuffed or scored, or if they are excessively worn, out-of-round or tapered, obtain new cylinder liners; new pistons will also be required.

19   If the bores are in reasonably good condition and not worn to the specified limits and if the piston-to-bore clearances can be maintained properly, then it may only be necessary to renew the piston rings.

20   If this is the case, the bores should be honed to allow the new rings to bed in correctly and provide the best possible seal. The conventional type of hone has spring-loaded stones and is used with a power drill. You will also need some paraffin or honing oil and rags. The hone should be moved up and down the bore to produce a crosshatch pattern and plenty of honing oil should be used. Ideally the crosshatch lines should intersect at approximately a 60° angle. Do not take off more material than is necessary to produce the required finish. If new pistons are being fitted, the piston manufacturers may specify a finish with a different angle, so their instructions should be followed. Do not withdraw the

28.22 Always renew liner O-rings whenever liners are removed – oil before refitting

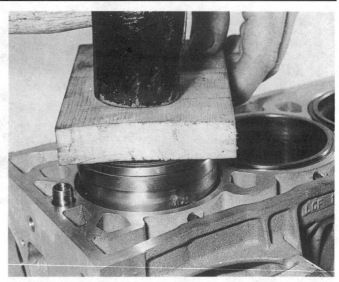

28.23 Ensuring O-rings are not displaced, tap liner as shown onto locating shoulder

hone from the bore while it is still being turned, but stop it first. After honing a bore, wipe out all traces of the honing oil. If equipment of this type is not available, or if you are not sure whether you are competent to undertake the task yourself, an engine overhaul specialist will carry out the work at moderate cost.

21   To remove the liners, invert the cylinder block/crankcase and support it on blocks of wood, then use a hard wood drift to tap out each liner from the crankshaft side. When all the liners are released, tip the cylinder block/crankcase on its side and remove each liner from the cylinder head side; discard the two sealing O-rings from the base of each. If the liners are to be re-used, mark each one by sticking masking tape on its right-hand (timing belt) face and writing the cylinder number on the tape.

22   To install the liners, thoroughly clean the liner mating surfaces in the cylinder block/crankcase and use fine abrasive paper to polish away any burrs or sharp edges which might damage the liner O-rings. Clean the liners and wipe dry, then fit new sealing O-rings to the two grooves at the base of each liner and apply a thin film of oil to the O-rings and to the liner surface on each side of the O-rings (photo).

23   If the original liners are being refitted, use the marks made on removal to ensure that each is refitted the same way round into its original bore. Insert each liner into the cylinder block/crankcase taking great care not to displace or damage the O-rings and press it home as far as possible by hand. Using a hammer and a block of wood, tap each liner lightly but fully onto its locating shoulder (photo). Wipe clean, then lightly oil all exposed liner surfaces to prevent rusting.

29.1 Measuring piston diameter

29   Piston/connecting rod assembly – inspection

1   Examine the pistons for ovality, scoring and scratches, and for wear of the piston ring grooves. Use a micrometer to measure the pistons (photo).

2   If the pistons or connecting rods are to be renewed it is necessary to have this work carried out by a Rover dealer or suitable engine overhaul specialist who will have the necessary tooling to remove and install the gudgeon pins.

3   If new rings are to be fitted to the original pistons, expand the old rings over the top of the pistons. The use of two or three old feeler gauge blades will be helpful in preventing the rings dropping into empty grooves (photo).

4   When the original piston rings have been removed, ensure that the ring grooves in the piston are free of carbon by cleaning them using an old ring. Break the ring in half to do this.

29.3 Removing piston rings using feeler gauge blades

29.5A Measuring piston ring-to-groove clearance

29.5B Measuring piston ring end gap

5   Check the ring-to-groove clearance by inserting each ring from the outside together with a feeler gauge blade between the ring's top surface and the piston land. Check the ring end gaps by inserting each ring into the cylinder bore and pushing it in with the piston crown to ensure that it is square in the bore, 20 mm from the top; use feeler gauges to measure the gap (photos).
6   Note that each piston should be considered as being matched to its respective liner and they must not be interchanged.

30   Crankshaft – inspection

Checking crankshaft endfloat

1   If the crankshaft endfloat is to be checked, this must be done when the crankshaft is still installed in the cylinder block/crankcase, but is free to move (see Section 27).
2   Check the endfloat using a dial gauge in contact with the end of the crankshaft (photo). Push the crankshaft fully one way and then zero the gauge. Push the crankshaft fully the other way and check the endfloat. The result can be compared with the specified amount and will give an indication as to whether new thrustwashers are required.
3   If a dial gauge is not available, feeler gauges can be used. First push the crankshaft fully towards the flywheel end of the engine, then use feeler gauges to measure the gap between the web of number 3 crankpin and the thrustwasher.

Inspection

4   Clean the crankshaft and dry it with compressed air, if available.

Warning: *Wear eye protection when using compressed air!* Be sure to clean the oil holes with a pipe cleaner or similar probe.
5   Check the main and crankpin (big-end) bearing journals for uneven wear, scoring, pitting and cracking.
6   Rub a penny across each journal several times (photo). If a journal picks up copper from the penny, it is too rough.
7   Remove any burrs from the crankshaft oil holes with a stone, file or scraper.
8   Using a micrometer, measure the diameter of the main bearing and crankpin (big-end) journals and compare the results with the Specifications at the beginning of this Chapter (photo). Check carefully that each journal's diameter is within the tolerances of the size grade corresponding to the code number on the crankshaft right-hand web (main bearing) or indicated by the code letter on the left-hand web (crankpin/big-end bearing); see Section 34 or 35 as appropriate. If any diameter measured is incorrect for the grade indicated, re-check the measurement carefully; if the journal is fit for further service the correct grade code should be substituted when selecting new bearing shells.
9   By measuring the diameter at a number of points around each journal's circumference, you will be able to determine whether or not the journal is out-of-round. Take the measurement at each end of the journal (near the webs) to determine if the journal is tapered.
10   If the crankshaft journals are damaged, tapered, out-of-round or worn beyond the limits specified in this Chapter, the crankshaft must be renewed unless an engine overhaul specialist can be found who will regrind it and supply the necessary undersize bearing shells.
11   Check the oil seal journals at each end of the crankshaft for wear and damage. If either seal has worn an excessive groove in its journal, consult an engine overhaul specialist who will be able to advise whether a repair is possible or whether a new crankshaft is necessary.

30.2 Checking crankshaft endfloat using a dial gauge

30.6 Using a penny to check the condition of a crankshaft journal

30.8 Measuring the diameter of a crankshaft journal

Fig. 2.20 Typical bearing shell failures (Sec 31)

31   Main and big-end bearings – inspection

1   Even though the main and big-end bearings should be renewed during the engine overhaul, the old bearings should be retained for close examination, as they may reveal valuable information about the condition of the engine. The bearing shells are graded by thickness, the grade of each shell being indicated by the colour code marked on it.

2   Bearing failure occurs because of lack of lubrication, the presence of dirt or other foreign particles, overloading the engine and corrosion. Regardless of the cause of bearing failure, it must be corrected before the engine is reassembled to prevent it from happening again.

3   When examining the bearing shells, remove them from the cylinder block/crankcase, the main bearing ladder, the connecting rods and the connecting rod big-end bearing caps and lay them out on a clean surface in the same general position as their location in the engine. This will enable you to match any bearing problems with the corresponding crankshaft journal. **Do not** touch any shell's bearing surface with your fingers while checking it, or the delicate surface may be scratched.

4   Dirt and other foreign particles get into the engine in a variety of ways. It may be left in the engine during assembly, or it may pass through filters or the crankcase ventilation system. It may get into the oil and from there into the bearings. Metal chips from machining operations and normal engine wear are often present. Abrasives are sometimes left in engine components after reconditioning, especially when parts are not thoroughly cleaned using the proper cleaning methods. Whatever the source, these foreign objects often end up embedded in the soft bearing material and are easily recognized. Large particles will not embed in the bearing and will score or gouge the bearing and journal. The best prevention for this cause of bearing failure is to clean all parts thoroughly and keep everything spotlessly clean during engine assembly. Frequent and regular engine oil and filter changes are also recommended.

5   Lack of lubrication (or lubrication breakdown) has a number of interrelated causes. Excessive heat (which thins the oil), overloading (which squeezes the oil from the bearing face) and oil leakage (from excessive bearing clearances, worn oil pump or high engine speeds) all contribute to lubrication breakdown. Blocked oil passages, which usually are the result of misaligned oil holes in a bearing shell, will also oil starve a bearing and destroy it. When lack of lubrication is the cause of bearing failure, the bearing material is wiped or extruded from the steel backing of the bearing. Temperatures may increase to the point where the steel backing turns blue from overheating.

6   Driving habits can have a definite effect on bearing life. Full throttle, low speed operation (labouring the engine) puts very high loads on bearings, which tends to squeeze out the oil film. These loads cause the bearings to flex, which produces fine cracks in the bearing face (fatigue failure). Eventually the bearing material will loosen in pieces and tear away from the steel backing. Short-distance driving leads to corrosion of bearings because insufficient engine heat is produced to drive off the condensed water and corrosive gases. These products collect in the engine oil, forming acid and sludge. As the oil is carried to the engine bearings, the acid attacks and corrodes the bearing material.

7   Incorrect bearing installation during engine assembly will lead to bearing failure as well. Tight fitting bearings leave insufficient bearing running clearance and will result in oil starvation. Dirt or foreign particles trapped behind a bearing shell result in high spots on the bearing which

lead to failure. **Do not** touch any shell's bearing surface with your fingers during reassembly; there is a risk of scratching the delicate surface or of depositing particles of dirt on it.

32   Engine overhaul – reassembly sequence

1   Before reassembly begins ensure that all new parts have been obtained and that all necessary tools are available. Read through the entire procedure to familiarise yourself with the work involved, and to ensure that all items necessary for reassembly of the engine are at hand. In addition to all normal tools and materials, a thread-locking compound will be needed. A tube of liquid sealant will also be required for the joint faces that are fitted without gaskets. It is recommended that Rover's own product is used, which is specially formulated for this purpose; the sealant and everything necessary for its application is included in a Liquid Sealant Kit which is available under Part Number LVV 10001 or 10002.

2   In order to save time and avoid problems, engine reassembly can be carried out in the following order.

    (a)   Crankshaft (Sec 34).
    (b)   Piston/connecting rod assemblies (Sec 35).
    (c)   Oil pump (Sec 13).
    (d)   Sump (Sec 12).
    (e)   Flywheel (Sec 16).
    (f)   Cylinder head (Sec 11).
    (g)   Timing belt inner cover, tensioner and toothed pulleys, and timing belt (Secs 6, 7 and 8).
    (h)   Engine external components.

3   At this stage, all engine components should be absolutely clean and dry, with all faults repaired and should be laid out (or in individual containers) on a completely clean work surface.

33   Piston rings – refitting

1   Before installing new piston rings, check the end gaps; it is assumed that the ring-to-groove clearance has been checked and found to be correct (Sec 29).

2   When measuring new rings, lay out each piston set with a piston/connecting rod assembly and keep them together as a matched set from now on.

3   If the end gap of a new ring is found to be too large or too small, double-check to ensure that you have the correct rings before proceeding. If the end gap is still too small, it must be opened up by careful filing of the ring ends using a fine file; if it is too large, this is not as serious unless the specified service limit is exceeded, in which case very careful checking is required of the dimensions of all components as well as of the new parts.

Fig. 2.21 Piston ring fitting details and top surface markings (Sec 33)

Fig. 2.22 Piston ring end gap locations (Sec 33)

A   Top compression ring
B   Second compression ring
C   Oil control ring
D   Oil control ring spring

4   Once all rings have been checked, they can be installed; ensure that each ring is refitted only to its matched piston and bore.
5   Install the new rings by fitting them over the top of the piston, starting with the oil control ring spring. Note that all the rings must be fitted with the word 'TOP' uppermost – see Fig. 2.21.
6   With all the rings in position, space the ring gaps as shown in Fig. 2.22, noting that the 'FRONT' marking shown is usually in fact an arrow mark on the piston crown and indicates the timing belt end of the engine.

34   Crankshaft – refitting and main bearing running clearance check

Selection of bearing shells

1   The main bearing running clearance is controlled in production by selecting one of three grades of bearing shell. The grades are indicated by a colour-coding marked on the edge of each shell which governs the shell's thickness, as follows.

(a)   Green – Thin.
(b)   Blue – Intermediate.
(c)   Red – Thick.

2   If shells of differing grades are to be fitted to the same journal, the thicker shell **must always** be fitted to the main bearing ladder location; bear this carefully in mind when ordering replacement shells for numbers 2, 3 and 4 bearings.
3   If the bearing shells are to be renewed, first check and record the main bearing code letters stamped on the right-hand front face of the main bearing ladder (Fig. 2.23); the letters are read with the ladder inverted, number 1 bearing's code letter then being at the top and the remainder following in order from the engine's timing belt end.
4   Secondly, check and record the crankshaft journal code numbers stamped on the crankshaft's right-hand web (Fig. 2.23); number 1 journal's code number being the first. If the original crankshaft is to be re-used, the size grade can be checked by direct measurement (Sec 30).
5   Note that if the crankshaft is found to be excessively worn it must be renewed and the code numbers of the new component must be used instead to select a new set of bearing shells.
6   Matching the codes noted to the following table, select a new set of bearing shells.

Ladder code letter	Crankshaft code number	Shells
A	1	Blue, Blue
A	2	Red, Blue
A	3	Red, Red
B	1	Blue, Green
B	2	Blue, Blue
B	3	Red, Blue
C	1	Green, Green
C	2	Blue, Green
C	3	Blue, Blue

Main bearing running clearance check

7   Clean the backs of the bearing shells and the bearing locations in both the cylinder block/crankcase and the main bearing ladder.
8   Press the bearing shells into their locations, ensuring that the tab on each shell engages in the notch in the cylinder block/crankcase or main bearing ladder location, and taking care not to touch any shell's bearing surface with your fingers.

Fig. 2.23 Crankshaft main bearing size code locations (Sec 34)

Fig. 2.24 Apply thin bead of sealant to cylinder block/crankcase mating surface along paths shown by heavy black lines, then spread to an even film (Sec 34)

Fig. 2.25 Crankshaft main bearing ladder bolt tightening sequence (Sec 34)

Fig. 2.26 Apply thin bead of sealant to oil rail mating surface as shown by heavy black lines, then spread to an even film (Sec 34)

9   Press the bearing shells with the oil grooves into the upper locations (in the cylinder block/crankcase). Note the following points (photo).

(a)   On all engines grooved bearing shells are fitted to numbers 2, 3 and 4 upper bearing locations; note the central locating tabs of the grooved shells.

(b)   On early engines grooved bearing shells were fitted only to numbers 2 and 4 upper bearing locations at the factory; on reassembly of one of these units, a grooved shell must be fitted at number 3 upper bearing location as well, instead of the plain item originally used. Note, however, that this will require a grooved shell with an offset locating tab instead of the central tab that is used on all other grooved shells; see your Rover dealer for details.

(c)   If bearing shells of differing grades are to be fitted to the same journal, the thicker shell must always be fitted to the main bearing ladder location (see paragraph 1 above).

(d)   On all engines, if the original main bearing shells are being re-used these must be refitted to their original locations in the cylinder block/crankcase and main bearing ladder.

10   The main bearing running clearance should be checked if there is any doubt about the amount of crankshaft wear that has taken place, if the crankshaft has been reground and is to be refitted with non-genuine undersized bearing shells, or if non-genuine bearing shells are to be fitted. If the original crankshaft or a genuine Rover replacement part is to be installed, the shell selection procedure given above will produce the correct clearances and a further check will not be necessary. If the clearance is to be checked, it can be done in either of two ways.

11   One method (which will be difficult to achieve without a range of internal micrometers or internal/external expanding calipers) is to refit the main bearing ladder to the cylinder block/crankcase, with bearing shells in place. With the ladder retaining bolts tightened to the specified torque, refit the oil rail and the cylinder head, tightening the cylinder head bolts as described in Section 11, then measure the internal

diameter of each assembled pair of bearing shells. If the diameter of each corresponding crankshaft journal is measured and then subtracted from the bearing internal diameter, the result will be the main bearing running clearance.

12   The second (and more accurate) method is to use an American product known as Plastigage. This consists of a fine thread of perfectly round plastic which is compressed between the bearing shell and the journal. When the shell is removed, the plastic is deformed and can be measured with a special card gauge supplied with the kit. The running clearance is determined from this gauge. Plastigage is sometimes difficult to obtain but enquiries at one of the larger specialist quality motor factors should produce the name of a stockist in your area. The procedure for using Plastigage is as follows.

13   With the main bearing upper shells in place, carefully lay the crankshaft in position. Do not use any lubricant; the crankshaft journals and bearing shells must be perfectly clean and dry.

14   Cut several lengths of the appropriate size Plastigage (they should

34.9 Ensure grooved bearing shells (arrows) are installed exactly as described in text – early engine shown

34.14 Lay the length of Plastigage on the journal to be measured, parallel to the crankshaft centre-line

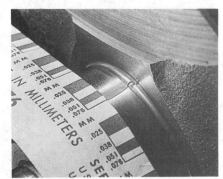

34.18 Using the scale on the envelope provided to check (at its widest point) the width of the crushed Plastigage and measure the bearing running clearance

34.24A If piston/connecting rod assemblies are refitted before the main bearing ladder is installed ...

34.24B ... care is required to hold the crankshaft steady while the connecting rod big-end cap bolts are tightened ...

34.24C ... but crankshaft can be rotated to required position

34.28 Tighten oil rail nuts to specified torque wrench setting

34.30A Fitting a new crankshaft left-hand oil seal

34.30B Always use new bolts when refitting flywheel

34.30C Use fabricated tool as shown to lock flywheel while slackening or tightening flywheel bolts

34.31A Use grease to stick new gasket in place when refitting oil pump

34.31B Fitting a new crankshaft right-hand oil seal

be slightly shorter than the width of the main bearings) and place one length on each crankshaft journal axis (photo).

15   With the main bearing lower shells in position, refit the main bearing ladder (see below) and the oil rail, tightening their fasteners to the specified torque wrench settings. Take care not to disturb the Plastigage.

16   Refit the cylinder head (using the original gasket, to save over-compressing the new one) and tightening its bolts as described in Section 11. Do not rotate the crankshaft at any time during this operation.

17   Remove the cylinder head, the oil rail and the main bearing ladder. Do not disturb the Plastigage or rotate the crankshaft.

18   Compare the width of the crushed Plastigage on each journal to the scale printed on the Plastigage envelope to obtain the main bearing running clearance (photo).

19   If the clearance is not as specified, the bearing shells may be the wrong grade (or excessively worn if the original shells are being re-used). Before deciding that different grade shells are needed, make sure that no dirt or oil was trapped between the bearing shells and the ladder or cylinder block/crankcase when the clearance was measured. If the Plastigage was wider at one end than at the other, the journal may be tapered.

20   Carefully scrape away all traces of the Plastigage material from the crankshaft and bearing shells using a fingernail or other object which is unlikely to score the shells.

Final crankshaft refitting

21   Carefully lift the crankshaft out of the cylinder block once more.

22   Using a little grease, stick the thrustwashers to each side of the number 3 main bearing upper location; ensure that the oilway grooves on each thrustwasher face outwards.

23   Place the bearing shells in their locations as described in paragraphs 7 to 9 above. If new shells are being fitted, ensure that all traces of the protective grease are cleaned off using paraffin. Wipe dry the shells and connecting rods with a lint-free cloth. Liberally lubricate

each bearing shell in the cylinder block/crankcase, then lower the crankshaft into position so that numbers 2 and 3 cylinder crankpins are at TDC.

24   Refit the piston/connecting rod assemblies (Sec 35); the crankshaft should now be at the (number 1 and 4 cylinders) TDC position (photos).

25   Thoroughly degrease the mating surfaces of the cylinder block/crankcase and the main bearing ladder. Apply continuous thin beads of sealant to the cylinder block/crankcase mating surface as shown in Fig. 2.24, then spread them to an even film with a small brush. **Note:** *If the Rover sealant is being used, assembly must be completed as soon as possible after the sealant has been applied (maximum of 20 minutes); if another sealant is being used, follow its manufacturer's instructions.*

26   Lubricate the bearing shells, then refit the main bearing ladder, ensuring that the shells are not displaced and that the locating dowels engage correctly. Working progressively, by a turn at a time and in the sequence shown (Fig. 2.25) tighten the ladder bolts to the specified torque wrench setting; the crankshaft cannot now be rotated.

27   Thoroughly degrease the mating surfaces of the oil rail and the main bearing ladder. Apply continuous beads of sealant to the oil rail mating surface as shown in Fig. 2.26, then spread them to an even film with a small brush (see note, paragraph 25 above).

28   Refit the oil rail, tightening its nuts to the specified torque wrench setting (photo).

29   Using a new sealing O-ring, refit the oil pump pick-up/strainer pipe to the oil rail, then refit the sump (Sec 12); tighten all nuts and bolts to their specified torque wrench settings.

30   Fit a new crankshaft left-hand oil seal (Sec 15), then refit the flywheel (Sec 16) (photos).

31   Refit the oil pump (Sec 13), then install a new crankshaft right-hand oil seal (Sec 15) (photos).

32   Refit the cylinder head (Sec 11). Rotate the crankshaft to the 90° BTDC position so that the crankshaft toothed pulley timing marks align as described in Section 7, paragraph 17.

33   Refit the dipstick tube to the cylinder block/crankcase, tightening its bolts to the specified torque wrench setting.

34   Refit the timing belt inner cover, the toothed pulley(s) and tensioner, and the belt itself (Secs 6, 7 and 8).

35   Using a torque wrench, check that the amount of force required to rotate the crankshaft does not exceed 31 Nm; if the effort required is greater than this, the engine must be dismantled again to trace and rectify the cause. This value takes into account the increased friction of a new engine and is much higher than the actual pressure required to rotate a run-in engine, so do not make allowances for 'tight' components; if excessive pressure is required to rotate the crankshaft, the engine has not been rebuilt to the required standard and **must** be dismantled again.

35   Piston/connecting rod assembly – refitting and big-end bearing running clearance check

Selection of bearing shells

1   The big-end bearing running clearance is controlled in production by selecting one of three grades of bearing shell. The grades are indicated by a colour-coding marked on the edge of each shell which governs the shell's thickness, as follows.

    (a)   *Yellow – Thin.*
    (b)   *Blue – Intermediate.*
    (c)   *Red – Thick.*

2   If shells of differing grades are to be fitted to the same journal, the thicker shell **must always** be fitted to the big-end bearing cap location.

3   If the bearing shells are to be renewed, first check and record the codes stamped on the front face of each big-end bearing cap and connecting rod (photo); the number stamped on the big-end bearing cap is the bearing size code, the number stamped on the connecting rod is the piston/rod assembly's cylinder number and the letter stamped on the connecting rod is its weight code.

4   Secondly, check and record the crankpin/big-end journal code letters stamped on the crankshaft's left-hand web (Fig. 2.27); number 1 journal's code letter being the first. If the original crankshaft is to be

Fig. 2.27 Crankpin (big-end) journal size code location (Sec 35)

re-used, the code letter can be checked by direct measurement (Sec 30).

5   Note that if the crankshaft is found to be excessively worn it must be renewed and the code letters of the new component must be used instead to select a new set of bearing shells.

6   Matching the codes noted to the following table, select a new set of bearing shells.

Cap code number	Crankshaft code letter	Shells
5	A	Blue, Blue
5	B	Red, Blue
5	C	Red, Red
6	A	Blue, Yellow
6	B	Blue, Blue
6	C	Red, Blue
7	A	Yellow, Yellow
7	B	Blue, Yellow
7	C	Blue, Blue

Big-end bearing running clearance check

7   Refer to Section 34, paragraph 10. If the clearance is to be checked, it can be done in either of two ways.

8   One method is to refit the big-end bearing cap to the connecting rod, with bearing shells in place. With the cap retaining bolts tightened to the specified torque, use an internal micrometer or vernier caliper to measure the internal diameter of each assembled pair of bearing shells. If the diameter of each corresponding crankshaft journal is measured and then subtracted from the bearing internal diameter, the result will be the big-end bearing running clearance.

9   The second method is to use Plastigage as described in Section 34, paragraphs 12 to 20. Place a strand of Plastigage on each (cleaned) crankpin journal and refit the (clean) piston/connecting rod assemblies, shells and big-end bearing caps, tightening the bolts to the specified torque wrench settings. Take care not to disturb the Plastigage. Dismantle the assemblies without rotating the crankshaft and use the scale printed on the Plastigage envelope to obtain the big-end bearing running clearance. On completion of the measurement, carefully scrape off all traces of Plastigage from the journal and shells using a fingernail or other object which will not score the components.

Final piston/connecting rod assembly refitting

10   Note that the following procedure assumes that the cylinder liners have been refitted to the cylinder block/crankcase (Sec 28) and that the crankshaft and main bearing ladder are in place. It is of course possible to refit the piston/connecting rod assemblies to the cylinder bores, to refit the crankshaft and to reassemble the piston/connecting rods on the crankshaft before refitting the main bearing ladder (see Section 34).

11   Clean the backs of the bearing shells and the bearing recesses in both the connecting rod and the big-end bearing cap. If new shells are being fitted, ensure that all traces of the protective grease are cleaned off using paraffin. Wipe dry the shells and connecting rods with a lint-free cloth.

35.3 Big-end bearing size code number 'A' (on cap), piston/connecting rod assembly's cylinder number 'B', connecting rod weight code letter 'C'

35.15A Arrow (or 'FRONT' marking) on piston crown must point to timing belt end of engine (arrow)

35.15B Using a piston ring compressor to clamp piston rings while piston/connecting rod assembly is refitted to cylinder bore

35.17A Tighten connecting rod big-end bearing cap bolts to specified torque wrench setting (first stage) ...

35.17B ... then use angular torque gauge to tighten bolts through angle specified (second stage)

12   Press the bearing shells into their locations, ensuring that the tab on each shell engages in the notch in the connecting rod or big-end bearing cap and taking care not to touch any shell's bearing surface with your fingers. Note the following points.

(a)   *If bearing shells of differing grades are to be fitted to the same journal, the thicker shell must always be fitted to the big-end bearing cap location (see paragraph 1 above).*

(b)   *On all engines, if the original big-end bearing shells are being re-used these must be refitted to their original locations in the connecting rod and big-end bearing cap.*

13   Lubricate the cylinder bores, the pistons and piston rings then lay out each piston/connecting rod assembly in its respective position.
14   Starting with assembly number 1, make sure that the piston rings are still spaced as shown in Fig. 2.22, then clamp them using a piston ring compressor.
15   Insert the piston/connecting rod assembly into the top of liner number 1, ensuring that the arrow (or 'FRONT' marking) on the piston crown faces the timing belt end of the engine; note that the stamped marks on the connecting rod and big-end bearing cap should face the front (alternator bracket side) of the engine. Using a block of wood or hammer handle against the piston crown, tap the assembly into the liner until the piston crown is flush with the top of the liner (photos).
16   Ensure that the bearing shell is still correctly installed. Taking care not to mark the liner bores, liberally lubricate the crankpin and both bearing shells, then pull the piston/connecting rod assembly down its bore and onto the crankpin. Noting that the faces with the stamped marks must match (which means that the bearing shell locating tabs abut each other), refit the big-end bearing cap, tightening its bolts finger-tight at first.
17   Use a torque wrench to tighten the bolts evenly to the (first stage) torque wrench setting specified, then use an angular torque gauge to tighten the bolts evenly through the (second stage) angle specified (photos).
18   Repeat the procedure for the remaining three piston/connecting rod assemblies.
19   Thoroughly degrease the mating surfaces of the oil rail and the

main bearing ladder. Apply continuous thin beads of sealant to the oil rail mating surface as shown in Fig. 2.26, then spread them to an even film with a small brush (see note, Section 34, paragraph 25).
20   Refit the oil rail, tightening its nuts to the specified torque wrench setting.
21   Using a new sealing O-ring, refit the oil pump pick-up/strainer pipe to the oil rail, then refit the sump (Sec 12); tighten all nuts and bolts to their specified torque wrench settings.
22   Refit the cylinder head (Sec 11). Rotate the crankshaft to the 90° BTDC position so that the crankshaft toothed pulley timing marks align as described in Section 7, paragraph 17.
23   Refit the dipstick tube to the cylinder block/crankcase, tightening its bolts to the specified torque wrench setting.
24   Refit the hydraulic tappets and camshaft(s) (Sec 10).
25   Refit the timing belt inner cover, the toothed pulley(s) and tensioner, and the belt itself (Secs 6, 7 and 8).
26   Using a torque wrench, check that the amount of force required to rotate the crankshaft does not exceed 31 Nm; if the effort required is greater than this, the engine must be dismantled again to trace and rectify the cause. This value takes into account the increased friction of a new engine and is much higher than the actual pressure required to rotate a run-in engine, so do not make allowances for 'tight' components; if excessive pressure is required to rotate the crankshaft, the engine has not been rebuilt to the required standard and **must** be dismantled again.

36   Engine – initial start-up after overhaul

1   With the engine refitted in the car, double-check the engine oil and coolant levels. Make a final check that everything has been reconnected and that there are no tools or rags left in the engine compartment.
2   With the spark plugs removed and the ignition system disabled by earthing the ignition HT coil distributor spark plug (HT) lead with a jumper lead, turn the engine over on the starter until the oil pressure warning lamp goes out.

3   Refit the spark plugs and connect all the spark plug (HT) leads (Chapter 1).

4   Start the engine, noting that this may take a little longer than usual due to the fuel system components being empty.

5   While the engine is idling, check for fuel, water and oil leaks. Don't be alarmed if there are some odd smells and smoke from parts getting hot and burning off oil deposits. If the hydraulic tappets have been disturbed, some valve gear noise may be heard at first; this should disappear as the oil circulates fully around the engine and normal pressure is restored in the tappets.

6   Keep the engine idling until hot water is felt circulating through the top hose, check the ignition timing and idle speed and mixture (as appropriate), then switch it off.

7   After a few minutes, recheck the oil and coolant levels and top up as necessary (Chapter 1).

8   If they were tightened as described, there is no need to re-tighten the cylinder head bolts once the engine has first run after reassembly.

9   If new pistons, rings or crankshaft bearings have been fitted, the engine must be run-in for the first 500 miles (800 km). Do not operate the engine at full throttle or allow it to labour in any gear during this period. It is recommended that the oil and filter be changed at the end of this period.

Chapter 3 Cooling, heating and ventilation systems

Contents

Specifications

System type .... Pressurised, pump-assisted thermo-syphon with front-mounted radiator and thermostatically-controlled electric cooling fan

Thermostat
Type... Wax
Start to open temperature .... 76 to 80°C
Fully open temperature .... 82 or 88°C (actual value stamped in unit end)
Full lift height.. 9.0 mm

Expansion tank cap pressure .... 0.9 to 1.0 bar

Cooling fan operating temperature.............................. 88 to 92°C

System capacity.. 4.5 litres

Antifreeze properties and quantities
50% antifreeze (by volume):
    Commences freezing .... –36°C
    Frozen solid .... –48°C
    Quantities (system refill) .... 2.25 litres antifreeze, 2.25 litres water
Antifreeze type.. Ethylene glycol-based antifreeze with non-phosphate corrosion inhibitors, suitable for mixed-metal engines, containing no methanol and meeting specifications BS6580 and BS5117 (Duckhams Universal Antifreeze and Summer Coolant)

Torque wrench settings

	Nm	lbf ft
Coolant temperature gauge sender unit........................	15	11
Inlet manifold pre-heater temperature switch (carburettor engines)........	15	11
Coolant temperature sensor (fuel-injected engines)	15	11
Thermostat housing cover bolts	9	6.5
Thermostat housing/dipstick tube-to-cylinder block/crankcase bolt........	9	6.5
Coolant rail-to-cylinder block/crankcase bolts	9	6.5
Water pump fasteners:		
Pump-to-timing belt upper left-hand (inner) cover bolt.......................	9	6.5
Pump-to-cylinder block/crankcase bolts	10	7.5
Heater air inlet box and blower motor-to-body bolts and nuts...........	7	5

Fig. 3.1 Components of the cooling system (Sec 1)

1	Radiator
2	Electric cooling fan and cowl assembly
3	Rubber mounting bush
4	Radiator top mounting
5	Bottom hose
6	Top hose
7	Coolant rail
8	Thermostat housing cover
9	Gasket
10	Thermostat
11	Thermostat housing
12	Sealing O-ring
13	Sealing O-ring
14	Water pump
15	Expansion tank
16	Coolant hose – heater/inlet manifold return
17	Coolant hose – heater/inlet manifold feed
18	System bleed plug
19	System bleed screw
20	Coolant temperature gauge sender unit
21	Coolant cross-pipe – radiator-to-top hose
22	Coolant hose – expansion tank return
23	Sealing ring
24	Electric cooling fan thermostatic switch
25	Locking ring
26	Coolant hose – expansion tank-to-inlet manifold
27	Coolant hose – expansion tank-to-coolant rail

Note: *Fuel-injection engine shown – carburettor version similar*

1   General information

Cooling system

The cooling system is of the pressurised, pump-assisted thermo-syphon type. It consists of the front-mounted radiator (which is of copper/brass, with moulded plastic side tanks), a translucent expansion tank mounted on the right-hand inner wing, a thermostatically-controlled electric cooling fan mounted on the rear of the radiator, a thermostat and a centrifugal water pump, as well as the connecting hoses. The water pump is driven by the engine's timing belt.

The location of the system's components and the direction of coolant flow are shown in Figs. 3.1 and 3.2.

Warning: *Do not attempt to remove the expansion tank filler cap or to disturb any part of the cooling system while it or the engine is hot, as there is a very great risk of scalding. If the expansion tank filler cap must be removed before the engine and radiator have fully cooled down (even though this is not recommended) the pressure in the cooling system must first be released. Cover the cap with a thick layer of cloth, to avoid scalding, and slowly unscrew the filler cap until a hissing sound can be heard. When the hissing has stopped, showing that pressure is released, slowly unscrew the filler cap until it can be removed; if more hissing sounds are heard, wait until they have stopped before unscrewing the cap completely. At all times keep well away from the filler opening.*

Warning: *Do not allow antifreeze to come in contact with your skin or painted surfaces of the vehicle. Rinse off spills immediately with plenty of*

Fig. 3.2 Direction of coolant flow (Sec 1)

1   Radiator bottom hose
2   Heater matrix
3   Inlet manifold
4   Thermostat
5   Radiator top hose
6   Radiator
7   Electric cooling fan
     thermostatic switch
A   Engine hot
B   Engine cold

Note: Carburettor engine shown –
fuel-injected version similar

Fig. 3.3 Location of heating and ventilation system components (Sec 1)

1   Air inlet box
2   Heater air
     distribution
     control
3   Adjustable
     face-level vents
4   Windscreen
     demister ducts
5   Side window
     demister ducts
6   Heater
     temperature
     control

water. Never leave antifreeze lying around in an open container or in a puddle in the driveway or on the garage floor. Children and pets are attracted by its sweet smell. Antifreeze is fatal if ingested.

Warning: *If the engine is hot, the electric cooling fan may start rotating even if the engine is not running, so be careful to keep hands, hair and loose clothing well clear when working in the engine compartment.*

Heating and ventilation systems

The heater has a three-speed blower housed in the engine compartment, face level vents in the centre and at each end of the facia and air ducts to the front footwells. Illuminated sliding controls for air temperature and distribution are housed, with the heater blower switch, in the facia instrument panel and operate flap valves to deflect the air flowing through the heater. Cold air enters through the grille at the rear of the bonnet, is boosted when required by the blower's radial fan and flows through the ducts, according to the control setting; stale air is exhausted through tailgate ducts. If warm air is required, the cold air is passed over the copper/brass heater matrix which is heated by the engine's coolant.

2   Cooling system hoses – renewal

Note: *Refer to the warnings given in Section 1 of this Chapter before starting work*

1   If the checks described in Chapter 1 reveal a faulty hose, it must be renewed as follows.
2   First drain the cooling system (Chapter 1); if the antifreeze is not due for renewal, the drained coolant may be re-used if it is collected in a clean container.

2.5 Connecting the radiator top hose to the coolant outlet elbow

3   To disconnect any hose use a screwdriver to slacken the clips, then move them along the hose clear of the outlet. Carefully work the hose off its outlets. While the hoses can be removed with relative ease when new or hot, **do not** attempt to disconnect any part of the system when it is still hot (see Sec 1).
4   Note that the radiator hose outlets are fragile; do not use excessive force when attempting to remove the hoses. If a hose proves stubborn try to release it by rotating it on its outlets before attempting to work it off. If all else fails, cut the hose with a sharp knife then slit it so that it can be peeled off in two pieces. While expensive, this is preferable to buying a new radiator.
5   When refitting a hose first slide the clips onto the hose, then work the hose onto its outlets (photo). If the hose is stiff, use soap as a lubricant or soften it by first soaking it in boiling water, but take care to prevent scalding.
6   Work each hose end fully onto its outlet, check that the hose is settled correctly and is properly routed, then slide each clip along the hose until it is behind the outlet flared end before tightening it securely.
7   Refill the system with coolant (Chapter 1).
8   Check carefully for leaks as soon as possible after disturbing any part of the cooling system.

3   Radiator and expansion tank – removal, inspection and refitting

Note: *Refer to the warnings given in Section 1 of this Chapter before starting work*

Removal
Radiator

1   Drain the cooling system (Chapter 1).
2   Remove the electric cooling fan assembly (Sec 5).
3   Disconnect the remaining coolant hoses from the radiator as required; if necessary the radiator top hose and expansion tank hose can be disconnected so that the coolant cross-pipe is removed with the radiator and subsequently disconnected.
4   Disconnect the electric cooling fan thermostatic switch wires.
5   Withdraw the radiator, taking care not to damage its matrix on the exhaust manifold (photo). Detach the cross-pipe (where appropriate).

Expansion tank

6   The expansion tank can be removed, as soon as the system has been drained (Chapter 1), by unscrewing its mounting nuts and disconnecting its hoses (photos).

Expansion tank filler cap

7   Unscrew the filler cap from the top of the expansion tank.

Inspection
Radiator

8   If the radiator was removed because of clogging (causing overheating) then try reverse flushing (Chapter 1) or, in severe cases, use a radiator cleanser strictly in accordance with the manufacturer's instructions; ensure that the cleanser is suitable for use in a copper/brass radiator.

3.5 Removing the radiator with the coolant cross-pipe

3.6A Disconnecting expansion tank coolant hose from inlet manifold

3.6B Disconnecting coolant rail hose from expansion tank – note one of mounting nuts (arrow)

9   Use a soft brush and an air line or garden hose to clear the radiator matrix of leaves, insects etc.

10   Minor leaks from the radiator can be cured using Holts Radweld. Major leaks or extensive damage should be repaired by a specialist, or the radiator should be renewed or exchanged for a reconditioned unit.

11   If the radiator is to be repaired or exchanged, detach first the thermostatic switch (Sec 6) and any remaining coolant hoses.

12   Check the condition of the mountings and renew them if necessary.

Expansion tank

13   Empty any remaining coolant from the tank and flush it with fresh water to clean it. If the tank is leaking it must be renewed, but it is worth first attempting a repair using a proprietary sealant or suitable adhesive.

Expansion tank filler cap

14   The cap should be cleaned and checked whenever it is removed. Check that its sealing surfaces and threads are clean and undamaged and that they mate correctly with those of the expansion tank.

15   The cap's performance can be checked only using a cap pressure-tester (cooling system tester) with a suitable adaptor. On applying pressure, the cap's pressure relief valve should hold until the specified pressure is reached, at which point the valve should open.

16   If there is any doubt about the cap's performance, it must be renewed; ensure that the replacement is of exactly the correct type and rating.

Refitting

Radiator

17   Refitting is the reverse of the removal procedure, noting the following points.

   (a)   *Ensure that the radiator is seated correctly and without strain on its mountings.*

   (b)   *Position the hose clips carefully so that they do not foul any other component.*

   (c)   *Refill the cooling system (Chapter 1).*

Expansion tank

18   Refitting is the reverse of the removal procedure, noting the following points.

   (a)   *Ensure that the hoses, especially that between the tank and the radiator, are correctly routed with no kinks or sharp bends and are secured by the clips provided.*

   (b)   *Refill the cooling system (Chapter 1).*

Expansion tank filler cap

19   Refitting is a reversal of removal.

4   Thermostat – removal, testing and refitting

Note: *Refer to the warnings given in Section 1 of this Chapter before starting work*

Removal

1   Note that access to the thermostat is very limited; depending on the tools available, it may be easier to raise the front of the car and to work from underneath – ensure the car is securely supported on axle stands (see *'Jacking, towing and wheel changing'*). In most cases, however, access is better if the air cleaner and carburettor/throttle body (as appropriate) are removed first and is best if the complete inlet manifold is removed (Chapter 4). If the inlet manifold is removed, the thermostat housing cover can be unbolted to remove the thermostat without disturbing the housing itself (photo). Whichever method is used, first drain the cooling system (Chapter 1).

2   Where fitted, either remove the thermostatically-operated vacuum switch (Chapter 5) or disconnect the vacuum pipes from the switch so that it can be removed with the thermostat housing.

3   Unbolt the coolant rail from the rear of the cylinder block/crankcase, then slacken their clips and disconnect the coolant rail hose and

4.1 The thermostat can be removed without disturbing its housing if the inlet manifold is removed first

4.3 Thermostat removal – inlet manifold removed for clarity – disconnecting coolant hoses (arrows) ...

4.4 ... unscrew bolt securing dipstick tube and thermostat housing to cylinder block/crankcase ...

4.5 ... and withdraw complete thermostat housing – always renew sealing O-ring (arrowed)

4.9 Note temperature specification stamped in thermostat end

4.11 Thermostat housing refitted and coolant hoses correctly secured

5.9A Unscrew bolts (arrows) to release radiator top mountings from bonnet lock platform ...

5.9B ... check condition of mounting rubbers and renew if necessary

5.10A Pull radiator backwards at top edge to undo cross-pipe screw at right-hand end (arrow) ...

5.10B ... it may be necessary to disconnect radiator top hose from cross-pipe – note remaining cross-pipe screw (arrow)

5.11 Unscrewing remaining screw securing electric cooling fan and cowl assembly

heater/inlet manifold return hose from the thermostat housing (photo).

4   Undo the thermostat housing/dipstick tube-to-cylinder block/crankcase bolt (photo).

5   Remove the thermostat housing from the cylinder block/crankcase (photo).

6   Remove the sealing O-ring; this must be renewed whenever it is disturbed. Unbolt the housing cover and discard the gasket, then withdraw the thermostat.

Testing

7   If the thermostat remains in the open position at room temperature it is faulty and must be renewed as a matter of course.

8   To test it fully, suspend the (closed) thermostat on a length of string in a container of cold water, with a thermometer beside it; ensure that neither touches the side of the container.

9   Heat the water and check the temperature at which the thermostat begins to open; compare this value with that specified. Continue to heat the water until the thermostat is fully open; the temperature at which this should happen is stamped in the unit's end (photo). Remove the thermostat and measure the height of the fully opened valve, then allow the thermostat to cool down and check that it closes fully.

10   If the thermostat does not open and close as described, if it sticks in either position, or if it does not open at the specified temperature, it must be renewed.

Refitting

11   Refitting is the reverse of the removal procedure, noting the following points (photo).

(a)   Clean the thermostat housing, housing cover and cylinder block/crankcase mating surfaces thoroughly.

(b)   Always fit a new cover gasket and sealing O-ring – smear the O-ring with grease to aid refitting.

(c)   Tighten all bolts to their specified torque wrench settings.

(d)   Ensure the coolant hose clips are positioned so that they do not foul any other component, then tighten them securely.

(e)   Refit any components removed for improved access.

(f)   Refill the cooling system (Chapter 1).

5   Electric cooling fan – testing, removal and refitting

Testing

1   The cooling fan motor is supplied with current via the ignition switch and fuse 4; the circuit being completed by the radiator-mounted thermostatic switch.

2   If the fan does not appear to work, run the engine until normal operating temperature is reached, then allow it to idle. If the fan does not cut in within a few minutes, switch off the ignition and disconnect the

5.12 Disconnecting radiator electric cooling fan wiring – note cowl wiring clip (arrow)

5.14 Withdrawing electric cooling fan and cowl assembly – note cross-pipe had to be disconnected in this case

5.15A Drilling out rivets securing fan to cowl ...

5.15B ... cooling fan is clipped to motor shaft

two wires from the thermostatic switch. Bridge these two wires with a length of spare wire and switch on the ignition. If the fan now operates, the thermostatic switch is probably faulty and must be tested further (Sec 6).

3 If the fan still fails to operate check that full battery voltage is available at the switch's light green wire terminal; if not, check the feed for a blown fuse or other fault. If the feed is good, check that there is continuity between the fan motor's black wire terminal and a good earth point on the body; if not, then the earth connection is faulty and must be remade. The circuit earth connection is one of those at earth header 2, attached to the left-hand inner wing panel next to the battery.

4 If the switch and wiring are in good condition, the fault must be in the motor itself. This can be checked by disconnecting it from the wiring loom and connecting a 12 volt supply directly to it. If the motor does not work it must be renewed; see the note in paragraph 15 below.

Removal

Note: *Refer to the warnings given in Section 1 of this Chapter before starting work*

5 Disconnect the battery negative lead.

6 Disconnect the vacuum pipe from the intake air temperature control valve, release the two clips securing the air intake duct to the air cleaner assembly and (as appropriate) unscrew the bolt or release the quarter-turn fastener(s) securing the duct to its support bracket(s).

7 Where fitted, unfasten the rubber strap and unbolt the support bracket from the cylinder head; unclip the vacuum pipe and withdraw the bracket.

8 Remove the two screws securing the cold air intake duct to the body front panel, then withdraw the complete intake duct assembly, taking care not to lose the hot air intake connector hose (Chapter 4).

9 Unbolt the radiator top mountings from the bonnet lock platform and remove both mounting brackets (photos).

10 Remove the two (hex-head) screws securing the coolant cross-pipe to the radiator, release the cross-pipe and secure it as far away from the working area as possible, over the cylinder head and exhaust manifold. **Note:** *The cooling fan and cowl assembly are very difficult to remove past the cross-pipe.* If the extra room is needed, drain the cooling system (Chapter 1) and disconnect the radiator top hose from the cross-pipe (photos).

11 Unscrew the remaining (hex-head) screw securing the cooling fan and cowl assembly to the radiator (photo).

12 Disconnect the fan motor wires and release the wiring from the cowl clip (photo).

13 Release the radiator from its lower mountings; it is seated on two pegs on its bottom edge which locate in rubber bushes in the body front panel.

14 Slide the cooling fan and cowl assembly towards the centre of the radiator, rotate it to release it from the radiator and withdraw it (photo). Take care not to damage the radiator matrix.

15 Note that if only the fan, its motor or the cowl is to be renewed, check with a Rover dealer before attempting to strip the assembly; if the separate items are not available, the assembly must be renewed complete and there is no point in trying to dismantle it. If they are available separately, the fan motor is secured by pop rivets to the cowl; these must be drilled out to release the motor and new rivets must be

inserted on reassembly. The fan is secured by a clip to the motor shaft (photos).

Refitting

16 Refitting is the reverse of the removal procedure; if the coolant was drained, refill the system (Chapter 1).

6 Cooling system electrical switches – testing, removal and refitting

Note: *Refer to the warnings given in Section 1 of this Chapter before starting work*

Testing

Electric cooling fan thermostatic switch

1 Refer to Section 5 for details of a quick test which should eliminate most faulty switches. If the switch is to be renewed, or to be tested thoroughly, it must be removed.

2 To carry out a thorough test of the switch, use two spare wires to connect to it either a multimeter (set to the resistance function) or a battery and bulb test circuit. Suspend the switch in a pan of water which is being heated. Measure the temperature of the water with a thermometer. Do not let either the switch or the thermometer touch the pan itself.

3 The switch contacts should close to the 'On' position (ie, continuity should exist) when the water reaches the temperature specified. Stop heating the water and allow it to cool down; the switch contacts should open at the same temperature or just below.

4 If the switch's performance is significantly different from that specified, or if it does not work at all, it must be renewed.

Coolant temperature gauge sender unit

5 The coolant temperature gauge mounted in the instrument panel is fed with a stabilised 10 volt supply from the instrument panel feed (via the ignition switch and fuse 3), its earth being controlled by the sender unit.

6 The sender unit is screwed into the coolant outlet elbow mounted on the left-hand end of the cylinder head, underneath the distributor (photo). It contains a thermistor, which is an element whose electrical resistance decreases at a predetermined rate as its temperature rises; thus when the coolant is cold, the sender's resistance is high, current flow through the gauge is reduced and the gauge needle points to the 'C' (cold) end of the scale. If the unit is faulty it must be renewed.

7 If the gauge develops a fault, check first the other instruments; if they do not work at all, check the instrument panel feed. If the readings are erratic, there may be a fault in the voltage stabiliser which will necessitate the renewal of the gauge unit or printed circuit (Chapter 12). If the fault is in the temperature gauge alone, check it as follows.

8 If the gauge needle remains at the 'C' end of the scale, disconnect the sender unit wire and earth it to the cylinder head; if the needle then deflects when the ignition is switched on the sender unit is proven faulty

6.6 Coolant temperature gauge sender unit

6.10 Inlet manifold pre-heater temperature switch (carburettor engines)

6.17 Radiator electric cooling fan thermostatic switch

and must be renewed. If the needle still does not move, remove the instrument panel (Chapter 12) and check the continuity of the green/blue wire between the gauge and the sender unit and the feed to the gauge unit. If continuity is shown, and the fault still exists, then the gauge is faulty and the gauge unit must be renewed.

9   If the gauge needle remains at the 'H' end of the scale, disconnect the sender unit wire; if the needle then returns to the 'C' end of the scale when the ignition is switched on the sender unit is proven faulty and must be renewed. If the needle still does not move, check the remainder of the circuit as described above.

Inlet manifold pre-heater temperature switch – carburettor engines

10   The switch screwed into the underside of the inlet manifold (carburettor engines) controls the inlet manifold heater circuit; refer to Chapter 4 for details (photo).

11   The switch contacts should be closed to the 'On' position (ie, continuity should exist) only at temperatures below 50°C; test the switch as described in paragraphs 2 to 4 above.

Thermostatically-operated vacuum switch

12   Refer to Chapter 5.

Coolant temperature sensor – fuel-injected engines

13   The sensor screwed into the underside of the inlet manifold is a thermistor (see paragraph 6 above) which is supplied with approximately 5 volts by the engine management system ECU; the ECU also controls the sensor's earth path and, by measuring the amount of current in the sensor circuit, determines the engine's temperature. This information is used, in conjunction with other inputs, to control idle speed, injector opening time duration and ignition timing.

14   If the sensor circuit should fail to provide adequate information, the ECU's back-up facility assumes a value corresponding to 60°C. The sensor itself can be tested only by having a Rover dealer check the complete system using the correct diagnostic equipment; **do not** attempt to 'test' the circuit using any other equipment, or the ECU will be damaged.

Removal

Electric cooling fan thermostatic switch

15   When the engine and radiator are cold, either drain the cooling system (Chapter 1) down to the level of the switch or unscrew the expansion tank filler cap to release any remaining pressure and have ready a suitable plug that can be used temporarily to stop the escape of coolant while the switch is removed. If the latter method is used, take care not to damage the radiator and do not use anything which will leave foreign matter inside the radiator.

16   Disconnect the battery negative lead.

17   Disconnect the switch wires and rotate the locking ring to release it, then withdraw the switch from the radiator and prise out the sealing ring (photo).

Coolant temperature gauge sender unit

18   When the engine and radiator are cold, either drain the cooling system (Chapter 1) down to the level of the sender unit or unscrew the expansion tank filler cap to release any remaining pressure and have

ready a suitable plug that can be used temporarily to stop the escape of coolant while the unit is removed. If the latter method is used, take care not to damage the threads and do not use anything which will leave foreign matter inside the cooling system.

19   Disconnect the battery negative lead.

20   Disconnect the unit's wiring and unscrew the unit from the coolant outlet elbow.

Inlet manifold pre-heater temperature switch – carburettor engines

21   Removal is as described in paragraphs 18 to 20 above.

Thermostatically-operated vacuum switch

22   Refer to Chapter 5.

Coolant temperature sensor – fuel-injected engines

23   Removal is as described in paragraphs 18 to 20 above.

Refitting

Electric cooling fan thermostatic switch

24   On refitting, renew the sealing ring if it is worn or compressed and clean carefully the radiator seat before pressing in the sealing ring and switch. Refit the locking ring and rotate it to tighten it securely. Reconnect the switch and battery, then refill the cooling system or check the coolant level, as necessary (Chapter 1).

Coolant temperature gauge sender unit

25   On refitting, apply a suitable sealant to the unit threads and tighten it to its specified torque wrench setting. Reconnect the unit and battery, then refill the cooling system or check the coolant level, as necessary (Chapter 1).

Inlet manifold pre-heater temperature switch – carburettor engines

26   Refitting is a reversal of removal. Note that the switch is fitted with a sealing washer that must be renewed whenever the switch is removed. Tighten the switch to the specified torque wrench setting.

Thermostatically-operated vacuum switch

27   Refer to Chapter 5.

Coolant temperature sensor – fuel-injected engines

28   Refitting is a reversal of removal. Note the specified torque wrench setting for the sensor.

7   Water pump – removal and refitting

Note: *Refer to the warnings given in Section 1 of this Chapter before starting work*

Removal

1   Water pump failure is usually indicated by coolant leaking from the gland behind the pump's bearing, or by rough and noisy operation,

usually accompanied by excessive pump spindle play. If the pump shows any of these symptoms it must be renewed as follows.
2   Drain the cooling system (Chapter 1).
3   Remove the timing belt (Chapter 2, Section 7).
4   Noting the locations of the two pillar bolts, unscrew the five bolts securing the water pump to the cylinder block/crankcase, then unscrew the single bolt securing the pump to the timing belt upper left-hand (inner) cover.
5   Withdraw the water pump and discard its sealing O-ring; this should never be re-used (photo). Carefully clean the cylinder block/crankcase mating surface and the pump socket.

Refitting

6   On refitting, install the pump using a new sealing O-ring and tighten the bolts to their specified torque wrench settings. The remainder of the refitting procedure is the reverse of removal; refer to the relevant sections of Chapters 1 and 2.

8   Heater components – removal and refitting

Note: *Refer to the warnings given in Section 1 of this Chapter before starting work*

Removal

Heater unit
1   Drain the cooling system (Chapter 1).
2   Slacken the hose clips and disconnect the heater feed and return hoses from the heater matrix outlets on the bulkhead (photos).
3   Remove the facia (Chapter 11).
4   Remove the side window demister ducts, the facia rail support stays, the face-level air duct and the windscreen demister ducts (Sec 9).
5   Unscrew the two bolts securing the heater to the body crossmember, then prise the heater off the clip securing it to the bulkhead and remove it, with the control panel; use old towels or rag to

7.5 Removing the water pump

soak up any remaining coolant that is released from the matrix. Note that the heater is a tight fit on the clip and will require considerable effort to remove it; take care not to damage the heater or any other component (photos).
6   The heater control cables can be disconnected now, if required, and the matrix removed (see below).

Heater matrix
7   Remove the heater unit (see paragraphs 1 to 5 above).
8   Withdraw the foam seal from the matrix pipes, remove the two screws and withdraw the pipe clamp.

8.2A Slackening hose clips ...

8.2B ... to disconnect heater feed and return hoses from bulkhead unions

8.5A Unscrew heater securing bolts (arrows) ...

8.5B ... and release heater from bulkhead clip with care (arrow)

8.9 Heater matrix pipe foam seal 'A', pipe clamp screws 'B', end plate screws 'C' (arrows)

Fig. 3.4 Heater unit and ducts (Sec 8)

1	Face-level air duct	3	Windscreen demister ducts
2	Side window demister ducts	4	Heater matrix
5	Heater duct	7	Heater unit case
6	Heater air blend flaps	8	Clip

9   Remove the four screws securing the heater end plate and withdraw the end plate, followed by the matrix (photo).
10   If the matrix is leaking it is best to obtain a new or reconditioned unit; home repairs are seldom successful. If it is blocked it can be cleared sometimes by reverse flushing using a garden hose (Chapter 1), using a proprietary radiator cleaning product if absolutely necessary.

Heater air inlet box and blower motor

11   Disconnect the battery negative terminal.
12   On cars with fuel-injected engines, remove the ECU mounting bracket-to-body screws and move aside the ECU.
13   If the extra working space is needed, remove also (if fitted) the charcoal canister (Chapter 4).
14   Disconnect the blower motor wiring by unplugging the connector on the top of the unit (photo). Release the clutch cable from its clip.
15   Unscrew the four bolts and three nuts securing the assembly's mounting plate to the bulkhead; be careful that all are unscrewed, as some are difficult to see (photo).
16   Working inside the car, remove the glovebox (Chapter 11).
17   Unscrew the remaining two bolts and one nut securing the assembly to the bulkhead; again, check carefully that all are unscrewed, as these are even more difficult to see (photo).
18   Remove the heater air inlet box and blower motor as an assembly, with its mounting plate (photo). If it resists removal, do not use force but check instead that all fasteners have been removed.
19   Note that if only the blower fan, its motor or the air inlet box is to be

8.14 Heater blower motor wiring connector plug (arrow)

Fig. 3.5 Heater air inlet box and blower motor assembly (Sec 8)

1   Bonnet-to-air inlet box foam seal
2   Blower radial fan
3   Blower motor
4   Air inlet box
5   Clip
6   Drain tube
7   Blower motor resistor and cowl unit
8   Mounting plate
9   Bulkhead aperture foam rubber seal

renewed, check with a Rover dealer before attempting to strip the assembly; if the separate items are not available, the assembly must be renewed complete and there is no point in trying to dismantle it. If they are available separately, the assembly can be dismantled by disconnecting the motor wires (black wire to the front), unbolting the air inlet box from the mounting plate and removing the box-to-bonnet seal (three clips) and drain tube; the two halves of the inlet box are secured by eight clips and by three screws around the motor. The fan is pressed on to the motor shaft (photos). On reassembly, clean off the old adhesive from the mating surfaces of the inlet box halves and apply a bead of suitable adhesive such as Bostik Sealer P.34 44S.

Heater blower motor resistor
Note: *If the resistor is thought to be faulty, check first with a Rover dealer as to whether it is available separately or not; it may only be available as part of the complete heater air inlet box/blower motor/mounting plate assembly*

8.15 Heater air inlet box and blower motor assembly mountings visible from engine compartment (arrows) ...

8.17 ... and through glovebox opening in facia (arrow)

8.18 Removing heater air inlet box and blower motor as an assembly with the mounting plate

8.19A Remove four bolts (arrows) to separate mounting plate from air inlet box ...

8.19B ... remove drain tube, release clips ...

8.19C ... and remove screws (arrows) ...

8.19D ... to separate inlet box halves

8.19E Remove blower motor, noting locating tongue ...

8.19F ... and withdraw fan from motor shaft

20   Remove the heater air inlet box and blower motor assembly (paragraphs 11 to 18 above).
21   Disconnect the wiring from the blower motor; note that the black wire is at the front.
22   Drill out the two pop rivets securing the resistor and cowl to the assembly's mounting plate (photo).

Heater blower switch
23   Refer to Chapter 12.

Refitting

Heater unit
24   Refitting is the reverse of the removal procedure, noting the following points.

   (a)   *Ensure that the foam rubber seals are refitted correctly so that all bulkhead apertures are closed off and that the sound deadening material is correctly replaced.*
   (b)   *Ensure that the heater ducts are connected so that there can be no gaps or air leaks.*
   (c)   *Ensure that the heater hoses are correctly reconnected; the feed hose (with the bleed plug) is connected to the heater matrix upper union.*
   (d)   *Refill the cooling system (Chapter 1).*

Heater matrix
25   Refitting is the reverse of the removal procedure.

Heater air inlet box and blower motor
26   Refitting is the reverse of the removal procedure, noting the following points.

   (a)   *Clean the mating surfaces of the bulkhead and of the assembly's mounting plate thoroughly.*
   (b)   *Ensure that the foam rubber seal is refitted correctly so that the bulkhead aperture is closed off; if necessary slacken the heater return hose clip so that the seal can be properly located.*

   (c)   *Ensure that the assembly mates correctly with the duct's seal, then tighten all fasteners to the specified torque wrench setting.*
   (d)   *If coolant was lost on disturbing the heater hose, top up the system (Chapter 1).*

Heater blower motor resistor
27   Refitting is the reverse of the removal procedure.

Heater blower switch
28   Refer to Chapter 12.

8.22 Heater blower motor resistor unit and cowl

9.1 Remove the facia to reach heater components

9.2 Withdrawing a side window demister duct

9.3 Facia rail support stay mountings (arrows)

9.5 Windscreen demister duct mounting nuts (arrows)

9.6 Removing a face-level vent – take care not to mark the facia

9   Heater ducts and vents – removal and refitting

Removal

Ducts

1   Remove the facia (Chapter 11) (photo).
2   Withdraw the side window demister ducts (photo).

3   Unbolt the facia rail support stays (photo).
4   Unclip the face-level air duct; it has a clip at each end and two in the centre.
5   Unscrew the two plastic nuts to release each of the windscreen demister ducts (photo).

Vents

6   The adjustable face-level vents can be removed by prising them gently out of the facia until their clips are released; take care not to mark the facia (photo).
7   The side window demister vents are secured by sealing flanges from behind the facia and so cannot be removed until the facia has been withdrawn.

Refitting

Ducts

8   Refitting is the reverse of the removal procedure; ensure that the ducts mate correctly with each other and with their respective vents, so that there are no air leaks.

Vents

9   Refitting is a reversal of removal. Fit new self-adhesive sealing strips on reassembly.

10.2 Heater control panel retaining screws (arrows) on rear of facia

10   Heater controls – removal, refitting and adjustment

Removal

1   Remove the facia (Chapter 11).

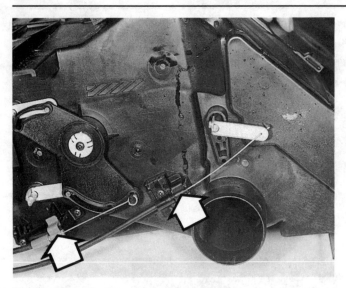

10.4 Control cable clips on heater unit (arrows)

2   Remove the three screws securing the control panel to the facia, release the panel and disconnect the illuminating bulb wires (photo).

3   Note that the control cables and their fittings on the heater unit are colour-coded; the temperature control being brown, while the distribution control is black.

4   Release the clip securing each cable outer to the heater unit and unclip each cable inner wire from its respective control lever. Withdraw the control panel (photo). **Note:** *The heater control cables are not available separately; do not attempt to disconnect them from the control panel levers.*

Refitting

5   Refitting is the reverse of the removal procedure.

Adjustment

6   No adjustment is possible; if the heater does not work properly, either the control panel or the assembly must be renewed to cure the fault.

Chapter 4 Fuel, exhaust
and emission control systems

Contents

Specifications

Part A: Carburettor engines

Fuel pump
Type... Mechanical, driven by eccentric on camshaft

Carburettor (general)
Type... Hobourn-SU constant-depression/variable choke
Designation:
    1.1 models .... KIF 38
    1.4 models .... KIF 44
Choke type .... Manual

Carburettor data

	1.1 models	1.4 models
Carburettor number:		
Without catalytic converter	MAC 10003 or 10043	MAC 10004
With catalytic converter	MAC 10010	MAC 10011
Throttle bore diameter	38 mm	44 mm
Piston spring colour code	Red	Red
Damper	LZX 2337	LZX 2337
Jet size	LZX 2211 (0.090 in)	LZX 2237 (0.100 in)
Needle:		
Without catalytic converter	AEH (MAC 103) or AEK (MAC 10043)	BGZ
With catalytic converter	AEJ	BGZ
Needle valve seat	LZX 1756	LZX 1756
Fast idle speed – at choke control first detent	1200 rpm	1200 rpm
Idle speed	850 ± 50 rpm	850 ± 50 rpm
CO level at idle speed – engine at normal operating temperature:		
Without catalytic converter	2.0 to 3.0 %	2.0 to 3.0 %
With catalytic converter – at gas sampling pipe	1.0 to 3.0 %	1.0 to 3.0 %

Recommended fuel

Minimum octane rating:

Without catalytic converter .... 95 RON unleaded (ie unleaded Premium) or 97 RON leaded (ie 4-star)

With catalytic converter .... 95 RON unleaded (ie unleaded Premium) **only**

Part B: Fuel-injected engines

System type .... Rover/Motorola Modular Engine Management System, using ECU-controlled single-point injection (MEMS-SPi) and speed/density method of airflow measurement

MEMS-SPi system data

Fuel pump type .... Electric, immersed in fuel tank

Fuel pump pressure:

Maximum – at 16 volts .... 2.7 bar

Regulated constant pressure – 1.4 K16-engined models with closed-loop catalytic converter .... 1.1 ± 0.1 bar

Regulated constant pressure – all other models .... 1.0 to 1.1 bar

Injector/pressure regulator assembly:

1.1 models .... JZX 3300

1.4 K8-engined models .... JZX 3296

1.4 K16-engined models .... JZX 3028

Throttle potentiometer voltage:

Throttle closed .... 0 to 1 volt

Throttle open .... 4 to 5 volt

Idle speed – nominal value given for reference purposes only:

1.4 K16-engined models with closed-loop catalytic converter .... 875 ± 50 rpm

All other models .... 850 ± 50 rpm

CO level at idle speed – engine at normal operating temperature:

Without catalytic converter – at tailpipe .... 0.5 to 2.0 %

With open-loop catalytic converter – at gas-sampling pipe .... 0.5 to 2.0 %

With closed-loop catalytic converter – at tailpipe – not adjustable .... 0.75 % maximum

Recommended fuel

Minimum octane rating:

Without catalytic converter .... 95 RON unleaded (ie unleaded Premium) or 97 RON leaded (ie 4-star)

With catalytic converter .... 95 RON unleaded (ie unleaded Premium) **only**

Part C: All models

Torque wrench settings	Nm	lbf ft
Air intake duct-to-cylinder head support bracket screw – K16 engine	8	6
Air cleaner assembly support bracket-to-carburettor screws	5	3.5
Fuel tank mounting bolts	12	9
Two-way valve-to-fuel tank filler neck nut	5	3.5
Fuel tank filler neck-to-body fasteners:		
Screws – three-door	5	3.5
Nuts – five-door	9	6.5
Electric fuel pump-to-fuel tank mounting nuts	9	6.5
Mechanical fuel pump-to-cylinder head mounting nuts	10	7.5
Fuel system pressure release bolt – at fuel filter	12	9
Fuel filter inlet union	40	29.5

Torque wrench settings (continued)

	Nm	lbf ft
Fuel filter outlet union	35	26
Throttle pedal mounting nuts	25	18.5
Upper-to-lower inlet manifold Torx screws – carburettor engines	10	7.5
Needle retaining (grub) screw	1.7 to 2.3	1.3 to 1.7
Throttle disc retaining screws	0.80 to 1.14	0.6 to 0.8
Carburettor vent and air bleed pipe mounting bolts	9	6.5
Intake air temperature sensor	7	5
Fuel pipe union nuts – at injector housing	24	17.5
Injector housing fuel pipe union adaptors	24	17.5
Injector housing-to-throttle body screws	5	3.5
Throttle body-to-inlet manifold nuts	18	13
Throttle potentiometer mounting screws	2	1.5
Inlet manifold mounting nuts and bolts	25	18.5
Inlet manifold support stays-to-cylinder block/crankcase bolts	25	18.5
Exhaust manifold mounting nuts	45	33
Exhaust system front pipe-to-manifold nuts:		
Without catalytic converter (spring-loaded mounting)	see text	see text
With catalytic converter	50	37
All exhaust system flange securing nuts	45	33
Exhaust system intermediate pipe-to-tailpipe clamp nut	18	13
Lambda sensor	45	33

Part A: Carburettor engines

1 General information and precautions

The fuel system consists of a fuel tank mounted under the rear of the car, a mechanical fuel pump and a carburettor. The fuel pump is operated by an eccentric on the camshaft and is mounted on the rear of the cylinder head. The air cleaner contains a disposable paper filter element and incorporates a flap valve air temperature control system which allows cold air from the outside of the car and warm air from the exhaust manifold to enter the air cleaner in the correct proportions.

The carburettor is the Hobourn SU-manufactured KIF type, a development by Rover of the previous HIF instrument. To reduce emissions and to improve driveability when the engine is cold, the inlet manifold is heated by the cooling system coolant and by an electric pre-heater system. Mixture enrichment for cold starting is by a manually-operated choke control.

The (service replacement) exhaust system consists of three sections; the front pipe and front silencer box, the intermediate pipe and middle silencer box, and the tailpipe and main silencer box. The system fitted in production differs in that the intermediate pipe and tailpipe are in one piece. The system is suspended throughout its entire length by rubber mountings. If a catalytic converter is fitted, it is situated between the front pipe and the (much shorter) intermediate pipe.

Warning: *Many of the procedures in this Chapter require the removal of fuel lines and connections which may result in some fuel spillage. Before carrying out any operation on the fuel system refer to the precautions given in Safety first! at the beginning of this Manual and follow them implicitly. Petrol is a highly dangerous and volatile liquid and the precautions necessary when handling it cannot be overstressed.*

2 Air cleaner assembly – removal and refitting

Removal

1 Release the two clips securing the air intake duct to the assembly, then undo the four screws securing the assembly to its mounting bracket.

2 Release the assembly from the intake duct and withdraw it until the thermac switch vacuum pipes can be disconnected; note that these are colour-coded (yellow to the temperature control valve, red to the inlet manifold) to ensure correct reconnection (photo).

3 Withdraw the assembly. Check the condition of the O-ring around the carburettor inlet and renew it if worn or damaged.

4 To remove the intake duct, refer to Section 3.

5 To remove the cold air intake duct remove the two retaining screws and disconnect the duct from the body front panel, release the clip securing the ignition HT lead, then slacken the clamp to separate the cold air duct from the intake duct (photos).

Refitting

6 Refitting is the reverse of the removal procedure; ensure that the vacuum pipes are correctly reconnected and are not trapped as the assembly is refitted, then check that the assembly sits properly on the carburettor inlet before tightening the screws securely.

3 Air cleaner air temperature control system – general information

Checking

1 The system is controlled by a thermac switch mounted in the air cleaner assembly; when the engine is started from cold, the switch is closed to allow inlet manifold depression to act on the air temperature control valve in the intake duct. This raises a vacuum servo in the valve assembly and draws a flap valve across the cold air intake, thus allowing only (warmed) air from the exhaust manifold to enter the air cleaner.

2 As the temperature rises of the exhaust-warmed air in the air cleaner, a bi-metallic strip in the thermac switch deforms and opens the switch to shut off the depression in the air temperature control valve assembly; the flap is lowered gradually across the hot air intake until, when the engine is fully warmed up to normal operating temperature, only cold air from the front of the car is entering the air cleaner.

3 To check the system, allow the engine to cool down completely, then disconnect the cold air intake duct from the air cleaner intake duct; the flap valve should be securely seated across the hot air intake. Start

Fig. 4.1 Location of fuel and ignition system components – carburettor engines (Sec 1)

1   Carburettor
2   Throttle pedal switch
3   Choke control
4   Manifold pre-heater relay
5   Fusible link box
6   Ignition HT coil
7   Distributor
8   Inlet manifold pre-heater
    temperature switch
9   Manifold PTC heater
10 Idle bypass solenoid
11 Vacuum capsule
12 Amplifier module
13 Fuel pump

2.2 Note colour-coding of thermac switch vacuum pipes before disconnecting

2.5A Cold air intake duct is secured by two screws to body front panel

2.5B Slacken clamp to disconnect cold air intake duct from air cleaner assembly intake duct

3.4 Disconnect vacuum pipe from control valve to check operation of system components

Fig. 4.2 Air cleaner air temperature control system components – carburettor engines (Sec 3)

1 Carburettor	3 Thermac switch
2 Air temperature control	4 Air cleaner intake duct
valve	5 Hot air intake

the engine; the flap should immediately rise to close off the cold air intake and should then lower steadily as the engine warms up until it is eventually seated across the hot air intake again.

4   To check the thermac switch, disconnect the vacuum pipe from the control valve when the engine is running (photo). With the engine cold, full inlet manifold depression should be felt sucking at the pipe end; none at all when the engine is fully warmed up.

5   To check the air temperature control valve, disconnect the cold air intake duct from the air cleaner intake duct; the flap valve should be securely seated across the hot air intake. Disconnect the vacuum pipe and suck hard at the control valve stub; the flap should rise to shut off the cold air intake.

6   If either component is faulty, it must be renewed.

Thermac switch – renewal

7   Remove the air cleaner assembly (Sec 2).
8   Remove the air cleaner filter element (Chapter 1).
9   Bend up the tags on the switch clip and remove the clip, then withdraw the switch and its seal (photo).
10   Refitting is the reverse of the removal procedure; ensure that the switch mating surfaces are clean and that the switch and seal are correctly located before fastening the clip.

Air temperature control valve – renewal

11   Disconnect the vacuum pipe from the air temperature control valve, then disconnect the cold air intake duct from the air cleaner intake duct (photo).
12   Release the two clips securing the air intake duct to the air cleaner assembly and withdraw the duct, taking care not to lose the hot air intake connector hose (photo).

13   The air temperature control valve can be renewed only with the complete intake duct assembly.
14   Refitting is the reverse of the removal procedure.

4   Fuel pump – testing, removal and refitting

Note: *Refer to the warning note in Section 1 before proceeding*

Testing

1   To test the fuel pump on the engine, temporarily disconnect the outlet pipe which leads to the carburettor, and hold a wad of rag over the pump outlet while an assistant spins the engine on the starter. *Keep the hands away from the electric cooling fan.* Regular spurts of fuel should be ejected as the engine turns.
2   The pump can also be tested by removing it. With the pump outlet pipe disconnected but the inlet pipe still connected, hold the wad of rag by the outlet. Operate the pump lever by hand, moving it in and out; if the pump is in a satisfactory condition a strong jet of fuel should be ejected.

Removal

3   Identify the pump inlet and outlet hoses then disconnect and plug them (photo). Place wads of rag to catch any spilled fuel and cover the hose unions to prevent the entry of dirt and the escape of fuel.

3.9 Thermac switch is clipped into air cleaner assembly

3.11 Disconnecting vacuum pipe from air temperature control valve – note clamp (arrow) securing cold air intake duct to air cleaner intake duct

3.12 Do not lose hot air intake connector hose when removing air cleaner intake duct

4.3 Plug fuel hoses when disconnecting them – pump inlet hose disconnected, outlet hose arrowed

4.5 Removing fuel pump and insulating block

5.4 Location of fuel gauge sender unit

4   Unscrew the nuts securing the pump to the cylinder head and remove the washers.
5   Withdraw the fuel pump from the engine and remove the insulating block (photo).

Refitting

6   Refitting is the reverse of the removal procedure; clean the mating surfaces and renew the insulating block if its sealing surfaces are marked or damaged. Tighten the pump mounting nuts to the specified torque wrench setting.

5   Fuel gauge sender unit – removal, refitting and testing

Note: *Refer to the warning note in Section 1 before proceeding*

Removal

1   Jack up the rear of the car and support it on axle stands (see *'Jacking, towing and wheel changing'*).
2   Disconnect the battery negative lead.
3   Drain the fuel tank and slacken the tank rear mounting bolts, then remove the tank front mounting bolts (Sec 6) and lower the tank until the sender unit (in the tank's front left-hand corner) can be reached.
4   Disconnect the sender unit wiring and hose (photo).
5   Release the sender unit's locking ring by turning it anti-clockwise; Rover recommend the use of Service Tool Number 18G 1001, but for those without access to such equipment a pair of slip-jointed pliers will serve as an adequate substitute.
6   Withdraw the sender unit, noting the sealing ring; this must be renewed if worn or damaged.

Refitting

7   Refitting is the reverse of the removal procedure.

Testing

8   The fuel gauge mounted in the instrument panel is fed with a stabilised 10 volt supply from the instrument panel feed (via the ignition switch and fuse 3), its earth being controlled by the sender unit.
9   If the gauge develops a fault, check first the other instruments; if they do not work at all, check the instrument panel feed. If the readings are erratic, there may be a fault in the voltage stabiliser which will necessitate the renewal of the gauge unit or printed circuit (Chapter 12). If the fault is in the fuel gauge alone, check it as follows.
10   If the gauge needle remains at the 'E' end of the scale, disconnect the sender unit wire and earth it; if the needle then deflects when the ignition is switched on, the sender unit is proven faulty and must be renewed. If the needle still does not move, remove the instrument panel (Chapter 12) and check the continuity of the green/black wire between the gauge and the sender unit and the feed to the gauge unit. If

continuity is shown, and the fault still exists, then the gauge is faulty and the gauge unit must be renewed.
11   If the gauge needle remains at the 'F' end of the scale, disconnect the sender unit wire; if the needle then returns to the 'E' end of the scale when the ignition is switched on check the sender unit as described below, then check that the green/black wire is sound. If the needle still does not move, check the remainder of the circuit as described above.
12   To test the sender unit, remove it from the tank and connect a multimeter (set to its resistance function) between the wire terminals and measure the resistance with the float in various positions; when the float is lowered to the empty position a reading of approximately 270 ohms should be obtained, decreasing steadily through 65 ohms at the half-full point, to a reading of 15.5 ohms when the float is raised to the full position. If the unit is faulty it must be renewed.

6   Fuel tank – removal and refitting

Note: *Refer to the warning note in Section 1 before proceeding*

Removal

1   A fuel tank drain plug is not provided; it is therefore preferable to carry out the removal operation when the tank is nearly empty. Before proceeding, disconnect the battery negative lead and syphon or hand pump the remaining fuel from the tank.
2   Chock the front wheels, then jack up the rear of the car and support its body on axle stands. Remove the right-hand roadwheel (see *'Jacking, towing and wheel changing'*).
3   Remove the exhaust tailpipe (Sec 18); if the production-fit system is still fitted, unhook its rubber mountings and move the system aside without straining it, but be careful to support its weight as much as possible. If the tailpipe does become a hindrance, it must be removed, even if this means cutting a perfectly good component.
4   Use a trolley jack to support the weight of the rear suspension subframe, then remove the subframe right-hand (front) mounting and lower the subframe as far as possible without straining the brake flexible hose (Chapter 10).
5   Slacken its retaining clip and disconnect the filler hose from the tank, then release their clips and disconnect the various fuel feed, breather and vent hoses from the tank (photo). Plug all hoses and cover their unions to prevent the entry of dirt and the escape of fuel.
6   Disconnect the wiring from the fuel gauge sender unit (Sec 5).
7   Release the handbrake cable from its retaining clips and move it above the tank.
8   Unbolt the tank from the body and withdraw it from the car (photos).
9   If the tank is contaminated with sediment or water, remove the sender unit (Sec 5) and swill the tank out with clean fuel. If the tank is damaged or leaks, it should be repaired by a specialist or alternatively renewed. *Do not under any circumstances attempt to solder or weld a fuel tank.*

Refitting

10   Refitting is the reverse of the removal procedure; tighten all nuts and bolts to their specified torque wrench settings and ensure that all hoses are correctly routed and securely fastened so that there can be no risk of fuel leakage.

7   Fuel tank filler components – removal and refitting

Note: *Refer to the warning note in Section 1 before proceeding*

Removal

1   A fuel tank drain plug is not provided; it is therefore preferable to carry out the removal operation when the tank is nearly empty. Before proceeding, disconnect the battery negative lead and syphon or hand pump the remaining fuel from the tank.
2   Chock the front wheels, then jack up the rear of the car and support it on axle stands. Remove the right-hand roadwheel (see *'Jacking, towing and wheel changing'*).
3   Remove the fuel filler cap.
4   On three-door models, remove the two screws securing the filler neck to the body.
5   On five-door models, remove the filler neck grommet, then undo the two nuts securing the filler neck to the body (photo).
6   On all models, slacken the clips of the filler hose and of the large- and small-diameter vent hoses, then disconnect the hoses and remove the filler neck and hose assembly (photo). Plug all hoses and cover their unions to prevent the entry of dirt and the escape of fuel.
7   The hoses can be disconnected, if required, by releasing their clips; note that the breather two-way valve is secured by a nut (photo).

Refitting

8   Refitting is the reverse of the removal procedure; tighten all nuts and bolts to their specified torque wrench settings and ensure that all

6.5 Slacken or release clips (arrows) to disconnect hoses from tank

hoses are correctly routed and securely fastened so that there can be no risk of fuel leakage.

8   Throttle cable – removal, refitting and adjustment

Removal

1   Working inside the car, release the clip securing the cable inner wire to the pedal (photo).

6.8A Fuel tank front mounting bolt

6.8B Fuel tank front left-hand mounting bolt

6.8C Fuel tank rear mounting bolts (arrows)

7.5 Fuel tank filler neck is secured by two nuts (one shown) on five-door models

7.6 Slacken filler hose clips (arrows) to release filler neck

7.7 Fuel tank breather two-way valve and mounting nut

8.1 Throttle cable inner wire securing clip 'A', cable fastener 'B', throttle pedal mounting nut 'C'

2   Working inside the engine compartment, slacken the cable adjuster nut and locknut, release the cable from the adjuster bracket and disengage the cable end nipple from the carburettor pulley (photo).
3   Release the cable fastener from the bulkhead and withdraw the cable into the engine compartment.

Refitting

4   Refitting is the reverse of the removal procedure; adjust the cable as follows.

Adjustment

5   With the pedal fully released, check that there is maximum clearance at the lost motion gap (see Fig. 4.3) and no slack in the cable. Have an assistant fully depress the pedal and check that the throttle opens fully, then check that it returns to the at-rest position when released.
6   To adjust the cable, slacken the adjuster locknut (underneath the adjuster bracket) and pull the cable upwards until the lost motion gap clearance is felt to have been taken up, all cable free play has been taken up and the throttle spindle is just starting to move.
7   From this position, unscrew the adjuster nut until a gap of 5 mm is present between the underside of the nut and the top of the adjuster bracket; tighten the locknut without disturbing this setting.
8   Recheck the adjustment.

10.2 Release clip to disconnect choke cable from carburettor – note fast idle adjusting screw (arrow)

8.2 Disconnecting throttle cable from carburettor

Fig. 4.3 Throttle lost motion gap – carburettor engines (Sec 8)

9   Throttle pedal – removal and refitting

Note: *Refer to Chapter 12 for details of throttle pedal switch removal and refitting*

Removal

1   Disconnect the throttle cable inner wire from the pedal (Sec 8).
2   Unhook the return spring and undo the nuts securing the pedal assembly to the bulkhead; withdraw the pedal.

Refitting

3   Refitting is the reverse of the removal procedure; tighten to the specified torque wrench setting the pedal nuts, then adjust the cable (Sec 8).

10   Choke cable – removal, refitting and adjustment

Note: *Refer to Chapter 12 for details of choke switch removal and refitting*

Removal

1   Remove the air cleaner (Sec 2).
2   Release the clip securing the cable outer to the carburettor, then disconnect the cable inner from the carburettor pulley (photo).

10.3 Remove cable sealing grommet from bulkhead to remove choke cable

3   Prise the cable sealing grommet out of the bulkhead aperture and slide the grommet off the cable (photo). Tie a length of string to the end of the cable.
4   Working inside the car, remove the ashtray and disconnect the switch wire from the choke cable, then prise out the clip securing the cable to the facia and withdraw the cable, removing the switch if required. Untie the drawstring as soon as it appears.

Refitting and adjustment

5   Refitting is the reverse of the removal procedure; use the drawstring to pull the new cable through the facia and bulkhead into the engine compartment.
6   Adjust the cable so that when the choke control is pulled fully out the choke cam has no further travel. When the control is pushed fully in the choke cam should return to the fully-off position so that there is clearance between the cam and the fast idle adjusting screw; provided

that the choke returns fully, no cable free play should be evident.
7   The cable is adjusted by releasing the carburettor clip and repositioning the cable outer as necessary.

11   Unleaded petrol – general information and usage

Note: *The information given in this Chapter is correct at the time of writing and applies only to petrols currently available in the UK. If updated information is thought to be required check with a Rover dealer. If travelling abroad consult one of the motoring organisations (or a similar authority) for advice on the petrols available and their suitability for your vehicle*

1   The fuel recommended by Rover for Metro models is given in the Specifications Section of this Chapter, followed by the equivalent petrol currently on sale in the UK.
2   RON and MON are different testing standards; RON stands for Research Octane Number (also written as RM), while MON stands for Motor Octane Number (also written as MM).
3   All Rover Metro models are designed to run on 95 (RON) octane petrol. Super/Super Plus (unleaded) petrols can be used without modification, if nothing else is available; 4-star (leaded) petrol can **only** be used if the car is **not** fitted with a catalytic converter. **Note:** *The only cars which MUST use unleaded petrol at all times are those with catalytic converters; see Section 40.*

12   Carburettor – general information

The carburettor features an electrically-controlled idle bypass system that is separate from the main fuel/air mixture circuit provided by the piston, jet and metering needle (Sec 14), a manual choke, an overrun valve and a full load enrichment device.
The idle bypass system is described in Section 14; see also Fig. 4.4.
The manual choke (Fig. 4.5) uses the constant manifold depression to draw fuel and air into a fixed orifice; a helical groove in the spindle keyed to the choke cam is arranged so that extra fuel/air mixture can pass from the orifice only when the choke cam is rotated slightly from

Fig. 4.4 Carburettor idle bypass system (Sec 12)

1   Carburettor piston
2   Plunger
3   Idle air bypass screw
4   Throttle pedal switch
5   Idle bypass solenoid

Fig. 4.5 Operation of the carburettor choke assembly (Sec 12)

A	Path of fuel	1	Fixed orifice
B	Path of air	2	Choke spindle
C	Path of air/fuel mixture	3	Helical groove

decelerating) a high depression is generated in the manifold, downstream of the throttle disc. A passage connects the space behind a diaphragm to this point so that the diaphragm is sucked off its seat against spring pressure; the air passing through the air bleed hose can then enter through two passages which means that the depression across the fuel pick-up is too low for fuel to be drawn from the float chamber into the system (Fig. 4.6 *'Engine under light load'*).

At high engine loads, with the throttle fully open (accelerating, full-throttle running) manifold depression drops to the point where the diaphragm is seated by its spring and the air can enter only through a small jet; this increases air speed and raises the depression over the fuel pick-up to the point where additional fuel is drawn up from the float chamber, mixed with the air bleed and passed into the carburettor venturi downstream of the piston (Fig. 4.6 *'Engine under full load'*).

Some models are fitted with a spring-loaded poppet valve in the throttle disc, so that when the throttle is closed at high engine speeds the high manifold depression sucks the valve open, admitting enough air to burn completely the small amount of fuel that is sucked through the jet under these conditions, thus reducing exhaust emissions.

13 Carburettor – removal and refitting

Note: *Refer to the warning note in Section 1 before proceeding*

Removal

1   Remove the air cleaner assembly (Sec 2).
2   Disconnect the throttle cable (Sec 8).
3   Disconnect the choke cable (Sec 10).
4   Disconnect the breather hose and the vacuum pipes; if required they can (where possible) be removed with the carburettor. Disconnect the idle bypass solenoid wiring, making notes of the connections so that they can be correctly reconnected, then disconnect the float chamber vent hose and the full load air bleed hose (photo).
5   Release its clip and disconnect the fuel pump outlet hose from the carburettor. Place wads of rag around the union to catch any spilled fuel, plug the hose as soon as it is disconnected and cover the hose union to prevent the entry of dirt and the escape of fuel.
6   Unscrew the four Torx screws securing the upper inlet manifold to the lower inlet manifold, then remove the carburettor assembly. Plug the inlet port with a wad of clean cloth, then check that the manifold mating surfaces are clean and flat and renew the gasket if necessary (photos).
7   If required, the air cleaner assembly support brackets, the air cleaner adaptor and the upper inlet manifold can be unbolted from the carburettor body. Again, check that the mating surfaces are clean and flat, renew the sealing O-rings as a matter of course and renew the gasket if it is damaged.

Refitting

8   Refitting is the reverse of the removal procedure; tighten all screws and bolts to their specified torque wrench settings (where given). Check, and adjust if necessary, the cable adjustments (Secs 8 and 10 of this Chapter) and the idle speed and mixture (Chapter 1).

the at-rest position; the amount of extra fuel delivered increases to a maximum point when the choke cam is rotated through 60°.

The full load enrichment device also uses manifold depression. At light engine loads, with the throttle partially closed (idling, cruising or

13.4 Breather hose 'A', float chamber vent and full load air bleed hoses 'B', idle bypass solenoid wiring 'C', fuel pump outlet hose 'D'

13.6A Unscrew upper-to-lower inlet manifold Torx screws ...

13.6B ... to remove carburettor assembly

Fig. 4.6 Carburettor full load enrichment device (Sec 12)

1 Diaphragm
2 Float chamber
3 Jet
A Path of fuel
B Path of air
C Path of air/fuel mixture

Engine under light load

Engine under full load

A
B
C

14 Carburettor – diagnosis, overhaul and adjustments

Diagnosis

1 The SU carburettor does not usually suffer from jet blockages and wear is usually only found between the needle and jet, although it is worth checking the fit of the piston in the suction chamber whenever the carburettor is dismantled. If the idle speed is too high and cannot be reduced by normal adjustment, it is worth checking the throttle disc overrun valve spring (if fitted); if this has weakened, the throttle disc must be renewed.

2 If a carburettor fault is suspected, always check first that the ignition timing is accurate and the spark plugs are in good condition and correctly gapped, that the throttle and choke cables are correctly adjusted, that the carburettor piston damper is topped-up, that the float chamber vent hose and (especially if the mixture is very rich) the full load air bleed hose are clear and that the air cleaner filter element is clean; see the relevant Sections of Chapter 1 or of this Chapter. If the engine is running very roughly, check the compression pressures (Chapter 2) and bear in mind the possibility that one of the hydraulic tappets might be faulty, producing an incorrect valve clearance.

3 If careful checking of all of the above produces no improvement, the carburettor must be removed for cleaning and overhaul.

Fig. 4.7 Exploded view of SU KIF carburettor (Sec 14)

1   Piston damper
2   Suction chamber
3   C-clip
4   Piston
5   Piston spring
6   Needle retaining (grub) screw
7   Needle spring
8   Needle
9   Needle guide
10 Idle speed screw
11 Spring
12 Idle speed adjusting knob
13 Throttle spindle seal
14 Screw
15 Throttle disc – with overrun valve
16 Throttle spindle
17 Return spring
18 Fast idle lever
19 Lockwasher
20 Nut
21 Fast idle adjusting screw
22 Choke assembly
23 Sealing O-rings
24 Throttle return spring lever
25 Throttle lever
26 Sealing O-ring
27 Diaphragm
28 Idle air bypass screw
29 Sealing O-ring
30 Full load enrichment device cover
31 Spring
32 Idle bypass solenoid

33 Float pivot
34 Pivot seal
35 Carburettor body
36 Sealing O-ring
37 Jet adjusting screw
38 Fuel strainer
39 Float needle seat
40 Float needle
41 Float
42 Jet bearing
43 Jet bearing nut
44 Jet
45 Bi-metal lever assembly
46 Spring
47 Jet retaining screw
48 Sealing O-ring
49 Float chamber cover

14.7 Prise C-clip from piston upper end ...

14.8 ... to separate piston (and piston spring) from suction chamber

Overhaul

Note: *Refer to the warning note in Section 1 before proceeding*

4   Note that in the rare event of a complete carburettor overhaul being necessary, it may prove more economical to renew the carburettor as a complete unit. Check the price and availability of a replacement carburettor and of its component parts before starting work; note that most sealing washers, screws and gaskets are available in kits, as are some of the major sub-assemblies. In most cases it will be sufficient to dismantle the carburettor and to clean the jets and passages.
5   Remove the carburettor and unbolt the air cleaner assembly support brackets, the air cleaner adaptor and the upper inlet manifold (Sec 13).
6   Releasing their clips where necessary, disconnect all vacuum pipes and breather hoses from the carburettor, then clean away all external dirt.
7   Unscrew the piston damper and tip out the oil, then push the piston upwards until the C-clip can be prised out of its upper end (photo).
8   Mark the suction chamber in relation to the carburettor body. Remove the three retaining screws (noting that one also secures the carburettor's metal identification tag) and withdraw the suction chamber, noting the piston spring (photo).
9   Carefully lift the piston and needle assembly out of the carburettor, unscrew the needle retaining grub screw and withdraw the needle with its spring and guide.
10   Mark the float chamber cover in relation to the carburettor body,

remove its retaining screws and withdraw the cover with its sealing O-ring.
11   Unscrew the jet retaining screw, remove the spring and withdraw the jet and bi-metal lever assembly. Disengage the lever from the jet.
12   Unscrew the float pivot, noting its seal, then remove the float and the float needle. Unscrew the needle seat and tip out the fuel strainer.
13   Unscrew, if required, the jet bearing nut and withdraw the bearing.
14   Unscrew the idle bypass solenoid.
15   **Do not** alter the setting of the idle speed adjusting knob, the idle air bypass screw or the jet adjusting screw; once disturbed these can only be reset correctly using an exhaust gas analyser and a tachometer. Note that the idle air bypass screw cannot be removed until the full load enrichment device has been removed from the carburettor body (it is secured by four Torx-type screws) and that the jet adjusting screw recess is sealed by a tamperproof plug.
16   If any of these screws are to be removed for cleaning, screw each in until it seats lightly (in the case of the idle air bypass screw, this means screwing it anti-clockwise until it seats in the cover), counting the **exact** number of turns required to do this, then unscrewing it; on refitting reverse the process to return the screw to its original location, then have the carburettor settings checked by a Rover dealer once the engine is running.
17   If the choke assembly is thought to be blocked it can be removed from the carburettor body so that the passages can be blown clear with compressed air; if this is not available a blast of commercial carburettor cleaner (applied from an aerosol via the thin plastic tube usually supplied) will serve to clear most obstructions. The same approach can be applied to the full load enrichment device. **Note:** *Be careful to wear full eye protection when using compressed air or chemicals in such a way.*
18   Check the throttle linkage for wear, especially the fit of the spindle in the carburettor body. If wear is found, seek the advice of a Rover dealer or SU carburettor specialist; at the time of writing, no replacement parts are listed which would permit the repair of such faults.
19   With the carburettor dismantled as far as is practicable and all components cleaned carefully, check them for signs of wear or damage and renew any faulty component. Renew all seals, gaskets and O-rings disturbed as a matter of course.
20   Check the float needle seat and tip, renewing them if they show wear ridges. Renew the float if it appears to be leaking.
21   Check the tapered needle, jet and jet bearing; renew them as a matched set if they show any sign of wear, or if there is any doubt about their condition.
22   Clean the mating surfaces of the piston and the suction chamber with methylated spirit, then wipe them dry; *do not use any form of abrasive cleaner.* Insert the piston (without the spring and damper) into the suction chamber, hold them horizontally and spin the piston; it should rotate freely in the suction chamber without sticking or touching the chamber walls. The piston and suction chamber must be renewed as a matched pair if either is worn or damaged.
23   On reassembly, refit the idle bypass solenoid, tightening it securely but not overtightening it.
24   Fit the jet bearing and bearing nut, if removed.
25   Do not forget the fuel strainer when refitting the float needle seat or the seal when refitting the float pivot, and ensure that the needle is refitted with its tapered tip engaged in the needle seat; as noted below, no data is available concerning float height adjustment.
26   Fit the jet to the bi-metal lever, ensuring that the jet head moves freely in the lever cut-out, then refit the assembly to the carburettor, ensuring that the lever engages correctly with the jet adjusting screw. Refit the spring and tighten the jet retaining screw securely; see below for details of jet adjustment.
27   Fit a new sealing O-ring to the float chamber cover. Refit the float chamber cover, aligning the marks made on dismantling; it will fit correctly only one way. Tighten securely, but do not overtighten, the cover screws.
28   Fit the needle and spring to the guide, then fit the assembly to the piston so that the guide cut-out faces the grub screw hole and the bottom of the guide is flush with the bottom of the piston. Tighten the needle retaining grub screw carefully (note the specified torque wrench setting); if this is overtightened, it will distort the guide and make subsequent needle removal and refitting very difficult.
29   Temporarily refit the piston and needle assembly to the carburettor body, engaging the piston slot on its locating projection and ensuring that the needle enters the jet. Fit the suction chamber over the

piston and align it on its mounting screws (or use the marks made on dismantling). Mark the correct relative positions of the piston and the suction chamber with a soft pencil, then remove them from the carburettor.

30   Fit the piston spring to the piston, then offer up the assembly to the suction chamber, aligning the pencil marks so that the piston spring is not 'wound up'. Push the piston fully up into the suction chamber and refit the C-clip to secure the assembly.

31   Ensuring that the pencil marks remain in alignment (so that the piston spring is not 'wound up' by the piston being rotated relative to the suction chamber) refit the piston/suction chamber assembly to the carburettor, engaging the piston slot on its locating projection and ensuring that the needle enters the jet. Do not forget the identification tag when refitting the suction chamber screws; tighten securely, but do not overtighten, the screws.

32   Fill the piston damper chamber with oil (Chapter 1) and tighten the damper securely.

33   The remainder of the refitting procedure is the reverse of removal.

Adjustments

Note: *Refer to the warning note in Section 1 before proceeding*

Idle speed and mixture

34   Refer to Chapter 1.

Fast idle speed

35   Check the throttle and choke cable adjustments (Secs 8 and 10).

36   Warm the engine up to normal operating temperature and check that the idle speed and mixture are correctly set (Chapter 1); if the car is not equipped with a tachometer, connect a tachometer to the engine following its manufacturer's instructions.

37   Pull out the choke control to the first detent position and check that the engine speed increases to the specified amount.

38   If adjustment is required, screw in or out the fast idle adjusting screw (see photo 10.2) until the engine speed is correct.

Fuel level

39   The carburettor fuel level is adjusted by bending the float arm to alter the float height, usually measured with the carburettor inverted; however since the necessary information is not provided by the manufacturer, the car should be taken to a Rover dealer or SU carburettor specialist if the fuel level is thought to be incorrect.

Jet adjustment

Note: *Accurate jet adjustment is not easy for the inexperienced and can only be carried out using an exhaust gas analyser. If the jet adjustment is thought to be incorrect or is to be checked, owners without the required equipment and the skill to use it are advised to have the work carried out by a Rover dealer or SU carburettor specialist*

40   Warm the engine up to normal operating temperature and check that the ignition timing, idle speed and mixture are correctly set and that the carburettor piston damper is topped-up (Chapter 1); connect a tachometer to the engine following its manufacturer's instructions.

41   Remove the tamperproof cap from the jet adjusting screw recess at the front left-hand corner of the carburettor body.

42   Counting the exact number of turns required to do so, screw the idle air bypass screw anti-clockwise until it seats lightly, then start the engine, switch on the headlamps, heated rear window and heater blower motor (first speed only) and adjust the idle speed to 700 to 750 rpm (Chapter 1).

43   Connect the exhaust gas analyser following its manufacturer's instructions.

44   Turning the jet adjusting screw either way (clockwise to richen the mixture) by half a turn at a time and waiting for the analyser reading to respond and stabilise before making a further alteration, set the mixture to a base CO level of 5.5 % $\pm$ 0.5 %. When the analyser reading is steady at the correct level, switch off all electrical loads.

45   Screw the idle air bypass screw clockwise by the number of turns previously noted to return it to its original setting, then set the true idle mixture to the specified value, as described in Chapter 1.

46   Stop the engine when the adjustment is correct, disconnect the test equipment and fit a new tamperproof cap to the jet adjusting screw recess.

14.51 Note connections before disconnecting idle bypass solenoid wiring

Idle bypass system

47   As well as the carburettor idle air bypass passage and screw, the system incorporates the solenoid and the throttle pedal switch and is supplied with current via fusible link number 1, the ignition switch and fuse number 1.

48   When the throttle is closed and the ignition is switched on the solenoid is energised, its plunger being retracted to open the bypass passage (see Fig. 4.4); this allows air to bypass the carburettor piston and thus makes the idle mixture independent of the needle metering. Screwing in (clockwise) the idle air bypass screw reduces the amount of air bypassing the piston and richens the idle mixture.

49   As soon as the throttle pedal is depressed, the throttle pedal switch opens, the solenoid is de-energised and the bypass passage is shut off.

50   To check the system, listen closely by the carburettor while an assistant switches on the ignition and depresses and releases the throttle pedal several times; the solenoid should be heard to be clicking in and out.

51   If no clicking can be heard, remove the air cleaner assembly (Sec 2) and use a meter or similar (Chapter 12) to check the solenoid earth and feed; use a meter to check that the throttle pedal switch contacts open and close as described. If the solenoid or switch is faulty it must be renewed. Note that fuse number 1 also controls the ignition system; if it blows repeatedly, the solenoid may be at fault (photo).

52   Refer to Chapter 12 for details of throttle pedal switch removal and refitting.

15   Inlet manifold pre-heater – removal and refitting

General

1   The system incorporates the manifold PTC (Positive Temperature Coefficient) heater, the relay and the manifold temperature switch; the relay energising coil is supplied with current via fusible link number 1, the ignition switch and fuse number 1.

2   When the ignition is switched on and the engine (coolant) is cold, the relay-energising current earths through the manifold temperature switch, closing the relay contacts and allowing current to flow from the battery via fusible link number 4 to the heater. This ensures that the inlet manifold is warm enough, even before the effect of the coolant heating becomes apparent, to prevent fuel droplets condensing in the manifold, thus improving driveability and reducing exhaust emissions when the engine is cold.

3   As soon as the engine warms up to temperatures above 50°C, the switch contacts close and the circuit is shut off.

15.6A Remove inlet manifold and extract circlip ...

15.6B ... to remove manifold PTC heater

15.8 Location of inlet manifold pre-heater temperature switch

4   If the engine suddenly develops flat spots when cold, the system may be faulty.

Manifold PTC heater – removal and refitting

Removal

5   Remove the inlet manifold (Sec 16).
6   Extract the circlip securing the heater to the manifold, then withdraw the heater and prise out and discard the rubber sealing ring (photos).

Refitting

7   Refitting is the reverse of the removal procedure; fit a new sealing ring as a matter of course and ensure that the heater locating projection is correctly engaged in the manifold recess.

Inlet manifold pre-heater temperature switch – general

8   Refer to Chapter 3, Section 6 for details of switch testing, removal and refitting (photo).

Manifold heater relay – general

9   Refer to Chapter 12 for details.

16   Inlet manifold – removal and refitting

Removal

Note: *The following procedure describes the removal of the manifold with the carburettor. Access to some of the components concerned is, however, much better if the carburettor is first removed separately (Sec 13); if this is done, the following procedure should be amended as required*

Note: *Refer to the warning note in Section 1 before proceeding*

1   Disconnect the battery negative lead.
2   Remove the air cleaner assembly (Sec 2).
3   Either drain the cooling system completely (Chapter 1), or clamp the coolant hoses connected to the inlet manifold to minimise coolant loss and be prepared to catch the coolant that will be released from the manifold and cylinder head.
4   Disconnect all coolant hoses from the manifold, as described in Chapter 3 (photo).
5   Trace the float chamber vent hose and the full load air bleed hose from the carburettor down to their metal pipes and unscrew the nut and bolts securing the pipes to the cylinder block/crankcase.
6   Disconnect the breather hose from the cylinder head cover.
7   Disconnect the idle bypass solenoid wiring, making notes of the connections so that they can be correctly reconnected, then disconnect the manifold pre-heater switch and heater wiring.
8   Release its clip and disconnect the fuel pump outlet hose from the carburettor. Place wads of rag around the union to catch any spilled fuel,

Fig. 4.8 Inlet manifold fastener tightening sequence – K8 engines (Sec 16)

16.4 Disconnect hoses arrowed when removing inlet manifold

plug the hose as soon as it is disconnected and cover the hose union to prevent the entry of dirt and the escape of fuel.
9   Disconnect the vacuum pipe from the distributor; secure the pipes so that they cannot be damaged during removal and refitting.
10   Disconnect the brake vacuum servo unit vacuum hose from the manifold (Chapter 9); discard the sealing washers.
11   The manifold support stays are bolted to the manifold at their upper ends and to the cylinder block/crankcase at their lower ends; slacken the bolts at one end and unbolt the other as convenient (photos).
12   Unscrew the nuts and bolts securing the manifold to the cylinder head and withdraw it; remove and discard the gasket (photo).
13   Clean the manifold and cylinder head mating surfaces and check that they are flat and unmarked.

16.11A Inlet manifold support stay upper end bolt (arrow)

16.11B Inlet manifold support stay lower end bolt (arrow)

16.12 Removing the inlet manifold – complete with carburettor

16.14A Always fit a new manifold gasket

16.14B Refitting the inlet manifold – less carburettor

16.14C Tighten manifold nuts and bolts in sequence to specified torque wrench setting

Refitting

14   Refitting is the reverse of the removal procedure, noting the following points (photos).

   (a)   *Always fit a new manifold gasket.*
   (b)   *Working in the sequence shown in Fig. 4.8, tighten the manifold retaining nuts and bolts evenly, to the specified torque wrench setting.*
   (c)   *Refill the cooling system or check the coolant level as required, then wash off any spilt coolant (Chapter 1).*
   (d)   *Renew the vacuum servo unit vacuum hose banjo union sealing washers.*
   (e)   *Tighten all other disturbed nuts and bolts to their specified torque wrench settings (where given).*

17   Exhaust manifold – removal and refitting

Removal

1   Disconnect the battery negative lead.
2   Jack up the front of the car and support it securely on axle stands (see *'Jacking, towing and wheel changing'*).
3   Unbolt the radiator top mountings to permit movement (Chapter 3).
4   Disconnect the exhaust front pipe from the manifold (Sec 18).
5   Remove the cold air intake duct and the air cleaner intake duct (Secs 2 and 3).
6   Unscrew the nuts securing the manifold to the cylinder head and withdraw it; remove and discard the gasket.

17.8A Refitting exhaust manifold – always renew gasket

17.8B Exhaust manifold nut tightening sequence – K8 engines

7   Clean the manifold and cylinder head mating surfaces and check that they are flat and unmarked. Check all threads and the exhaust front pipe mating surface; clean off any corrosion and repair or renew any damaged component.

Refitting

8   Refitting is the reverse of the removal procedure, noting the following points (photos).

(a)   *Always fit a new manifold gasket.*
(b)   *Working in the sequence shown in photo 17.8B, tighten the manifold retaining nuts evenly to the specified torque wrench setting.*
(c)   *Tighten all other disturbed nuts and bolts to their specified torque wrench settings (where given).*

18   Exhaust system – general information and component renewal

Note: *If a catalytic converter is fitted, remember that it is FRAGILE – do not use hammers, mallets etc to strike any part of the system and take care not to drop it or strike it against anything else while handling it*

General

1   The exhaust system components are shown in Figs. 4.9 and 4.10. The (service replacement) exhaust system is in three sections; the front pipe (attached to the exhaust manifold by a spring-tensioned flange on models without catalytic converters, by a flanged joint on models with catalytic converters) and front silencer box, the intermediate pipe and middle silencer box (attached to the front pipe by a flanged joint) and the tailpipe and main silencer box (attached to the intermediate pipe by a clamped sleeve joint). If a catalytic converter is fitted, it is situated between the front pipe and the (much shorter) intermediate pipe, with a flanged joint at each end; the front pipe then has a gas-sampling pipe (fitted to permit mixture checks using an exhaust gas analyser) and a flexible section. **Note:** *The exhaust system fitted in production differs in that the intermediate pipe and tailpipe are in one piece; the pipe must be cut to separate the two when either is to be renewed.*
2   The system is suspended throughout its entire length by rubber mountings (photo).
3   If the car still has the exhaust system fitted in production by the factory, the tailpipe and intermediate pipe must be cut at the point marked by two dimples in the pipe; the two can then be removed individually (photo). On fitting new components, the service replacement tailpipe has a sleeved joint which fits over the intermediate pipe and is secured by a clamp; if the intermediate pipe is to be renewed first, an adaptor sleeve (which will require securing clamps) is available from Rover dealers. Apart from this complication, all sections can be removed individually if required, in no particular sequence.
4   To remove the system or part of the system, first jack up the front or

Fig. 4.9 Typical exhaust system components – without catalytic converter (Sec 18)

1 Intermediate pipe and	5 Nut
tailpipe – production fit	6 Front pipe
2 Rubber mounting	7 Gasket
3 Rubber mounting	8 Nut
4 Heat shield	

Note: *Arrow indicates cutting point for removal of production-fit intermediate pipe and tailpipe*

18.2 Exhaust system is suspended on rubber mountings

18.3 Cutting production-fit intermediate pipe and tailpipe to remove

18.8 Note arrangement of plain, insulating and cup washers before unscrewing nuts

Fig. 4.10 Typical exhaust system components – with catalytic converter (Sec 18)

1 Intermediate pipe and tailpipe – production fit	11 Nut
2 Rubber mounting	12 Catalytic converter
3 Rubber mounting	13 Bolt
4 Nut	14 Gasket
5 Rear heat shield	15 Washer
6 Bolt	16 Nut
7 Front heat shield	17 Front pipe
8 Bolt	18 Nut
9 Gasket	19 Washer
10 Washer	20 Gas-sampling pipe

Note: Arrow indicates cutting point for removal of production-fit intermediate pipe and tailpipe

rear of the car and support it on axle stands (see 'Jacking, towing and wheel changing'). Alternatively position the car over an inspection pit or on car ramps.

System renewal

5   Disconnect the front pipe from the exhaust manifold (see paragraph 8 or 10, as appropriate, below) and cut or disconnect (as appropriate) the intermediate pipe from the tailpipe (see paragraph 3 above). Unhook the rubber mountings and withdraw the tailpipe from above the rear suspension subframe, then remove the front part of the system.
6   Renew all gaskets and seals as a matter of course; check, and renew if necessary, all fasteners, the clamp (if appropriate) and the rubber mountings.
7   Refitting is the reverse of the removal procedure, noting the following points.

    (a)   Apply a smear of anti-seize compound (such as Holts Copaslip) to the threads of all nuts (except self-locking nuts) and bolts as well as to the sleeve joint.
    (b)   Assemble the system loosely on its mountings and check that it cannot touch any part of the body or suspension, even when deflected within the full extent of the rubber mountings.
    (c)   Tighten all disturbed nuts and bolts to their specified torque wrench settings and connect the front pipe to the manifold as described in paragraph 9 or 11 below.
    (d)   Start the engine and check the system for leaks, especially once it is fully warmed up; retighten any slack fasteners.

Component renewal

Front pipe

8   To remove the front pipe on cars without catalytic converters, unscrew and remove the two nuts, then remove the cup washers, the springs and the plain washers securing the pipe to the manifold (photo). Unscrew the nuts and prise the intermediate pipe away from the front pipe, then withdraw the front pipe; collect the seal from its upper end and the gasket from its lower end.
9   Refitting is the reverse of the removal procedure, noting the following points (photos).

    (a)   Clean the mating surfaces of the front pipe and of the manifold and intermediate pipe.
    (b)   Apply a smear of anti-seize compound (such as Holts Copaslip) to the bolts and to the threads of the studs and nuts (except self-locking nuts).
    (c)   Always renew the gasket and seal, and check the condition of the springs and washers.
    (d)   Offer up the front pipe to its mountings and fit the gasket and nuts to connect it to the intermediate pipe.
    (e)   Align the pipe on the manifold then refit the plain washer, the insulating washer, the spring and the cup washer to each stud before refitting the nuts. Tighten the nuts until the cup washer touches the stud shoulder. DO NOT OVERTIGHTEN the nuts beyond this point; the springs will provide the seal required.
    (f)   Tighten the front-to-intermediate pipe flange nuts to the specified torque wrench setting.

18.9A Clean manifold-to-front pipe mating surfaces and apply anti-seize compound to studs

18.9B Tighten retaining nuts as described in text

18.15 Heat shield mounting nuts (arrows)

10 To remove the front pipe on cars with catalytic converters, unscrew the three nuts securing the pipe to the manifold and the two nuts securing the front pipe to the catalytic converter; prise the converter away from the front pipe, unhook the rubber mounting and withdraw the front pipe. Collect the seal from its upper end and the gasket from its lower end.

11 Refitting is the reverse of the removal procedure, noting the following points.

(a) Clean the mating surfaces of the front pipe and of the manifold and the catalytic converter.

.(b) Apply a smear of anti-seize compound (such as Holts Copaslip) to the threads of the studs and nuts (except self-locking nuts).

(c) Always renew the gasket and seal and check carefully the condition of the rubber mounting.

(d) Offer up the front pipe and hook it onto the rubber mounting, then fit the seal, gasket and nuts to connect it to the manifold and catalytic converter.

(e) Tighten the flange nuts to their specified torque wrench settings.

Catalytic converter

12 To remove the catalytic converter, undo the nuts securing its front and rear ends, then prise away the front and intermediate pipes; collect the gaskets and withdraw the converter. On refitting, clean the mating surfaces, fit new gaskets and tighten the nuts to the specified torque wrench settings.

Intermediate pipe

13 To remove the intermediate pipe first cut the tailpipe as described in paragraph 3 above, or disconnect it as described below (as appropriate). Unscrew the nuts and prise away the front pipe/catalytic converter; collect the gasket. Unhook the rubber mountings and remove the intermediate pipe. On refitting, clean the mating surfaces, fit new gaskets, renew the rubber mountings if necessary and tighten the nuts to the specified torque wrench setting.

Tailpipe

14 To remove the tailpipe, either cut it (see paragraph 3 above) or slacken the clamp nut and separate the tailpipe from the intermediate pipe. Unhook the rubber mountings and remove the tailpipe. Refitting is the reverse of the removal procedure; tighten the clamp nut to its specified torque wrench setting and renew the rubber mountings if necessary,

Heat shields

15 The various heat shields can be unfastened from the body and manoeuvred clear of the exhaust system; it may be necessary to unhook one or more of the system's rubber mountings if the extra space is required (photo).

Part B: Fuel-injected engines

19 General information and precautions

The fuel system consists of a fuel tank mounted under the rear of the car with an electric fuel pump immersed in it, a fuel filter, fuel feed and return lines and the throttle body assembly (which incorporates the single fuel injector and the fuel pressure regulator), as well as the Electronic Control Unit (ECU) and the various sensors, electrical components and related wiring. The air cleaner contains a disposable paper filter element and incorporates a flap valve air temperature control system which allows cold air from the outside of the car and warm air from the exhaust manifold to enter the air cleaner in the correct proportions.

To reduce emissions and to improve driveability when the engine is cold, the inlet manifold is heated by the cooling system coolant and by an electric pre-heater system. Mixture enrichment for cold starting is a pre-programmed function of the system.

The ECU fully controls both the ignition system and the fuel injection system, integrating the two in a complete engine management system; refer to Chapter 5 for information on the ignition side of the system and to Chapter 12 for details of electrical components such as the ignition switch, throttle pedal switch, fuel cut-off inertia switch and the relays.

The exhaust system is as described in Section 1 of this Chapter.

Warning: *Many of the procedures in this Chapter require the removal of fuel lines and connections which may result in some fuel spillage. Before carrying out any operation on the fuel system refer to the precautions given in Safety first! at the beginning of this Manual and follow them implicitly. Petrol is a highly dangerous and volatile liquid and the precautions necessary when handling it cannot be overstressed.*

20 Air cleaner assembly – removal and refitting

Removal

1 Release the two clips securing the air intake duct to the assembly, then undo the three screws securing the assembly to the throttle body (photo).

2 Release the assembly from the intake duct and withdraw it, collecting the throttle body seal and the intake duct sealing O-ring (where fitted), then disconnect the following (photo).

(a) Disconnect the thermac switch vacuum pipes; note that these are colour-coded (yellow to the temperature control valve, red to the inlet manifold) to ensure correct reconnection.

(b) Disconnect the ECU manifold absolute pressure sensor fuel trap vacuum hoses; note that these are colour-coded (green to the ECU, white to the inlet manifold) to ensure correct reconnection.

(c) Release its wire clip and disconnect the intake air temperature sensor wiring.

3 Check the condition of the throttle body seal and the intake duct sealing O-ring (where fitted); renew either if worn or damaged.

4 To remove the intake duct, refer to Section 21.

5 To remove the cold air intake duct remove the two retaining screws and disconnect the duct from the body front panel, release the clip securing the ignition HT lead, then slacken the clamp and unfasten the rubber strap (where fitted) to separate the cold air duct from the intake duct.

Refitting

6 Refitting is the reverse of the removal procedure; ensure that the vacuum pipes and hoses are correctly reconnected and are not trapped as the assembly is refitted, then check that the assembly sits properly on the throttle body before tightening the screws securely.

21 Air cleaner air temperature control system – general information

Checking

1 Refer to Section 3 of this Chapter.

Fig. 4.11 Location of fuel and ignition system components – fuel-injected engines (Sec 19)

1   Throttle pedal switch
2   Fuel cut-off inertia switch
3   Fuel pump
4   Throttle potentiometer
5   Fuel pressure regulator
6   Fuel injector
7   Stepper motor
8   Intake air temperature sensor
9   Manifold PTC heater
10 Coolant temperature sensor
11 Distributor
12 Crankshaft sensor
13 Diagnostic connector
14 Electronic Control Unit (ECU)
15 Relay module
16 Ignition HT coil
17 Lambda sensor relay*
18 Purge control valve*
19 Charcoal canister*
20 Lambda sensor*
*Not fitted to all models

Thermac switch – renewal

2   Refer to Section 3 of this Chapter; remove the air cleaner assembly as described in Section 20.

Air temperature control valve – renewal

3   Disconnect the vacuum pipe from the air temperature control valve, then slacken the clamp and disconnect the cold air intake duct from the air cleaner intake duct.

4   On K8-engined models, release the two quarter-turn fasteners securing the intake duct to its support bracket.

Fig. 4.12 Fuel delivery system – fuel-injected engines (Sec 19)

1 Fuel tank	6 Fuel injector
2 Fuel pump	7 Fuel pressure regulator
3 Swirl pot	8 Fuel return line
4 Non-return valve	9 Venturi
5 Fuel filter	

20.1 Releasing clips to separate intake duct from air cleaner assembly

20.2 Thermac switch vacuum pipes 'A', fuel trap vacuum hoses 'B', intake air temperature sensor wiring 'C', throttle body seal 'D'

21.5A Unfastening cold air intake duct rubber strap – note vacuum pipe 'A' and clamp screw 'B'

21.5B Unfastening screw securing intake duct to support bracket

22.3 Disconnecting throttle cable from throttle cam pulley

Fig. 4.13 Air cleaner air temperature control system components – fuel-injected engines (Sec 21)

1   Thermac switch
2   Air cleaner filter element
3   Air temperature control valve
4   Flap valve
5   Hot air intake
6   Air cleaner intake duct
7   Manifold absolute pressure sensor
8   ECU

5   On K16-engined models, undo the single screw securing the intake duct to its support bracket, then unfasten the rubber strap (photos).
6   Release the two clips securing the air intake duct to the air cleaner assembly and withdraw the duct, taking care not to lose the hot air intake connector hose.
7   The air temperature control valve can be renewed only with the complete intake duct assembly.
8   Refitting is the reverse of the removal procedure.

22   Throttle cable – removal, refitting and adjustment

Removal

1   Working inside the car, release the clip securing the cable inner wire to the pedal (see photo 8.1).

Fig. 4.14 Throttle cable adjustment – fuel-injected engines (Sec 22)

1   Throttle lever-to-lost
    motion link clearance –
    should be equal on each
    side

2   Adjuster nut
3   Adjuster locknut

2   Working inside the engine compartment, remove the air cleaner assembly (Sec 20).
3   Slacken the cable adjuster nut and locknut, release the cable from the adjuster bracket and disengage the cable end nipple from the throttle cam (photo).
4   Release the cable fastener from the bulkhead and withdraw the cable into the engine compartment.

Refitting

5   Refitting is the reverse of the removal procedure; adjust the cable as follows.

(a) With the cable connected to the throttle cam and (loosely) engaged on the adjuster bracket, switch on the ignition and position the stepper motor by MOVING THE CAM ONLY to open and fully close the throttle.
(b) Tighten the adjuster nut (underneath the adjuster bracket) until the clearance is equal on each side of the throttle lever at the lost motion link (Fig. 4.14).
(c) Tighten the locknut securely and recheck the setting.
(d) Switch off the ignition and refit the air cleaner assembly.

Adjustment

6   With the pedal fully released, check that there is equal clearance on each side of the throttle lever at the lost motion link (see Fig. 4.14) and no slack in the cable. Have an assistant fully depress the pedal and check that the throttle opens fully, then check that it returns to the at-rest position when released.
7   To adjust the cable, switch on the ignition and position the stepper motor by **moving the cam only** to open and fully close the throttle. Note that it is essential for accurate positioning of the stepper motor that the throttle pedal switch contacts remain closed, so that the ECU recognises the throttle movement as a command and indexes the stepper motor to 25 steps.
8   Slacken the adjuster locknut (above the adjuster bracket) and adjuster nut, then tighten the adjuster nut until the clearance is equal on

each side of the throttle lever at the lost motion link; tighten the locknut without disturbing this setting. Recheck the adjustment and switch off the ignition.

23   Throttle pedal – removal and refitting

Refer to Section 9.

24   Unleaded petrol – general information and usage

Refer to Section 11.

25   Fuel-injection system – general information

The Rover/Motorola Modular Engine Management System uses ECU-controlled single-point injection (MEMS-SPi) and the speed/density method of airflow measurement. The whole system is best explained if considered as three sub-systems; the fuel delivery, air metering and electrical control systems.

The fuel delivery system (see Fig. 4.12) incorporates the fuel tank, which has an electric fuel pump immersed in a swirl pot inside it to prevent aeration of the fuel. When the ignition is switched on the pump is supplied with current through one of the relays incorporated in the relay module, under the control of the ECU; the pump feeds petrol via a non-return valve (to prevent fuel draining out of the system components and back to the tank when the pump is not working) to the fuel filter and from the filter to the injector. Fuel pressure is controlled by the pressure regulator, which lifts to allow excess fuel to return to the tank swirl pot, where a venturi causes the returning fuel to draw cool fuel from the tank into the swirl pot. In the event of sudden deceleration (ie, an accident) the inertia switch cuts off the power to the pump so that the risk of fire is minimised from fuel spraying out of broken fuel lines under pressure.

The air metering system includes the intake air temperature control system (Secs 3 and 21; see also Fig. 4.13) and the air cleaner, but its main components are in the throttle body assembly. This incorporates the injector, which sprays fuel onto the back of the throttle disc, the throttle potentiometer, which is linked to the throttle disc spindle and sends the ECU information on the rate of throttle opening by transmitting a varying voltage, and the stepper motor, which is controlled by the ECU and operates the throttle disc spindle lever via a cam and pushrod to provide idle speed control. **Note:** *There is no provision for the adjustment or alteration of the idle speed except by reprogramming the ECU using Rover diagnostic equipment; if checking the idle speed, remember that it will vary constantly under ECU control.*

The electrical control system consists of the ECU, with all the sensors that provide it with information and the actuators by which it controls the whole system's operation. The ECU's manifold absolute pressure sensor is connected, by hoses and a fuel (vapour) trap mounted in the air cleaner assembly, to the inlet manifold (see Fig. 4.13); variations in manifold pressure are converted into graduated electrical signals which are used by the ECU to determine the load on the engine. The intake air temperature sensor is self-explanatory, the crankshaft sensor gives it the engine speed and crankshaft position, the coolant temperature sensor gives it the engine temperature, the throttle pedal switch tells it when the throttle is closed; the throttle potentiometer is explained above and the lambda sensor (where fitted) in Section 38. In addition, the ECU senses battery voltage (adjusting the injector pulse width to suit and using the stepper motor to increase the idle speed and, therefore, the alternator output if it is too low), incorporates short-circuit protection and diagnostic capabilities and can both receive and transmit information via the diagnostic connector, thus permitting engine diagnosis and tuning by Rover diagnostic equipment. If either the coolant temperature sensor, the intake air temperature sensor or the manifold absolute pressure sensor circuits should fail to provide adequate information, the ECU has a back-up facility which assumes a value corresponding to a coolant temperature of 60°C, an intake air temperature of 35°C and an engine load based on the engine speed and throttle position; these are used to implement a back-up air/fuel mixture ratio.

All these signals are compared by the ECU, using digital techniques, with set values pre-programmed (mapped) into its memory; based on this information, the ECU selects the response appropriate to those values and controls the ignition HT coil (varying the ignition timing as required), the fuel injector (varying its pulse width – the length of time the injector is held open – to provide a richer or weaker mixture, as appropriate), the stepper motor (controlling the idle and fast idle speeds), the fuel pump relay (controlling the fuel delivery), the manifold heater relay (controlling the inlet manifold pre-heater system) and the main relay, the purge control valve (where fitted) and the lambda sensor and relay (where fitted) accordingly. The mixture, idle speed and ignition timing are constantly varied by the ECU to provide the best settings for cranking, starting and engine warm-up (with either a hot or cold engine), idle, cruising and acceleration. A rev-limiter circuit is built into the ECU which switches off the injector earth (ie, the fuel supply) if engine speed exceeds 6860 rpm, switching it back on at 6820 rpm. The injector earth is also switched off on the overrun (coolant temperature above 80°C, throttle pedal switch contacts closed, engine speed above 1500 rpm) to improve fuel economy and reduce exhaust emissions.

The ECU idle control is an adaptive system; it learns the engine load and wear characteristics over a period of time and adjusts the idle speed to suit. If the ECU is renewed, or one from another car is fitted, it will take a short period of normal driving for the new ECU to learn the engine's characteristics and restore full idle control.

26 Fuel system – depressurisation

Note: *Refer to the warning note in Section 19 before proceeding*

Warning: *The following procedures will merely relieve the pressure in the fuel system – remember that fuel will still be present in the system components and take precautions accordingly before disconnecting any of them*

1   The fuel system referred to in this Section is defined as the tank-mounted fuel pump, the fuel filter, the fuel injector and the pressure regulator in the injector housing, and the metal pipes and flexible hoses of the fuel lines between these components. All these contain fuel which will be under pressure while the engine is running and/or while the ignition is switched on.
2   The pressure will remain for some time after the ignition has been switched off and must be relieved before any of these components is disturbed for servicing work.
3   The first method is simply to remove the fuel pump fuse (number 17) and to start the engine; allow the engine to idle until it dies. Turn the engine over once or twice on the starter to ensure that all pressure is released, then switch off the ignition; do not forget to refit the fuse when work is complete.
4   The second method is to place wads of rag around the area to catch the spilled fuel and to slacken the pressure release bolt fitted above the fuel filter, in the filter outlet pipe. Remove the black plastic cap and slacken the bolt with a spanner counter-holding the pipe boss (photo).
5   When all pressure is released, tighten the bolt to its specified torque wrench setting; again, use a spanner to counter-hold the pipe boss, to prevent damage to the pipe or filter.

27 Fuel system pressure check

Note: *Refer to the warning note in Section 19 before proceeding*

1   The following procedure is based on the use of the Rover pressure gauge and adaptor (Service Tool Numbers 18G 1500 and 18G 1500/3).
2   Depressurise the fuel system (Sec 26).
3   Unscrew the pressure release bolt and screw in the adaptor, then connect the pressure gauge.
4   Turn the engine over on the starter motor; the pressure should reach the specified value. Stop cranking the engine and watch the gauge; the pressure drop in the first minute should not exceed 0.7 bar.

26.4 Slackening pressure release bolt to depressurise fuel system

Fig. 4.15 Fuel pump mountings – fuel-injected engines (Sec 28)

1 *Fuel feed hose (yellow band)*	4 *Nut*
2 *Clip*	5 *Fuel pump*
3 *Fuel return hose (unmarked)*	6 *Pump seal*

5   If the pressure first recorded was too high, renew the pressure regulator; this means renewing the complete injector housing assembly (Sec 33).
6   If the pressure first recorded was too low or if it falls too quickly, check the system carefully for leaks. If no leaks are found check the pump by substituting a new one and recheck the pressure. If the pressure does not improve the fault is in the pressure regulator and the complete injector housing assembly must be renewed; if this is the case it is worth dismantling the regulator to check that the fault is not due to its being jammed open with dirt, or similar (Sec 33).

28 Fuel pump – removal and refitting

Note: *Refer to the warning note in Section 19 before proceeding*

Removal

1   Remove the fuel tank (Sec 30).
2   Release their clips and disconnect the fuel feed (yellow band) and return (unmarked) hoses from the pump unions.
3   Release the pump wiring from any clamps or ties securing it.

33.1A Remove screw to release injector connector ...

33.1B ... then withdraw injector

33.6 Disconnecting fuel feed and return pipes from injector housing

4   Unscrew the mounting nuts and withdraw the pump from the tank, then remove the pump seal.

Refitting

5   Refitting is the reverse of the removal procedure, noting the following points.

   (a) Renew the pump seal if there is any doubt about its condition.
   (b) Tighten the pump mounting nuts to the specified torque wrench setting.
   (c) Ensure that the hoses are connected to the correct unions (see Fig. 4.15) and that their clips are securely fastened.

29   Fuel gauge sender unit – removal and refitting

Refer to Section 5.

30   Fuel tank – removal and refitting

Proceed as described in Section 6, but depressurise the fuel system before disconnecting any of the fuel lines; note that the fuel feed hose is identified by a yellow band and that there is also an (unmarked) fuel return hose to be disconnected. Unclip the pump wiring connector from the tank bracket and unplug it to disconnect the pump wiring.

31   Fuel tank filler components – removal and refitting

Refer to Section 7.

32   Fuel-injection system components – testing

1   Apart from the basic electrical tests outlined in Chapter 12, the ignition system checks given in Chapter 5 and the tests for the coolant temperature sensor (Chapter 3), the throttle pedal switch (Sec 14) and the fuel cut-off inertia switch (Chapter 12), there is nothing that can be done by the owner to test individual fuel system components.
2   Remember that the ECU's back-up facility will keep the engine running, albeit at reduced efficiency, if certain sensor circuits should fail (see Sec 25). Unfortunately, the effect of this will be that while a system fault will be evident to the driver, it will be masked in such a way as to make fault diagnosis very difficult; the only solution is to have the complete system checked using Rover diagnostic equipment.

3   If a fault arises, check first that it is not due to poor maintenance; ie, check that the air cleaner filter element is clean, the spark plugs are in good condition and correctly gapped, that the engine breather hoses are clear and undamaged (Chapter 1) and that the throttle cable is correctly adjusted (Sec 22). If the engine is running very roughly, check the compression pressures (Chapter 2) and bear in mind the possibility that one of the hydraulic tappets might be faulty, producing an incorrect valve clearance.
4   If the fault is thought to be due to a dirty injector, it is worth trying one of the proprietary injector-cleaning treatments such as Holts Redex Injector Treatment before renewing, perhaps unnecessarily, the injector.
5   If the fault persists, check the ignition system components (as far as possible) as described in Chapter 5.
6   If the fault is still not eliminated, work methodically through the system, checking all fuses, fusible links, wiring connectors and wiring, looking for any signs of poor connections, damp, dirt or other faults.
7   Once the system components have been checked for signs of obvious faults such as dirty or poorly-fastened connections, damp, or 'tracking' and have been tested as far as is possible take the car to a suitably-equipped Rover dealer for the full engine management system to be tested on the correct equipment.
8   **Do not** attempt to 'test' any component, particularly the ECU, with anything other than the correct test equipment, which will be available only at a good Rover dealer. If any of the wires are to be checked which lead to a component such as the ECU, always first unplug the relevant connector from the system components so that there is no risk of their being damaged by the application of incorrect voltages from test equipment.

33   Fuel-injection system components – removal and refitting

Note: *Refer to the warning note in Section 19 before proceeding*

Fuel injector

1   As a Rover replacement part, the injector is available only as part of the injector housing; it is removed and refitted as described below. Note, however that it is a Bosch-manufactured component and can be obtained separately through Bosch agents; to remove it from the housing, proceed as described in paragraphs 2 to 4 and 7 below, then remove the retaining screw to release its connector. The injector can then be lifted out of the housing (photos). Refitting is the reverse of the removal procedure; ensure that the connector makes good contact with the injector pins.

Injector housing

Removal

2   Depressurise the fuel system (Sec 26).
3   Disconnect the battery negative lead.
4   Remove the air cleaner assembly (Sec 20).

33.7 Disconnecting injector wiring

33.8A Injector housing-to-throttle body screws 'A', injector connector screw 'B', pressure regulator screws 'C'

33.8B Note gasket when removing injector housing from throttle body

33.13 Disconnecting stepper motor wiring

33.14A Location of stepper motor screws

33.14B Removing stepper motor assembly

5   Place rag around the area to catch the spilled fuel and examine closely the fuel pipe feed and return unions at the injector housing, looking for signs of leakage, then wipe them clean.

6   Using a spanner to hold each adaptor, unscrew the pipe union nuts and release the fuel feed and return pipes from the adaptors (photo). Plug each pipe and adaptor to prevent the entry of dirt into the system and the loss of fuel.

7   Release its wire clip and disconnect the injector wiring connector plug (photo).

8   Remove the injector housing-to-throttle body screws and withdraw the housing, collecting the gasket (photos).

9   If leakage is detected from the feed and return pipes or their union nuts, check the sealing surfaces of the nuts and adaptors, renewing as necessary the adaptor or the pipe assembly. If leakage is detected from the adaptors, unscrew each through one turn with a spanner, then through two turns by hand; if either is tight, the housing must be renewed. If the threads are sound, fit new sealing washers to the adaptors and refit them, tightening them to their specified torque wrench setting.

Refitting

10   Refitting is the reverse of the removal procedure, noting the following points.

(a)   Clean the mating surfaces of the injector housing and the throttle body and renew the gasket if there is any doubt about its condition.

(b)   Apply thread-locking compound (Rover recommend Loctite Screwlock or Nutlock) to the threads of the injector housing screws and tighten them to their specified torque wrench setting.

(c)   Unplug the fuel pipes and adaptors, clean the unions and refit the pipes, tightening them finger-tight only at first, then tighten them to their specified torque wrench setting WITHOUT using a holding spanner on the adaptors. To tighten a nut to a torque value using an open-ended spanner, hook a spring balance to the spanner's outer end and apply the desired force by pulling

the spring balance. Since a torque setting of 17.5 lbf ft is a turning force of 17.5 lb applied at a distance of 1 ft from the nut's centre, it is easy to calculate that a force of 17.5 x 2 (ie 35 lb) must be applied if the spanner is only 6 inches long; if the spanner is longer, the applied force can be reduced proportionately.

Fuel pressure regulator

11   The pressure regulator is available only as part of the injector housing; it is removed and refitted as described above.

Stepper motor

Removal

12   Remove the injector housing; see above.

13   Release its clip and disconnect the stepper motor wiring connector plug (photo).

14   Remove the stepper motor screws and withdraw the stepper motor assembly (photos). Do not attempt to dismantle the assembly.

Refitting

15   Refitting is the reverse of the removal procedure; adjust the throttle cable (Section 22, paragraphs 6 to 8) to ensure that the stepper motor is correctly indexed.

Throttle potentiometer

Removal

16   Although not strictly necessary, access is greatly improved if the air cleaner assembly is first removed (Sec 20).

17   Disconnect the battery negative lead.

18   Release its wire clip and disconnect the potentiometer wiring connector plug (photo).

19   Remove the two screws and withdraw the potentiometer, noting how its tongue engages with the throttle disc spindle lever (photo). Withdraw the spacer if required.

33.18 Disconnecting throttle potentiometer wiring – note mounting screws (arrows)

33.19 Ensure potentiometer tongue engages correctly with throttle lever – note spacer (arrowed)

33.27 Disconnecting breather hoses from throttle body

33.28 Removing throttle body assembly from inlet manifold

33.29 Renew throttle body gasket spacer if worn or damaged

33.31 Disconnecting ECU wiring

Refitting

20   Refitting is the reverse of the removal procedure, noting the following points.

   (a)   *Carefully clean the mating surfaces of the throttle body, the spacer and the potentiometer, then refit the spacer.*

   (b)   *Refit the potentiometer so that its tongue engages FORWARD of (ie 'inside') the throttle disc spindle lever, then rotate the throttle cam to check the action of the lever and tongue.*

   (c)   *Tighten the potentiometer screws to their specified torque wrench setting and rotate the cam to recheck the potentiometer action before reconnecting the wiring.*

Throttle body

Removal

Note: *This refers to the throttle body assembly, complete with the injector housing and stepper motor; it is also possible to remove these separately, as described above, before removing the throttle body itself*

21   Depressurise the fuel system (Sec 26).
22   Disconnect the battery negative lead.
23   Remove the air cleaner assembly (Sec 20).
24   Disconnect the fuel feed and return pipes from the injector housing; see paragraphs 5, 6 and 9 above.
25   Releasing their clips, unplug the connectors to disconnect the injector, stepper motor and throttle potentiometer wiring.
26   Disconnect the throttle cable (Sec 22).
27   Release their clips and disconnect the breather hoses (photo).
28   Unscrew the retaining nuts and remove the complete throttle body assembly from the inlet manifold (photo).

Refitting

29   Refitting is the reverse of the removal procedure, noting the following points (photo).

   (a)   *Carefully clean the mating surfaces of the throttle body and the inlet manifold.*

   (b)   *Renew the gasket spacer if there is any doubt about its condition.*

   (c)   *Tighten the throttle body-to-inlet manifold nuts to their specified torque wrench setting.*

   (d)   *Adjust the throttle cable (Sec 22).*

   (e)   *Reconnect the fuel feed and return pipes as described in paragraph 10(c) above.*

Fuel-injection/ignition system ECU

Removal

30   Disconnect the battery negative lead.
31   Unplug the connectors from the ECU and from the relay module (photo).
32   Release the engine wiring harness connector plug from the ECU mounting bracket, then undo the three screws securing the bracket to the body. Withdraw the assembly until the manifold absolute pressure sensor vacuum hose can be disconnected from the ECU.
33   Undo the three screws securing the ECU to its mounting bracket, then withdraw it (photo).

Refitting

34   Refitting is the reverse of the removal procedure; if a new or different ECU has been fitted, it may take a short while for full idle control to be restored (Sec 25).

Manifold absolute pressure sensor

35   This is part of the ECU and is removed and refitted as described above.
36   The sensor's vacuum hose runs from the inlet manifold to the ECU via a fuel (vapour) trap mounted in the air cleaner assembly (photo).
37   To remove the fuel trap, remove the air cleaner assembly cover (Chapter 1), release their clips and disconnect the hoses, then remove the single retaining screw and withdraw the trap.
38   On refitting, note that the hoses are colour-coded (green to the ECU, white to the inlet manifold) to ensure correct reconnection.

33.33 ECU mounting bracket retaining screws (arrows)

33.36 Manifold absolute pressure sensor is mounted in air cleaner assembly

33.42 Remove air cleaner intake duct to reach intake air temperature sensor

Intake air temperature sensor

Removal

39   Disconnect the battery negative lead.
40   Remove the air cleaner assembly intake duct (Sec 21).
41   Release its wire clip and disconnect the sensor wiring.
42   Unscrew the sensor and remove it (photo).

Refitting

43   Refitting is the reverse of the removal procedure; tighten the sensor to its specified torque wrench setting.

Coolant temperature sensor

44   Refer to Chapter 3, Section 6 (photo).

Relay module

45   Refer to Chapter 12; note that the module contains the main relay, the starter relay, the fuel pump relay and the manifold pre-heater relay and cannot be dismantled. If any of these relays is faulty, the complete unit must be renewed.

Accelerator pedal switch

46   Refer to Chapter 12.

Fuel cut-off inertia switch

47   Refer to Chapter 12.

33.44 Location of coolant temperature sensor (arrowed)

34   Inlet manifold pre-heater – removal and refitting

The system is as described in Section 15, noting the following points (photo).

(a)   The manifold pre-heater relay is one of those in the relay module; it is energised under ECU control.
(b)   There is no separate pre-heater temperature switch – the ECU uses the coolant temperature sensor.
(c)   Inlet manifold removal and refitting is as described in Section 35.

35   Inlet manifold – removal and refitting

Removal

Note: *The following procedure describes the removal of the manifold with the throttle body assembly. Access to some of the components*

34.1 Inlet manifold partially removed to show manifold PTC heater and coolant temperature sensor (arrows)

35.5A Disconnect coolant hoses (arrows) from inlet manifold ...

35.5B ... hoses can be clamped to minimise coolant loss

35.12 Ensure vacuum pipes and hoses are disconnected

35.14 Removing inlet manifold – note gasket

35.16 Always renew gasket when refitting manifold

concerned is, however, much better if the throttle body is first removed separately (Sec 33); if this is done, the following procedure should be amended as required

Note: *Refer to the warning note in Section 1 before proceeding*

1 Depressurise the fuel system (Sec 26).
2 Disconnect the battery negative lead.
3 Remove the air cleaner assembly (Sec 20).
4 Either drain the cooling system completely (Chapter 1), or clamp the coolant hoses connected to the inlet manifold to minimise coolant loss and be prepared to catch the coolant that will be released from the manifold and cylinder head.
5 Disconnect all coolant hoses from the manifold, as described in Chapter 3 (photos).
6 Release their clips and disconnect the breather hoses from the cylinder head cover.
7 Disconnect the brake vacuum servo unit vacuum hose from the manifold (Chapter 9); discard the sealing washers.
8 Releasing their clips, unplug the connectors to disconnect the injector, stepper motor and throttle potentiometer wiring.
9 Disconnect the coolant temperature sensor and manifold pre-heater wiring.
10 Disconnect the throttle cable (Sec 22).
11 Working as described in paragraphs 5, 6 and 9 of Section 33, disconnect the fuel feed and return pipes from the injector housing.
12 Disconnect the vacuum pipes and hoses as necessary; secure

them so that they cannot be damaged during removal and refitting (photo).
13 The manifold support stays are bolted to the manifold at their upper ends and to the cylinder block/crankcase at their lower ends; slacken the bolts at one end and unbolt the other, as convenient.
14 Unscrew the nuts and bolts securing the manifold to the cylinder head and withdraw it; remove and discard the gasket (photo).
15 Clean the manifold and cylinder head mating surfaces and check that they are flat and unmarked.

Refitting

16 Refitting is the reverse of the removal procedure, noting the following points (photo).

(a) Always fit a new manifold gasket.
(b) Working in the sequence shown in Fig. 4.8 or 4.16, as appropriate, tighten the manifold retaining nuts and bolts evenly, to the specified torque wrench setting.
(c) Adjust the throttle cable (Sec 22).

Fig. 4.16 Inlet manifold fastener tightening sequence – K16 engines (Sec 35)

Fig. 4.17 Exhaust manifold nut tightening sequence – K16 engines (Sec 36)

(d) Reconnect the fuel feed and return pipes as described in paragraph 10(c) of Section 33.

(e) Refill the cooling system or check the coolant level as required, then wash off any spilt coolant (Chapter 1).

(f) Renew the vacuum servo unit vacuum hose banjo union sealing washers.

(g) Tighten all disturbed fasteners to their specified torque wrench settings (where given).

36 Exhaust manifold – removal and refitting

Proceed as described in Section 17, but on refitting, tighten the manifold nuts in the sequence shown in photo 17.8B (K8 engines) or Fig. 4.17 (K16 engines), as appropriate.

37 Exhaust system – general information and component renewal

Proceed as described in Section 18; note that on models with closed-loop catalytic converters the lambda sensor must be removed (Sec 39) or its wiring must be disconnected whenever the exhaust system front pipe is disconnected from the manifold or removed.

Part C: Emission control systems

38 General information

Apart from their ability to use unleaded petrol and the various features which help to minimise emissions and are built into the fuel system, Metro models have at least the crankcase emission-control system described below and may be fitted with one or both of the other two systems:

Crankcase emission control

To reduce the emission of unburned hydrocarbons from the crankcase into the atmosphere, the engine is sealed and the blow-by gases and oil vapour are drawn from the crankcase, through a wire mesh oil separator in the cylinder head cover, into the inlet tract to be burned by the engine during normal combustion. On carburettor engines a single breather hose connects the cylinder head cover to the carburettor continuous-depression area. On fuel-injected engines a small-bore breather hose connects the cylinder head cover to the throttle body downstream of the throttle disc, while a larger-bore hose is connected above the throttle disc so that the same effect is obtained at all states of manifold depression.

Under conditions of high manifold depression (idling, deceleration) the gases will be sucked positively out of the crankcase. Under conditions of low manifold depression (acceleration, full-throttle running) the gases are forced out of the crankcase by the (relatively) higher crankcase pressure; if the engine is worn, the raised crankcase pressure (due to increased blow-by) will cause some of the flow to return under all manifold conditions.

Evaporative emission control

To minimise the escape into the atmosphere of unburned hydrocarbons, an evaporative emissions control system is fitted to some models. The fuel tank filler cap is sealed and a charcoal canister is mounted in the engine compartment to collect the petrol vapours generated in the tank when the car is parked. It stores them until they can be cleared from the canister (under the control of the fuel-injection/ignition system ECU via the purge control valve) into the inlet tract to be burned by the engine during normal combustion.

To ensure that the engine runs correctly when it is cold and/or idling and to protect the catalytic converter from the effects of an over-rich mixture, the purge control valve is not opened by the ECU until the engine has warmed up to above 70°C, the engine speed exceeds 1500 rpm and manifold absolute pressure is below 30 kPa; the valve solenoid is then modulated on and off to allow the stored vapour to pass into the inlet.

Exhaust emission control

To minimise the amount of pollutants which escape into the atmosphere, some models are fitted with a catalytic converter in the exhaust system (Sec 40). Either an open-loop control system, which has no feedback from the converter to the fuel system, or a closed-loop control system, in which the lambda sensor in the exhaust system provides the fuel-injection/ignition system ECU with constant feedback (which enables it to adjust the mixture to provide the best possible conditions for the converter to operate) may be fitted.

If a lambda sensor is fitted, it has a heating element built-in that is controlled by the ECU through the lambda sensor relay to quickly bring the sensor's tip to an efficient operating temperature. The sensor's tip is sensitive to oxygen and sends the ECU a varying voltage depending on the amount of oxygen in the exhaust gases; if the intake air/fuel mixture is too rich, the exhaust gases are low in oxygen so the sensor sends a low-voltage signal, the voltage rising as the mixture weakens and the amount of oxygen rises in the exhaust gases. Peak conversion efficiency of all major pollutants occurs if the intake air/fuel mixture is maintained at the chemically-correct ratio for the complete combustion of petrol of 14.7 parts (by weight) of air to 1 part of fuel (the 'stoichiometric' ratio). The sensor output voltage alters in a large step at this point, the ECU using the signal change as a reference point and correcting the intake air/fuel mixture accordingly by altering the fuel injector pulse width.

Fig. 4.18 Charcoal canister and purge control valve assembly mountings (Sec 39)

1 Hose – to inlet	4 Mounting bracket
2 Hose – to fuel filler breather pipe	5 Clamp screw
3 Purge control valve wiring connector	6 Mounting clamp

39 Emission control system components – testing and renewal

Crankcase emission control

1   Apart from the checks described in Chapter 1, the components of this system require no attention other than to check that the hose(s) are clear and that the wire mesh oil separators are flushed clean with a suitable solvent whenever the cylinder head cover is removed, as described in Chapter 2 (photo).

39.1 Always clean oil separators whenever cylinder head cover is removed

Evaporative emission control

Testing

2   If the system is thought to be faulty, disconnect the hoses from the charcoal canister/purge control valve assembly and check that they are clear by blowing through them. If the purge control valve or charcoal canister are thought to be faulty, the assembly must be renewed.

Renewal

3   Disconnect the battery negative lead.
4   Release their clips and disconnect the hoses from the valve and canister.
5   Unplug the connector to disconnect the purge control valve wiring.
6   Remove the assembly from its mounting bracket; do not attempt to dismantle it.
7   Refitting is the reverse of the removal procedure; the hose from the (underbody) fuel filler breather pipe is connected to the charcoal canister, while the hose from the inlet is connected to the purge control valve.

Exhaust emission control

Note: *If the CO level reading is too high (or if any other symptom is encountered which causes you to suspect a fault in the exhaust emission control system) always check first that the air cleaner filter element is clean, the spark plugs are in good condition and correctly gapped, that the engine breather and vacuum hoses are clear and undamaged (Chapter 1) and that the throttle cable is correctly adjusted (Sec 8 for carburettor-engines, Sec 22 for fuel-injected engines). If the engine is running very roughly, check the compression pressures (Chapter 2) and bear in mind the possibility that one of the hydraulic tappets might be faulty, producing an incorrect valve clearance. Check also that all wiring is in good condition, with securely-fastened connectors, that the fuel filter (fuel-injected engines only) has been renewed at the recommended intervals and that the exhaust system is entirely free of air leaks which might upset the operation of the catalytic converter. Only when all these have been checked and found to be in serviceable condition should the converter be suspected*

Testing – open-loop system

8   The performance of the catalytic converter can be checked only using a good-quality, carefully-calibrated exhaust gas analyser (Chapter 1).
9   Check that the CO level is as specified at the gas-sampling pipe when the engine is fully warmed up to normal operating temperature; if not, check the fuel and ignition systems (Chapter 1) until the fault is found and the level is restored to its correct value.
10   Once the CO level is known to be correct upstream of the catalytic converter, take the car on a brisk 4-mile road test and check the CO level

at the tailpipe **immediately** on return; it should be significantly lower than the level at the gas-sampling pipe (below 0.5 % approximately on fuel-injected engines, slightly higher on carburettor engines).
11   If the tailpipe CO level is little different from that at the gas-sampling pipe, repeat the check ensuring that it is made **immediately** on return from road test or the converter may not be at normal operating temperature and will not have reached its peak conversion efficiency. If the results are the same, the catalytic converter is proven faulty and must be renewed (Sec 18).

Testing – closed-loop system

12   The performance of the catalytic converter can be checked only using a good-quality, carefully-calibrated exhaust gas analyser (Chapter 1).
13   Where a gas-sampling pipe is fitted, the test described above can be carried out; if the CO level at the tailpipe is little different from that at the gas-sampling pipe, the catalytic converter is probably faulty and must be renewed (Sec 18), once the fuel-injection and ignition systems have been checked thoroughly using Rover diagnostic equipment and are known to be free from faults.
14   If a gas-sampling pipe is not fitted and the CO level at the tailpipe is too high, the complete fuel-injection and ignition systems must be checked thoroughly using Rover diagnostic equipment. Once these have been checked and are known to be free from faults, the fault must be in the catalytic converter, which must be renewed (Sec 18).

Catalytic converter – renewal

15   Refer to Section 18.

Lambda sensor – operational check

16   The manufacturer's maintenance schedule calls for regular checks of the lambda sensor's operation. This can be done only by attaching Rover diagnostic equipment to the sensor wiring and checking that the voltage varies from low to high values when the engine is running; **do not** attempt to 'test' any part of the system with anything other than the correct test equipment.

Lambda sensor – renewal

Note: *The lambda sensor is delicate and will not work if it is dropped or knocked, if its power supply is disrupted, or if any cleaning materials are used on it*

17   Release the sensor's wiring connector from its bracket on the transmission and unplug it to disconnect the sensor.
18   Raising and supporting the front of the car, if required, to remove the sensor from underneath, unscrew the sensor from the exhaust system front pipe; collect the sealing washer.
19   On refitting, clean the sealing washer and renew it if it is damaged or worn, then refit the sensor, tightening it to its specified torque wrench setting. Reconnect the wiring and refit the connector plug.

Lambda sensor relay – general

20   Refer to Chapter 12.

40   Catalytic converters – general information and precautions

The catalytic converter is a reliable and simple device which needs no maintenance in itself, but there are some facts of which an owner should be aware if the converter is to function properly for its full service life.

(a)   *DO NOT use leaded petrol in a car equipped with a catalytic converter – the lead will coat the precious metals, reducing their converting efficiency and will eventually destroy the converter.*

(b)   *Always keep the ignition and fuel systems well-maintained in accordance with the manufacturer's schedule (Chapter 1) – particularly, ensure that the air cleaner filter element, the fuel filter (where fitted) and the spark plugs are renewed at the correct interval – if the intake air/fuel mixture is allowed to become too rich due to neglect, the unburned surplus will enter and burn in the catalytic converter, overheating the element and eventually destroying the converter.*

(c)   If the engine develops a misfire, do not drive the car at all (or at least as little as possible) until the fault is cured – the misfire will allow unburned fuel to enter the converter, which will result in its overheating, as noted above.

(d)   DO NOT push- or tow-start the car – this will soak the catalytic converter in unburned fuel, causing it to overheat when the engine does start – see (b) above.

(e)   DO NOT switch off the ignition at high engine speeds – if the ignition is switched off at anything above idle speed, unburned fuel will enter the (very hot) catalytic converter, with the possible risk of its igniting on the element and damaging the converter.

(f)   DO NOT use fuel or engine oil additives – these may contain substances harmful to the catalytic converter.

(g)   DO NOT continue to use the car if the engine burns oil to the extent of leaving a visible trail of blue smoke – the unburned carbon deposits will clog the converter passages and reduce its efficiency; in severe cases the element will overheat.

(h)   Remember that the catalytic converter operates at very high temperatures – hence the heat shields on the car's underbody – and the casing will become hot enough to ignite combustible materials which brush against it. DO NOT, therefore, park the car in dry undergrowth, over long grass or piles of dead leaves.

(i)   Remember that the catalytic converter is FRAGILE – do not strike it with tools during servicing work, take great care when working on the exhaust system (Sec 18), ensure that the converter is well clear of any jacks or other lifting gear used to raise the car and do not drive the car over rough ground, road humps etc in such a way as to 'ground' the exhaust system.

(j)   In some cases, particularly when the car is new and/or is used for stop/start driving, a sulphurous smell (like that of rotten eggs) may be noticed from the exhaust. This is common to many catalytic converter-equipped cars and seems to be due to the small amount of sulphur found in some petrols reacting with hydrogen in the exhaust to produce hydrogen sulphide (H_2S) gas; while this gas is toxic, it is not produced in sufficient amounts to be a problem. Once the car has covered a few thousand miles the problem should disappear – in the meanwhile a change of driving style or of the brand of petrol used may effect a solution.

(k)   The catalytic converter, used on a well-maintained and well-driven car, should last for between 50 000 and 100 000 miles – from this point on, careful checks should be made at all specified service intervals of the CO level to ensure that the converter is still operating efficiently – if the converter is no longer effective it must be renewed.

Chapter 5 Ignition system

Contents

Specifications

Carburettor engines

General
System type .... Lucas constant energy inductive
Firing order.. 1–3–4–2 (No 1 cylinder at timing belt end)
Direction of crankshaft rotation... Clockwise (viewed from right-hand side of car)

Distributor
Type.. Lucas 67 DM4, incorporating centrifugal and vacuum advance
mechanisms and externally-mounted amplifier module

Identification:
    1.1 models .... NJC 10024
    1.4 models .... NJC 10026
Direction of rotor arm rotation .... Anti-clockwise (viewed from left-hand side of car)
Rotor arm .... GRA 2143
Amplifier module.. CDU 4175/NJQ 10001
Pick-up coil resistance.. 950 to 1150 ohms
Vacuum capsule identification:
    1.1 models 80–270–7
    1.4 models 80–200–8
Vacuum advance commences.. 107 mbar (80 mm Hg)
Maximum vacuum advance:
    1.1 models .... 14° @ 360 mbar (270 mm Hg)
    1.4 models .... 16° @ 267 mbar (200 mm Hg)
Deceleration check – vacuum disconnected:
    1.1 models .... 6° to 10° @ 2000 rpm
    1.4 models .... 4° to 8° @ 2500 rpm
Note: *Degree and speed values to be measured at crankshaft*

Ignition HT coil
Type.. AUU 1326 or ADU 8779
Manufacturer.. Bosch, Ducellier or Rudi Cajavec
Current consumption – average... 0.25 to 0.75 amps @ idle speed
Winding resistances:
    Primary .... 0.71 to 0.81 ohms @ 20°C
    Secondary... 5 to 15 K ohms @ 20°C

Ignition timing – @ 1500 rpm (vacuum pipe disconnected)
1.1 models:
    Carburettor numbers MAC 10003 and MAC 10010 .... 8° ± 1° BTDC
    Carburettor number MAC 10043.. 10° ± 1° BTDC
1.4 models.. 9° ± 1° BTDC

Torque wrench settings

	Nm	lbf ft
Spark plugs	25	19
Distributor cap screws	2	2
Amplifier module-to-distributor body (hex-head) screws	5	4
Distributor mounting bolts	25	19
Reluctor ring-to-flywheel setscrews	3	2
Ignition HT coil mounting screws	7	5

Fuel-injected engines

General

System type .... Rover/Motorola Modular Engine Management System (MEMS), fully electronic, controlled by ECU

Firing order .... 1–3–4–2 (No 1 cylinder at timing belt end)

Direction of crankshaft rotation .... Clockwise (viewed from right-hand side of car)

Distributor

Type .... Spark distribution only (ignition timing entirely controlled by ECU)

Direction of rotor arm rotation .... Anti-clockwise (viewed from left-hand side of car)

Distributor cap:

    Early 1.4 K16-engined models .... AUU 1186

    All other models .... NJD 10005

Rotor arm .... AUU 1641 (resistive type)

Electronic Control Unit (ECU)

1.1 K8-engined models MN3 10015

1.4 K8-engined models .... MNE 10016

1.4 K16-engined models – without catalytic converter:

    Up to VIN 662512 .... AUU 1518 or MNE 10039

    VIN 662513 on .... MNE 10050

1.4 K16-engined models – with open-loop catalytic converter .... MNE 10009 or MNE 10041

1.4 K16-engined models – with closed-loop catalytic converter .... MNE 10022 or MNE 10062

Ignition timing – @ idle speed (ECU-controlled)

1.1 K8-engined models .... 15° BTDC

1.4 K8-engined models .... 10° BTDC

1.4 K16-engined models – by ECU number:

    AUU 1518, MNE 10039 .... 13° ± 2° BTDC

    MNE 10009, MNE 10041, MNE 10050 .... 14° ± 2° BTDC

    MNE 10062 .... 14° ± 5° BTDC

    MNE 10022 .... Not available

Note: *Nominal value given for checking purposes only – not adjustable and may vary under ECU control*

Crankshaft sensor

Type .... ADU 7340

Ignition HT coil

Type:

    Early 1.4 K16-engined models .... NEC 10002 or NEC 10003

    All other models .... AUU 1326 or ADU 8779

Manufacturer .... Bosch, Ducellier or Rudi Cajavec

Current consumption – average .... 0.25 to 0.75 amps @ idle speed

Winding resistances:

    Primary .... 0.71 to 0.81 ohms @ 20°C

    Secondary .... 5 to 15 K ohms @ 20°C

Torque wrench settings

	Nm	lbf ft
Spark plugs	25	19
Distributor cap screws	2	2
Distributor rotor arm (hex-head) screw	10	8
Reluctor ring-to-flywheel setscrews	3	2
Ignition HT coil mounting screws	7	5
Crankshaft sensor mounting screws	6	4.5
Crankshaft sensor lead-to-flywheel cover plate screw	6	4.5

Fig. 5.1 Exploded view of the Lucas 67 DM4 distributor – carburettor engines (Sec 1)

1	Distributor cap
2	Rotor arm
3	Upper housing
4	Vacuum capsule
5	Stator pack, including thrust washer(s) and circlip
6	Pick-up coil
7	Clamp ring
8	Distributor shaft, including reluctor and advance assembly
9	Thrust washer
10	Lower housing
11	Sealing O-ring
12	Drive coupling, including thrust washer, spring and roll pin
13	Connector and gasket
14	Amplifier module

1 General information and precautions

Carburettor engines

The ignition system is fully-electronic in operation and of the inductive type, incorporating a contact-less distributor (driven off the camshaft left-hand end) and an amplifier module as well as the spark plugs, HT leads, ignition HT coil and associated wiring. The system is divided into two circuits; primary (low tension/LT) and secondary (high tension/HT). The primary circuit consists of the battery, ignition switch, ignition HT coil primary windings, amplifier module and distributor pick-up coil and wiring. The secondary circuit consists of the ignition HT coil secondary windings, the distributor cap and rotor arm, the spark plugs and the HT leads connecting these.

The distributor incorporates features which advance the ignition timing both mechanically and by vacuum operation. Its shaft, driven by the camshaft, incorporates a reluctor which has four shaped poles and is mounted on the centre of a centrifugal advance assembly whose two weights move outwards under centrifugal force as engine speed rises, thus rotating the reluctor on the shaft and advancing or retarding the spark; the amount of movement being controlled by light springs. A pick-up coil generates a weak magnetic field whenever the ignition is switched on; as the engine rotates the reluctor poles pass the coil, disturbing the field each time and sending a signal current to the amplifier module. Whenever this signal exceeds a threshold level determined by engine speed a high-voltage transistor in the amplifier is switched on, thus allowing HT coil current to flow; when this current has reached the required level it is held constant until the transistor is switched off, thus triggering the spark. The pick-up coil is clamped to a stator pack that is able to rotate under the control of the vacuum capsule mounted on the side of the distributor. The capsule consists of a diaphragm, one side of which is connected via a small-bore pipe to the carburettor and the other side to the stator pack; inlet manifold depression, which varies with engine speed and throttle position, causes the diaphragm to move thus rotating the stator pack and advancing or retarding the spark.

Models fitted with catalytic converters have a thermo-statically-operated vacuum switch screwed into the cooling system thermostat housing; the small-bore vacuum pipe being in two lengths that are connected from the carburettor to the switch and from the switch to the distributor. At coolant temperatures below 70°C the switch prevents any vacuum advance from taking place, causing raised exhaust gas temperatures due to the retarded ignition timing, thus bringing the catalytic converter more quickly to its efficient operating temperature. Once coolant temperatures rise above this point, the switch opens and normal vacuum advance is restored.

Fuel-injected engines

The ignition system is fully electronic in operation, incorporating the Electronic Control Unit (ECU) mounted on the engine compartment bulkhead, a distributor (driven off the inlet camshaft left-hand end) and a crankshaft sensor mounted in the left-hand rear end of the engine's cylinder block/crankcase to register with the reluctor ring fixed to the flywheel, as well as the spark plugs, HT leads, ignition HT coil and associated wiring. The system is divided into two circuits; primary (low tension/LT) and secondary (high tension/HT). The primary circuit consists of the battery, ignition switch, ignition HT coil primary windings, ECU and wiring. The secondary circuit consists of the ignition HT coil secondary windings, the distributor cap and rotor arm, the spark plugs and the HT leads connecting these.

The ECU controls both the ignition system and the fuel injection system, integrating the two in a complete engine management system; refer to Part B of Chapter 4 for information on any part of the system not given here.

As far as the ignition system is concerned, the ECU receives information in the form of electrical impulses or signals from the crankshaft sensor (which gives it the engine speed and crankshaft position), from the coolant temperature sensor (which gives it the engine temperature), from the throttle pedal switch (which tells it when the throttle is closed) and from the manifold absolute pressure sensor (which gives it the load on the engine). All these signals are compared by the ECU, using digital techniques, with set values pre-programmed (mapped) into its memory; based on this information, the ECU selects the ignition timing appropriate to those values and controls the ignition HT coil accordingly.

**2.2 Disconnecting the distributor wiring –
note amplifier module screws (arrows)**

**2.3 Disconnecting vacuum pipe from
distributor vacuum capsule**

**2.6 Marking relationship of distributor body
to cylinder head**

**2.7 Unscrewing distributor mounting bolts
– remaining bolt arrowed**

**2.8 Removing distributor – always renew
sealing O-ring (arrow)**

Note that this means that the distributor is just that, a distributor of the HT pulse to the appropriate spark plug; it has no effect whatsoever on the ignition timing. Also, the system is so sensitive that, at idle speed, the ignition timing may be constantly changing; this should be remembered if trying to check the ignition timing (see Chapter 1, ignition timing check and adjustment).

All models

Refer to Chapter 12 for details of the ignition switch.

Warning: *The voltages produced by the electronic ignition system are considerably higher than those produced by conventional systems. Extreme care must be taken when working on the system with the ignition switched on. Persons with surgically-implanted cardiac pacemaker devices should keep well clear of the ignition circuits, components and test equipment.*

2   Distributor – removal, overhaul and refitting

Removal

Carburettor engines

1   Disconnect the battery negative terminal.
2   Releasing its wire clip, unplug the wiring connector from the distributor (photo).
3   Disconnect and plug the vacuum pipe (photo).
4   Position the engine so that number 1 cylinder is at TDC on the compression stroke (Chapter 2, Section 3).
5   Remove the distributor cap (and rotor arm, if required) as described in Chapter 1.
6   Mark the relationship of the distributor body to the cylinder head, using a scriber or similar (photo).
7   Unscrew the distributor mounting bolts and withdraw the

distributor (photo). Do not disturb the crankshaft setting while the distributor is removed, or rotate the distributor shaft (unless the unit is to be overhauled).
8   Remove the distributor body sealing O-ring; this must be renewed whenever it is disturbed (photo).

Fuel-injected engines

9   Remove the distributor cap and rotor arm as described in Chapter 1.

Overhaul

Carburettor engines

10   Remove the distributor; withdraw the cap and rotor arm, if not already removed.
11   Remove the amplifier module (Sec 3), then remove its gasket and withdraw the connector.
12   Remove the screws and separate the upper housing from the lower.
13   Remove the clamp ring and pick-up coil from the upper housing.
14   Remove the circlip (and first thrust washer, if fitted) from the underside of the upper housing, disengage the stator pack from the vacuum capsule arm and withdraw the stator pack, followed by the (second) thrust washer.
15   Remove its retaining screw and withdraw the vacuum capsule. Note the numbers stamped on the capsule's mounting bracket; the eight-digit number is the Lucas part number, but the three remaining numbers indicate the capsule's design characteristics – the first and second numbers show (in mm Hg) the pressure at which vacuum advance begins and reaches its maximum, while the third shows the capsule's total advance in (distributor) degrees. Check that the capsule is the correct one for the car (see Specifications).
16   Check the distributor shaft endfloat; if it seems excessive, seek expert advice.
17   Remove the spring from the distributor drive coupling, then use a scriber or similar to mark the relationship of the coupling to the shaft; it is essential that the coupling is refitted correctly in relationship to the rotor arm on refitting. Release the distributor shaft by driving out the retaining

roll pin and removing the coupling; note the thrust washer behind it.

18　Withdraw the shaft, noting the thrust washer underneath the centrifugal advance assembly. Be very careful not to bend any of the reluctor poles and do not attempt to remove it from the shaft.

19　The advance assembly and shaft can be lubricated, but if any part of the assembly is found to be worn or damaged the complete distributor must be renewed; individual replacement parts are not available.

20　Clean and examine all components; if any are found to be worn or damaged, seek expert advice. A repair kit of sundry parts is available separately, also the coupling assembly, the pick-up coil and vacuum capsule, as well as the rotor arm and the distributor cap; if any other parts are worn or damaged, the complete distributor must be renewed.

21　In addition to the checks described in Chapter 1, use an ohmmeter or continuity tester to check that there is no continuity between any of the cap's terminal segments. Similarly, check that there is no continuity between the rotor arm body and its brass segment; note that the arm has a built-in resistance.

22　Re-assembly is the reverse of the dismantling procedure, noting the following points.

(a)　Apply a few drops of suitable oil to the advance assembly pivots and springs and to the shaft, upper housing and stator pack bearing surfaces.

(b)　Using the marks made on dismantling, be very careful to ensure that the coupling is located correctly on the shaft end (in relationship to the rotor arm) before driving in the roll pin to secure it, then ensure that the spring is fitted over the roll pin ends.

(c)　Grease the vacuum capsule arm before refitting it, use grease to stick the thrust washer to the underside of the upper housing, then refit and connect the stator pack and vacuum capsule, followed by the remaining thrust washer, if fitted, and circlip; tighten the capsule retaining screw securely.

(d)　Refit the pick-up coil to the upper housing and centre its terminals in the aperture before fitting the clamp ring so that its cut-out is over the aperture.

(e)　Refit the upper housing to the lower, tighten the screws lightly and check that the shaft is free to rotate – there must be no sign of the reluctor poles touching the stator pack arms, as either can easily be bent – before tightening the screws securely.

(f)　Refit the connector and its gasket.

(g)　Refit the amplifier module (Sec 3) and the rotor arm.

(h)　Fit a new sealing O-ring to the distributor body.

Fuel-injected engines

23　Check, and if necessary renew, the distributor cap and rotor arm (Chapter 1); in addition to those checks, note also the electrical tests given in paragraph 21 above.

Refitting

Carburettor engines – normal procedure

24　First check that number 1 cylinder is at TDC (Chapter 2, Section 3), then rotate the rotor arm to align with the distributor cap's number 1 terminal. Fit a new sealing O-ring to the distributor body and lubricate it with a smear of engine oil.

25　Aligning the marks made on removal, refit the distributor. If necessary, rotate the rotor arm very slightly to help the distributor drive dogs locate in the camshaft slots; they are offset and so will fit only one way. Refit the mounting bolts, tightening them to the specified torque wrench setting.

26　Refit the distributor cap, ensuring it is correctly located, then reconnect the HT leads (Chapter 1).

27　Reconnect the vacuum pipe and distributor wiring.

28　Check, and adjust if necessary, the ignition timing (Chapter 1).

Carburettor engines – full procedure

29　If a new distributor is to be fitted (or no marks were made on removal) , the following procedure will produce a basic setting which will enable the engine to start and run while the ignition timing is accurately set.

30　Remove the cylinder head cover and position the engine so that number 1 cylinder is at TDC on the compression stroke (Chapter 2, Section 3), then rotate the crankshaft slightly anti-clockwise until the flywheel mark aligns with the appropriate scale mark (see

Specifications), so that the engine is in the firing position.

31　Rotate the distributor rotor arm to align with the distributor cap's number 1 terminal.

32　Refit the distributor (see paragraph 24 above), positioning its body so that the mounting bolts are in the middle of their respective slots. Refit the cylinder head cover and connect the HT leads to the cap and spark plugs, ensuring that the leads are correctly routed and secured in their guides and that the firing order is followed.

33　Check, and adjust if necessary, the ignition timing (Chapter 1).

Fuel-injected engines

34　Refer to paragraphs 24 to 26 inclusive.

3　Ignition amplifier module – removal and refitting

Warning: *Do not attempt to open or repair the module; if it is faulty, it must be renewed*

Removal

1　Disconnect the battery negative terminal.

2　Releasing its wire clip, unplug the wiring connector from the distributor.

3　Remove the two screws and withdraw the module, taking care not to damage the terminal pins.

4　Check carefully that the mating surfaces of the module and distributor are completely clean and unmarked and that the pick-up coil terminal pins are clean and a secure fit in the module; if in doubt, it is permissible to remove the connector and its gasket and to **gently** squeeze together the female terminals to improve the fit. The pick-up coil-to-connector and connector-to-module connections must be checked with particular care if the module is thought to be faulty; similarly, check, clean and tighten (if necessary) the distributor wiring connector-to-module terminals. It is **essential** that there is good electrical contact between the module and the distributor and at all four LT wiring connections mentioned above.

Refitting

5　On refitting, apply a smear of heat-conducting silicone grease to the mating surfaces of the module and the distributor; the correct grease can be obtained from Rover dealers under Part Number BAU 5812, but if this is not available either a heat-sink compound, or an anti-seize compound (such as Holt's Copaslip), will serve as an adequate substitute.

6　Check that the terminal pins are not bent or damaged and that they engage correctly with the module's connections.

7　Tighten the module screws to the specified torque wrench setting, then reconnect the distributor wiring and battery.

4　Ignition HT coil – removal, testing and refitting

Removal

1　The coil is mounted on the left-hand side of the engine compartment, between the battery and the left-hand headlamp unit.

2　Disconnect the battery negative terminal.

3　Remove the two retaining screws securing the cold air intake duct to the body front panel and move the hose clear of the HT coil.

4　Peel back the rubber cover, then disconnect the HT lead. Note which terminals they are connected to and disconnect the two pairs of LT wires from the coil.

5　Slacken the two coil mounting screws, noting the location of the suppressor, and withdraw the coil; slacken its clamp screw, if required, to release it from its bracket.

Testing

6　Testing of the coil consists of using a multimeter set to its resistance

5.2 Removing crankshaft sensor – wiring lead screw arrowed

5.5 Reluctor ring-to-flywheel setscrews (arrows)

function, or a low-wattage test lamp, to check the primary (LT '+' to '–' terminals) and secondary (LT '+' to HT lead terminals) windings for continuity. If the meter is used the resistance of either winding can be checked and compared with the specified value. Note that since the readings obtained will vary slightly with temperature, the coil should be tested (where possible) after the engine has been running for at least 15 minutes so that the coil is at its normal operating temperature.

7   Using an ohmmeter or continuity tester, check that there is no continuity between the HT lead terminal and the coil body.

8   If the coil is faulty it must be renewed.

Refitting

9   Refitting is the reverse of the removal procedure.

5   Crankshaft sensor and reluctor ring – general

Removal

Crankshaft sensor

1   Disconnect the battery negative lead (Chapter 12).

2   Disconnect the sensor wiring at its connector plug on the flywheel rear cover plate, then undo the retaining screw to release the wiring lead (photo).

3   Remove the two retaining screws and withdraw the sensor from the cylinder block/crankcase.

Reluctor ring

Note: *While a reluctor ring is fitted to the flywheel of carburettor engines, it has no function on these models but should be checked whenever the flywheel is removed to ensure that its mountings are securely fastened*

4   Remove the transmission (Chapter 7), the clutch (Chapter 6) and the flywheel (Chapter 2).

5   Remove the setscrews securing the reluctor ring to the flywheel and withdraw it (photo).

Checking

Crankshaft sensor

6   Check the sensor for obvious signs of wear or damage and renew it if any are found. As no data is available to enable the sensor to be tested, if it is thought to be faulty it can be checked only by the substitution of a new component.

Reluctor ring

7   Check the ring for any signs of wear or damage and renew it if any are found.

Refitting

Crankshaft sensor

8   Refitting is the reverse of the removal procedure; tighten the screws to their specified torque wrench setting.

Reluctor ring

9   Refitting is the reverse of the removal procedure; tighten the screws to their specified torque wrench setting.

6   Thermostatically-operated vacuum switch – removal and refitting

Removal

1   Either drain the cooling system (Chapter 1), or be prepared for some loss of coolant as the switch is unscrewed.

2   As noted in Chapter 3, access to the thermostat housing is possible with the inlet manifold and carburettor in place, but is made much easier if these are first removed (Chapter 4).

3   Disconnect and plug the vacuum pipes.

4   Unscrew the switch and withdraw it, then plug the opening to prevent the entry of dirt; if the cooling system has not been drained, work quickly to minimise coolant loss.

Refitting

5   Refitting is the reverse of the removal procedure, noting the following points.

(a)   Wipe clean the threads of the switch and of the thermostat housing.
(b)   If a sealing washer is fitted, renew it whenever it is disturbed to prevent leaks; if no sealing washer is fitted, apply a smear of sealant to the switch threads.
(c)   Tighten the switch securely and reconnect the vacuum pipes.
(d)   Refit any components removed to improve access.
(e)   Refill or top up the cooling system (Chapter 1).

7   Ignition system – testing

Note: *Refer to the warning given in Section 1 of this Chapter before starting work. Always switch off the ignition before disconnecting or connecting any component and when using a multi-meter to check resistances. Any voltmeter or multi-meter used to test ignition system components must have an impedance of 10 M ohms or greater*

Carburettor engines

General

1   The components of electronic ignition systems are normally very

reliable; most faults are far more likely to be due to loose or dirty connections or to 'tracking' of HT voltage due to dirt, dampness or damaged insulation than to the failure of any of the system's components. **Always** check all wiring thoroughly before condemning an electrical component and work methodically to eliminate all other possibilities before deciding that a particular component is faulty.

2   The old practice of checking for a spark by holding the live end of an HT lead a short distance away from the engine is not recommended; not only is there a high risk of a powerful electric shock, but the HT coil or amplifier module will be damaged. Similarly, **never** try to 'diagnose' misfires by pulling off one HT lead at a time.

Engine will not start

3   If the engine either will not turn over at all, or only turns very slowly, check the battery and starter motor. Connect a voltmeter across the battery terminals (meter positive probe to battery positive terminal), disconnect the ignition coil HT lead from the distributor cap and earth it, then note the voltage reading obtained while turning over the engine on the starter for (no more than) ten seconds. If the reading obtained is less than approximately 9.5 volts, check the battery, starter motor and charging system (Chapter 12).

4   If the engine turns over at normal speed but will not start, check the HT circuit by connecting a timing light (following the manufacturer's instructions) and turning the engine over on the starter motor; if the light flashes, voltage is reaching the spark plugs, so these should be checked first. If the light does not flash, check the HT leads themselves followed by the distributor cap, carbon brush and rotor arm (Chapter 1, but note also the tests given in Section 2, paragraph 21, of this Chapter).

5   If there is a spark, check the fuel system for faults (Chapter 4).

6   If there is still no spark, check the voltage at the ignition HT coil '+' terminal (white wires); it should be the same as the battery voltage (ie, at least 11.7 volts). If the voltage at the coil is more than 1 volt less than that at the battery, check the feed back through the fusebox and ignition switch to the battery and its earth until the fault is found.

7   If the feed to the HT coil is sound, check the coil's primary winding (and also the secondary winding, while the opportunity exists) as described in Section 4, paragraph 6; renew the coil if faulty, but be careful to check carefully the condition of the LT connections themselves before doing so, to ensure that the fault is not due to dirty or poorly-fastened connectors.

8   If the HT coil is in good condition, the fault is probably within the amplifier module or distributor pick-up coil. So that the operation of these two can be checked quickly, Rover dealers have a Neon indicator, which when connected across the HT coil's LT terminals, flashes every time the amplifier triggers an HT pulse in the coil if the ignition is switched on and the engine is turned over on the starter. Owners can substitute a low-wattage bulb; if the bulb flickers or flashes when the engine is turned over, the amplifier and distributor are sound.

9   If the amplifier and distributor are sound, and the entire LT circuit is in good condition, the fault, if it lies in the ignition system, must be in the HT circuit components. These should be checked carefully, as outlined above.

10   If the indicator or bulb does not flash, the fault is in either the distributor pick-up coil or the amplifier module; owners should note, however, that by far the commonest cause of 'failure' of either of these is a poor connection, either between the amplifier module and the distributor body or in the LT circuit wiring connections themselves. If a voltmeter or multi-meter is available, check the feed to the amplifier (the voltage reading obtained should be the same as that measured at the HT coil LT '+' terminal), then check that there is no measurable resistance between the amplifier module fixing screws and engine earth and that there is no continuity between either module terminal and earth. If any doubt exists as to the condition of the connections, remove the module, clean and check carefully the module earth and the connections and, if necessary, improve their fit (Sec 3). If these checks fail to correct the fault, measure the resistance of the pick-up coil, comparing it with the specified value; renew the coil if the reading

obtained differs significantly from that given. If the fault still exists, the only solution is to try the effect of renewing the amplifier module.

Engine misfires

11   An irregular misfire suggests either a loose connection or intermittent fault on the primary circuit, or an HT fault on the coil side of the rotor arm.

12   With the ignition switched off, check carefully through the system ensuring that all connections are clean and securely fastened. If the equipment is available, check the LT circuit as described in paragraphs 6 to 10 above.

13   Check that the HT coil, the distributor cap and the HT leads are clean and dry. Check the leads themselves and the spark plugs (by substitution, if necessary), then check the distributor cap, carbon brush and rotor arm (Chapter 1).

14   Regular misfiring is almost certainly due to a fault in the distributor cap, HT leads or spark plugs. Use a timing light (paragraph 4 above) to check whether HT voltage is present at all leads.

15   If HT voltage is not present on any particular lead, the fault will be in that lead or in the distributor cap. If HT is present on all leads, the fault will be in the spark plugs; check and renew them if there is any doubt about their condition.

16   If no HT is present, check the HT coil; its secondary windings may be breaking down under load.

Fuel-injected engines

General

17   The general comments made above apply equally to this system, but note that in this case it is the ECU that is at risk if the system is triggered with an open (ie, not properly earthed) HT circuit; ECUs are very much more expensive to replace, so take care!

18   If you are in any doubt as to your skill and ability to test the ignition system components and to understand what is happening, or if you do not have the required equipment, take the car to a suitably-equipped Rover dealer; it is better to pay the labour charges involved in having the car checked by an expert than to risk damage to the system or to yourself.

Engine will not start

19   Check whether the fault is in the ignition system or not (paragraphs 3 and 4 above) and check the HT circuit as described.

20   If the HT circuit appears to be in good condition, the feed to the HT coil can be checked as described in paragraph 6, while the coil itself can be checked as described in paragraph 7. Note however that the ECU controls the coil's feed; **Do not** attempt to 'test' the ECU with anything other than the correct test equipment, which will be available only at a suitably-equipped Rover dealer. If any of the wires are to be checked which lead to the ECU, always first unplug the relevant connector from the ECU so that there is no risk of the unit being damaged by the application of incorrect voltages from test equipment.

21   If all components have been checked for signs of obvious faults such as dirty or poorly-fastened connections, damp, or 'tracking' and have been tested as far as is possible but the system is still thought to be faulty, the car must be taken to a Rover dealer for testing on the correct equipment.

Engine misfires

22   Refer to paragraphs 11 to 16 above, but note that the possible causes of partial failures which might result in a misfire are far too numerous to be eliminated without the correct test equipment. Once the ignition system components have been checked for signs of obvious faults such as dirty or poorly-fastened connections, damp, or 'tracking' and have been tested as far as is possible take the car to a suitably-equipped Rover dealer for the full engine management system to be tested on the correct equipment.

Chapter 6 Clutch

Contents

Specifications

Type .... Single dry plate with diaphragm spring, cable-operated, self-adjusting

Friction plate
Diameter:
1.1	180 mm
1.4	190 mm

Friction material total thickness – AP plate only:
New plate – 1.1 models	8.30 to 8.80 mm
Service limit – 1.1 models	6.60 mm
New plate – 1.4 models	8.00 to 8.40 mm
Service limit – 1.4 models	6.30 mm

Rivet depth – distance from friction material surface to rivet heads:
New plate – AP	1.3 mm minimum
Service limit – AP	0.2 mm
New plate – Valeo	0.9 mm minimum
Service limit – Valeo	0.1 mm

Maximum run-out – at outer edge of friction material:
AP	1.3 mm
Valeo	1.0 mm

Pressure plate
Diaphragm spring finger maximum clearance:
AP	0.65 mm
Valeo	1.00 mm

Diaphragm spring finger height above flywheel surface:

1.1 models:
New plate – AP	27.0 to 33.2 mm
Service limit – AP	38.3 mm
New plate – Valeo	30.1 to 32.0 mm
Service limit – Valeo	37.3 mm

1.4 models:
New plate – AP	27.6 to 33.1 mm
Service limit – AP	39.4 mm
New plate – Valeo	29.1 to 32.0 mm
Service limit – Valeo	35.9 mm

Maximum warpage of machined surface:
AP	0.08 mm
Valeo	0.20 mm

Torque wrench settings

	Nm	lbf ft
Pressure plate-to-flywheel bolts	18	13
Release bearing guide sleeve-to-bellhousing bolts	5	4

Fig. 6.1 Clutch components (Sec 1)

1   *Flywheel*
2   *Flywheel bolt*
3   *Friction plate*
4   *Pressure plate assembly*
5   *Pressure plate bolt*
6   *Release bearing*
7   *Release fork*
8   *Release lever*
9   *Upper bush*
10 *Lower bush*

1   General information

The clutch consists of a friction plate, a pressure plate assembly, a release bearing and the release mechanism; all of these components are contained in the large cast aluminium alloy bellhousing, sandwiched between the engine and the transmission. The release mechanism is mechanical, being operated by a cable.

The friction plate is fitted between the engine flywheel and the clutch pressure plate and is allowed to slide on the transmission input shaft splines. It consists of two circular facings of friction material riveted in position to provide the clutch bearing surface, and a spring-cushioned hub to damp out transmission shocks.

The pressure plate assembly is bolted to the engine flywheel and is located by three dowel pins; it comprises the clutch cover, the diaphragm spring and the pressure plate. When the engine is running, drive is transmitted from the crankshaft via the flywheel and clutch cover to the friction plate (these last three components being clamped securely together by the pressure plate and diaphragm spring) and from the friction plate to the transmission input shaft.

To interrupt the drive the spring pressure must be relaxed. This is achieved by a sealed release bearing fitted concentrically around the transmission input shaft; when the driver depresses the clutch pedal the release bearing is pressed against the fingers at the centre of the diaphragm spring. Since the spring is held by rivets between two annular fulcrum rings the pressure at its centre causes it to deform so that it flattens and thus releases the clamping force it exerts, at its periphery, on the pressure plate.

Depressing the clutch pedal pulls the control cable inner wire and this in turn rotates the release fork by acting on the lever at the fork's upper end, above the bellhousing. The fork itself is clipped to the left of the release bearing.

As the friction plate facings wear the pressure plate moves towards the flywheel; this causes the diaphragm spring fingers to push against the release bearing, thus reducing the clearance which must be present in the mechanism. To ensure correct operation, the clutch cable incorporates a spring-loaded self-adjusting mechanism, eliminating the need for periodic adjustments.

Note: *The clutch friction and pressure plates are manufactured by two suppliers, AP (Automotive Products) and Valeo. Both the friction plate and the pressure plate must come from the same supplier; they are not interchangeable between the two. Apart from the manufacturer's*

Fig. 6.2 Clutch release mechanism (Sec 1)

1 *Pedal*
2 *Cable*
3 *Release lever*
4 *Release fork*
5 *Release bearing*
6 *Diaphragm spring*
7 *Friction plate*

name which may be stamped on either component, AP components can be identified by the part number being applied with white paint, while on Valeo components the part number is applied either with green paint or with black paint with a green spot. All other clutch components are the same, irrespective of supplier.

2 Clutch cable – removal, inspection and refitting

Removal

1   Working in the engine compartment, compress the cable spring and remove the C-clip, then unhook the cable end fitting from the release fork lever (photos).

2   Release the cable from the bracket bolted to the transmission and from the bulkhead clip.
3   Working inside the car, unhook the cable from the pedal.
4   Return to the engine compartment and withdraw the cable forwards through the bulkhead.

Inspection

5   Examine the cable, looking for worn end fittings or a damaged outer casing and for signs of fraying of the inner wire. Check the cable's operation; the inner wire should move smoothly and easily through the outer casing, but remember that a cable that appears serviceable when tested off the car may well be much heavier in operation when compressed into its working position. Renew the cable if it shows any signs of excessive wear or of damage.

Refitting

6   Refitting is the reverse of the removal procedure, but apply a thin

2.1A Compress cable spring and remove C-clip ...

2.1B ... then unhook cable from release lever and withdraw from transmission bracket

Fig. 6.3 Clutch cable and pedal assembly (Sec 2 and 3)

1	*Pedal*	*8*	*Hex-head screw*
2	*Pedal rubber*	*9*	*Washer*
3	*Pedal pivot shaft and*	*10*	*Spring washer*
	bracket	*11*	*Bolt*
4	*Pedal pivot bush – 2 off*	*12*	*Spring washer*
5	*Circlip*	*13*	*Nut*
6	*Spring washer*	*14*	*Cable*
7	*Nut*		

smear of multi-purpose grease to the cable end fittings. Align the slot in the inner wire's end with the pedal hook and smear petroleum jelly on the cable outer's rubber bush before hooking the cable onto the pedal; press the bush firmly into the bulkhead so that the steel washer butts firmly against the bulkhead boss.

7   Ensure that the cable is routed correctly, with no sharp bends or kinks, also so that it is secured clear of components such as brake pipes, coolant hoses and wiring.

8   When the cable is refitted, depress the pedal several times through its full travel, releasing it fully at each stroke, to enable the self-adjusting mechanism to set itself. Check that the clutch operation is correct.

3   Clutch pedal – removal, inspection and refitting

Removal

1   Disconnect the cable from the pedal (Sec 2).

2   Remove the circlip and withdraw the pedal from its pivot.

Inspection

3   Carefully clean all components and renew any that are worn or damaged; check the bearing surfaces of the pivot bushes and shaft with particular care; the bushes can be renewed separately if worn.

Refitting

4   Refitting is the reverse of the removal procedure, but apply a thin smear of multi-purpose grease to the pedal pivot bearing surfaces.

4   Clutch assembly – removal, inspection and refitting

Warning: *Dust created by clutch wear and deposited on the clutch components may contain asbestos, which is a health hazard. DO NOT blow it out with compressed air or inhale any of it. DO NOT use petrol or petroleum-based solvents to clean off the dust. Brake system cleaner or methylated spirit should be used to flush the dust into a suitable receptacle. After the clutch components are wiped clean with rags, dispose of the contaminated rags and cleaner in a sealed, marked container*

Note: *Although some friction materials may no longer contain asbestos it is safest to assume that they do and to take precautions accordingly*

Removal

1   Unless the complete engine/transmission unit is to be removed from the car and separated for major overhaul (see Chapter 2), the clutch can be reached by removing the transmission (Chapter 7).

2   Before disturbing the clutch use chalk or a felt-tip pen to mark the relationship of the pressure plate assembly to the flywheel.

3   Working in a diagonal sequence, slacken by half a turn at a time the pressure plate bolts until spring pressure is released and the bolts can be unscrewed by hand.

4   Prise the pressure plate assembly off its locating dowels and collect the friction plate, noting which way round the friction plate is fitted (photo).

Inspection

Note: *Due to the amount of work necessary to remove and refit clutch components, it is usually considered good practice to renew the clutch friction plate, pressure plate assembly and release bearing as a matched set, even if only one of these is actually worn enough to require renewal*

5   Remove the clutch assembly.

6   When cleaning clutch components, read first the warning at the beginning of this Section; remove dust using a clean, dry cloth and working in a well-ventilated atmosphere.

7   Check the friction plate facings for signs of wear, damage or oil contamination. If the friction material is cracked, burnt, scored or damaged, or if it is contaminated with oil or grease (shown by shiny black patches), the friction plate must be renewed.

8   If the depth from the friction material surface to any of the rivets is worn to the service limit specified or less, the friction plate must be renewed (photo).

9   If the friction plate is an AP item (see Sec 1 for identification details), the total thickness of friction material can be measured (photo) and compared with the Specifications at the beginning of this Chapter. If the plate is excessively worn, or even close to the service limit, it must be renewed.

10   If the friction material is still serviceable, check that the centre boss splines are unworn, that the torsion springs are in good condition and securely fastened and that all the rivets are tightly fastened. If any wear or damage is found, the friction plate must be renewed.

11   If the friction material is fouled with oil, this must be due to an oil leak from the crankshaft left-hand oil seal, from the sump-to-main bearing ladder joint, from the main bearing ladder-to-cylinder block/crankcase joint or from the transmission input shaft; renew the seal or repair the joint, as appropriate, as described in Chapter 2 or 7.

12   Check the pressure plate assembly for obvious signs of wear or damage; shake it to check for loose rivets or worn or damaged fulcrum rings and check that the drive straps securing the pressure plate to the cover do not show signs (such as a deep yellow or blue discoloration) of overheating. If the diaphragm spring is worn or damaged, or if its pressure is in any way suspect, the pressure plate assembly should be renewed.

13   To check the condition of the diaphragm spring, place a circular

4.4 Note locating dowels (two arrowed) and which way round friction plate is fitted on removing clutch components

4.8 Measuring friction plate rivet depth

4.9 Measuring friction plate total thickness

piece of flat plate across the tips of the spring fingers and use feeler gauges to measure the clearance between each finger's tip and the plate. If any finger is distorted so that the clearance between its tip and the plate is at the specified service limit or greater, the pressure plate must be renewed.

14   To check the condition of the complete pressure plate assembly, first check that the friction plate is within tolerances (paragraphs 8 and/or 9 above), then refit the clutch assembly to the flywheel as described below. Measure the height of each diaphragm spring finger from the flywheel's machined bearing surface; if any finger's height is at the service limit specified or greater, the pressure plate assembly must be renewed.

15   Examine the machined bearing surfaces of the pressure plate and of the flywheel; they should be clean, completely flat and free from scratches or scoring. If either is discoloured from excessive heat or shows signs of cracks it should be renewed, although minor damage of this nature can sometimes be polished away using emery paper. Use a straight-edge, placed across the pressure plate surface at four different points, and feeler gauges to check the pressure plate surface, comparing any warpage found with the specified service limit.

16   Check the release bearing as described in Section 5 of this Chapter.

Refitting

17   On reassembly, ensure that the bearing surfaces of the flywheel and pressure plate are completely clean, smooth and free from oil or grease. Use solvent to remove any protective grease from new components.

18   Fit the friction plate so that the longer part of its central, splined, boss is towards the flywheel and so that its spring hub assembly faces away from the flywheel; there may also be a marking showing which way round the plate is to be refitted (photo).

19   Refit the pressure plate assembly, aligning the marks made on dismantling (if the original pressure plate is re-used) and locating the pressure plate on its three locating dowels. Fit the pressure plate bolts, but tighten them only finger-tight so that the friction plate can still be moved.

20   The friction plate must now be centralised so that when the transmission is refitted its input shaft will pass through the splines at the centre of the friction plate.

21   Centralisation can be achieved by passing a screwdriver or other long bar through the friction plate and into the hole in the crankshaft; the friction plate can then be moved around until it is centred on the crankshaft hole. Alternatively, a clutch aligning tool (photo) can be used to eliminate the guesswork; these can be obtained from most accessory shops or can be made up from a length of metal rod or wooden dowel which fits closely inside the crankshaft hole, and has insulating tape wound around it to match the diameter of the friction plate splined hole.

22   When the friction plate is centralised, tighten the pressure plate bolts evenly and in a diagonal sequence to the specified torque setting.

23   Apply a thin smear of molybdenum disulphide grease to the splines of the friction plate and the transmission input shaft, also to the release bearing bore and release fork shaft.

24   Refit the transmission (Chapter 7).

4.18 Check friction plate for markings on refitting – this side must be refitted next to the flywheel

5 Clutch release mechanism – removal, inspection and refitting

Note: *Refer to the warning concerning the dangers of asbestos dust at the beginning of Section 4*

Removal

1   Unless the complete engine/transmission unit is to be removed from the car and separated for major overhaul (see Chapter 2), the clutch release mechanism can be reached only by removing the transmission (Chapter 7).

2   Disengaging the release bearing from the fork ends, pull the release bearing off its guide sleeve (photo).

3   Drive out the roll pin from the top of the release fork using a hammer and a parallel punch, remove the lever and prise up the fork upper bush. Withdraw the release fork and extract the lower bush.

Inspection

4   Check the release mechanism, renewing any component which is worn or damaged. Carefully check all bearing surfaces and points of contact.

4.21 Using a clutch aligning tool to centralise clutch friction plate

5.2 Removing the clutch release bearing

5.7 Clutch release bearing installed correctly on the release fork

Fig. 6.4 Release fork and bushes (Sec 5)

1 Release lever	4 Release fork
2 Roll pin	5 Lower bush
3 Upper bush	

5   When checking the release bearing itself, note that it is often considered worthwhile to renew it as a matter of course. Check that the contact surface rotates smoothly and easily, with no sign of noise or roughness and that the surface itself is smooth and unworn, with no signs of cracks, pitting or scoring. If there is any doubt about its condition the bearing must be renewed.

6   Note that when cleaning clutch components, **do not** use solvents on the release bearing; it is packed with grease which may be washed out if care is not taken.

Refitting

7   Reassembly is the reverse of the dismantling procedure, noting the following points (photo).

(a) When refitting the release fork bushes, ensure that each bush's locating tags engage in the bellhousing slots. Apply a smear of molybdenum disulphide grease to the release fork shaft's bearing surfaces before refitting it and use a new roll pin if required to secure the release fork lever.

(b) Clean the release bearing bore and guide sleeve, then apply a smear of molybdenum disulphide grease to both bearing surfaces before engaging the bearing on the fork ends and sliding it onto the sleeve.

(c) Move the fork up and down to check that it fits correctly against the bearing, then move the release lever to check that the fork and bearing operate properly.

(d) Refit the transmission (Chapter 7).

Chapter 7 Transmission

Contents

Specifications

General

Type...	Manual, four or five (according to model) forward speeds and reverse. Synchro-mesh on all forward speeds
Designation..	Rover R65

Identification

Transmission code:

1.1C, 1.1L – standard..	4S/40/Y
1.1C, 1.1L – optional, 1.1S, 1.4SL, 1.4GS.......................................	5C/35/Y
GTa, GTi 16v	5C/37/Y

Reduction ratios

Transmission 4S/40/Y:

Final drive..	4.063 : 1 (65/16T)
1st...	3.417 : 1
2nd..	1.800 : 1
3rd...	1.138 : 1
4th...	0.810 : 1
Reverse..	3.583 : 1

Transmission 5C/35/Y:

Final drive..	3.556 : 1 (64/18T)
1st...	3.417 : 1
2nd..	1.947 : 1
3rd...	1.333 : 1
4th...	1.054 : 1
5th...	0.854 : 1
Reverse..	3.583 : 1

Transmission 5C/37/Y:

Final drive..	3.765 : 1 (64/17T)
1st...	3.417 : 1
2nd..	1.947 : 1
3rd...	1.333 : 1
4th...	1.054 : 1
5th...	0.854 : 1
Reverse..	3.583 : 1

Lubrication

Recommended oil...	Special gearbox oil – refer to your Rover dealer (Duckhams Hypoid PT 75W/80 Gear Oil – for topping-up only)
Capacity	2.0 litres
Recommended gearchange linkage grease	Rover Grease containing 3% molybdenum disulphide – Part Number AFU 1500.1509 (Duckhams LBM 10 Grease)

Torque wrench settings

	Nm	lbf ft
General		
Oil filler/level and drain plugs	25	19
Speedometer upper-to-lower cable nut	9	7
Speedometer pinion housing screw	18	13
Transmission-to-engine bolts	85	63
Flywheel cover plate screws	9	7
Flywheel rear cover plate bolt and nut	38	28
Engine/transmission left-hand mounting:		
Support member-to-subframe bolts	45	33
Mounting-to-support member bolts	45	33
Mounting-to-bracket bolts	45	33
Bracket-to-transmission bolts	80	59
Engine/transmission rear mounting:		
Mounting bracket-to-transmission 12 mm bolt(s)	85	63
Mounting bracket-to-transmission 10 mm bolt(s)	45	33
Mounting bracket-to-tie-rod through-bolt	85	63
Tie-rod-to-body bolt and nut	45	33
Overhaul		
Intermediate plate-to-bellhousing:		
Bolts	28	21
Torx screws	60	44
Transmission casing-to-bellhousing bolts	28	21
Input and output shaft left-hand bearing retainer Torx screws	30	22
Output shaft left-hand end nut	150	111
Left-hand end cover bolts	28	21

1 General information

The transmission is contained in a cast aluminium alloy casing bolted to the engine's left-hand end and consists of the gearbox and final drive differential, often called a transaxle.

Drive is transmitted from the crankshaft via the clutch to the input shaft, which has a splined extension to accept the clutch friction plate and rotates in sealed ball-bearings; from the input shaft drive is transmitted to the output shaft, which rotates in a roller bearing at its right-hand end and a sealed ball-bearing at its left-hand end. From the output shaft the drive is transmitted to the differential crownwheel, which rotates with the differential case and planetary gears, thus driving the sun gears and driveshafts. The rotation of the planetary gears on their shaft allows the inner roadwheel to rotate at a slower speed than the outer roadwheel when the car is cornering.

The input and output shafts are arranged side by side, parallel to the crankshaft and driveshafts, so that their gear pinion teeth are in constant mesh. In the neutral position the output shaft gear pinions rotate freely so that drive cannot be transmitted to the crownwheel.

Gear selection is by a floor-mounted lever acting through a remote control linkage on the selector mechanism. The selector mechanism causes the appropriate selector fork to move its respective synchro-sleeve along the shaft to lock the gear pinion to the synchro-hub. Since the synchro-hubs are splined to the output shaft, this locks the pinion to the shaft so that drive can be transmitted. To ensure that gear changing can be made quickly and quietly a synchro-mesh system is fitted to all forward gears, consisting of baulk rings and spring-loaded fingers as well as the gear pinions and synchro-hubs; the synchro-mesh cones are formed on the mating faces of the baulk rings and gear pinions.

2 Transmission oil – renewal

1   This operation is much quicker and more efficient if the car is first taken on a journey of sufficient length to warm the engine/transmission up to normal operating temperature.

2   Park the car on level ground, switch off the ignition and apply the handbrake firmly. For improved access, jack up the front of the car and support it securely on axle stands (see 'Jacking, towing and wheel changing'). Note that the car must be lowered to the ground and level, to ensure accuracy, when refilling and checking the oil level.

3   To avoid rounding-off the corners of the filler/level and drain plug hexagons, use only good quality close-fitting single-hexagon or surface drive spanners or sockets. Unscrew the filler/level plug, then position a suitable container under the drain plug at the rear of the transmission, below the left-hand driveshaft inner constant velocity joint, and unscrew the plug (photo).

4   Allow the oil to drain completely into the container. If the oil is hot, take precautions against scalding. Clean both the filler/level and the drain plugs, being especially careful to wipe any metallic particles off the magnetic inserts. Discard the original sealing washers; they should be renewed whenever they are disturbed.

5   When the oil has finished draining, clean the drain plug threads and those of the transmission casing, fit a new sealing washer and refit the drain plug, tightening it to the specified torque wrench setting. It the car was raised for the draining operation, now lower it to the ground.

6   Refilling the transmission is an extremely awkward operation. Above all, allow plenty of time for the oil level to settle properly before checking it. Note that the car must be parked on flat level ground when checking the oil level.

7   Refill the transmission with the exact amount of the specified type of oil, noting that only a few oils are recommended by Rover for refilling. Allow time for the oil to settle.

2.3 Transmission oil filler/level plug 'A' and drain plug 'B'

Fig. 7.1 Gearchange linkage components (Sec 4)

1   Knob
2   Collar
3   Gearchange upper lever
4   Gearchange lower lever
5   Hex-head screw
6   Bucket joint
7   Hex-head screw
8   Bellcrank assembly
9   Selector rod
10 Ball housing
11 Rubber washer
12 Control rod
13 Bolt
14 Thrustwasher
15 Spacer
16 Bush
17 Nut
18 Upper link rod
19 Dust cover
20 Lower link rod
21 Bush
22 Spacer
23 Mounting plate
24 Mounting rubber
25 Bolt
26 Nut

H.22274

8   Check the oil level (Chapter 1); if the correct amount was poured into the transmission and a large amount flows out on checking the level, refit the filler/level plug and take the car on a short journey so that the new oil is distributed fully around the transmission components, then check the level again.

9   Dispose of the old oil safely; **do not** pour it down a drain (see *'General repair procedures'* at the beginning of this Manual).

3   Gearchange linkage – adjustment

1   If a stiff, sloppy or imprecise gearchange leads you to suspect that a fault exists within the linkage, first dismantle it completely and check it for wear or damage (Sec 4), then reassemble it, applying a smear of the specified grease (see Specifications) to all bearing surfaces.

2   If this does not cure the fault, the car should be examined by an expert, as the fault must lie within the transmission itself. There is no adjustment as such in the linkage; note that while the length of the link rods can be altered, this is for initial setting-up only and is not intended to provide a form of compensation for wear.

3   If the link rods have been renewed, or if the length of the originals is incorrect, adjust them as follows.

4   Ensure that the car is parked on level ground, with the ignition switched off, the handbrake firmly applied and neutral selected. Remembering that the selector mechanism is spring-loaded so that the

gearchange lever rests naturally between the third and fourth gear positions, have an assistant hold the gearchange lever in its normal position in relation to the front seats.

5   Working in (or under) the engine compartment, slacken the locknut at each end of the rod to be adjusted; if not already done, disconnect the rod(s) from the transmission selector levers.

6   Check that the selector lever concerned is in its neutral position, with no signs of free play or damage, then hold the rod end socket over the lever ball and prevent the socket from rotating while turning the rod itself to alter its length by screwing it in or out of its end sockets.

7   When the rod's length is correct, check that the same amount of thread is visible at each end before tightening the locknuts securely; be careful not to alter the position of either socket when tightening the locknuts.

8   Connect the link rod(s) to the selector lever(s) and check that all gears can be selected, with the gearchange lever returning properly to its correct at-rest position.

4   Gearchange linkage – removal, overhaul and refitting

Removal

1   Park the car on level ground, switch off the ignition, check that the

Fig. 7.2 Using Rover service tool to disconnect gearchange linkage link rod balljoint from transmission selector lever (Sec 4)

18G 1592

18G 1594

Fig. 7.3 Using Rover service tool to connect gearchange linkage link rod balljoint to transmission selector lever (Sec 4)

transmission is in neutral and apply the handbrake firmly. Jack up the front of the car and support it securely on axle stands (see 'Jacking, towing and wheel changing').

2   Although not strictly necessary, work is a great deal easier if the exhaust front pipe is first removed (Chapter 4).

3   Disconnect the link rods from the transmission upper and lower selector levers using either Rover service tool Number 18G 1592 (Fig. 7.2) or a fabricated copy of it, or (with care) a pair of needle-nosed pliers (photo).

4   Unscrewing the nuts and/or releasing the balljoints as necessary, disconnect the gearchange control and selector rods from the bellcrank assembly; the assembly can then be unbolted from the suspension front subframe if required (photos).

5   Move inside the car. Although not strictly necessary, work is a great deal easier if the cassette storage holder is removed first; it is secured by two retaining screws. Unscrew the gearchange knob and collar, then remove the four screws and withdraw the gearchange lever outer

gaiter, its retaining plate and the inner gaiter (photos).

6   With the gaiters removed, the gearchange upper lever can be separated from the lower lever, if required. Also, the lever-to-control rod pivot components can be unbolted for examination (photo).

7   Returning under the car, unfasten the retaining nuts to release the mounting rubber and plate from the underbody; withdraw all remaining linkage components (photo).

Overhaul

8   Thoroughly clean all components and check them for wear or

4.3 Using pliers to disconnect gearchange linkage link rod from transmission upper selector lever

4.4A Gearchange linkage control rod bucket joint nut 'A' and selector rod balljoint 'B'

4.4B Gearchange linkage bellcrank assembly mounting screws (arrows)

4.5A Unscrew the gearchange knob and collar

4.5B Remove four retaining screws ...

4.5C ... to release gaiter retaining plate ...

4.6 ... and withdraw gaiters to expose gearchange lever and lever-to-control rod pivot

4.7 Gearchange linkage rear end components

damage, renewing all worn or faulty items. Note that the gearchange lever-to-control rod pivot bushes can be renewed separately if necessary.

9   Carefully check the condition of all linkage joints; if any show signs of stiffness or free play, they must be renewed. Check also the mounting rubber and the control rod's bush that passes through it; renew the rubber if it shows any sign of cracks, splits or other deterioration and renew the bush if it is a sloppy fit on the control rod end.

10   The bellcrank assembly must be renewed complete if it is worn or damaged.

Refitting

11   Refitting is the reverse of the removal procedure, noting the following points.

(a)   Apply a smear of the specified grease (see Specifications) to all pivots and bearing surfaces; pack the gearchange lever-to-control rod pivot with grease.

(b)   Tighten all fasteners securely.

(c)   Connect the link rods to the transmission upper and lower selector levers using either Rover service tool Number 18G 1594 (Fig. 7.3) or (with care) a pair of combination pliers. If adjustment is required, refer to Section 3.

5   Speedometer drive – removal and refitting

Removal

1   Open the bonnet and disconnect the speedometer drive upper cable from the lower cable, then remove the lower cable as described in Chapter 12, Section 21.

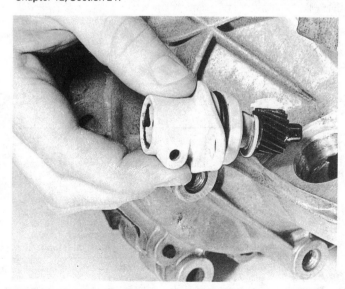

5.2 Removing the speedometer drive assembly

2   Unscrew the single (hex-head) screw and withdraw the speedometer drive assembly (photo). Remove and discard the sealing O-ring.

3   Renew the O-ring and oil seal as a matter of course whenever they are disturbed.

4   Renew the pinion if its teeth are worn or damaged and check the housing for cracks or damage. Note that the speedometer drivegear can be checked visually with the pinion assembly removed by shining a torch into the aperture. If any of the gear teeth are damaged the transmission must be removed from the car and dismantled so that the gear can be renewed; it is pressed onto the differential case.

Refitting

5   On reassembly, fit the new oil seal and O-ring to the housing, then refit the pinion, applying a smear of grease to all components before installation. Insert the assembly into the transmission, rotating the pinion until it is felt to engage the teeth of the drivegear, then press the housing into place. **Do not** use excessive force or the drive components may be damaged.

6   When the drive is correctly refitted tighten the retaining screw to the specified torque wrench setting and connect the cable(s) to the transmission.

7   Refit the lower cable as described in Chapter 12, Section 21.

6   Oil seals – renewal

Note: *The following text describes only the renewal of those oil seals which can be removed without dismantling the transmission. If oil leaks appear from any seal not mentioned here, or from any of the joint surfaces, the transmission must be removed from the car and dismantled*

Differential side (driveshaft) oil seals

1   Jack up the front of the car and support it securely on axle stands, then remove the roadwheel (see 'Jacking, towing and wheel changing').

2   Drain the transmission oil (Sec 2).

3   Remove the underwing shield (Chapter 11).

4   Relieve the pressure of the Hydragas system from the components by using a trolley jack or similar (with a block of wood interposed to prevent damage) to jack up the suspension via the lower balljoint until it is just beginning to take the weight of the car, then slip a wooden spacer between the suspension upper arm and the front subframe and lower the jack.

5   Unscrew the brake caliper mounting bolts, remove the caliper from the hub carrier and slip a clean spacer (of the same thickness as the brake disc) between the pads, then secure the caliper clear of the working area without stretching or kinking the brake flexible hose.

6   Disconnect the track rod balljoint from the hub carrier steering arm (Chapter 10).

7   Disconnect the suspension upper balljoint from the upper arm (Chapter 10); discard the lockwasher.

8   Unscrew the nut and completely remove the pinch-bolt, then disconnect the suspension lower balljoint from the hub carrier (Chapter 10).

6.10 Removing the driveshaft complete with the hub carrier

6.11 Prising out a driveshaft oil seal

6.12 Fitting a new driveshaft oil seal

9　Use a suitable lever to prise out the driveshaft until the circlip compresses into its groove and is released from the differential sun gear.

10　Withdraw the driveshaft assembly complete with the hub carrier (photo). Check the circlip at the driveshaft's inboard end; renew it if there is any doubt about its condition. To prevent the risk of the sun gear falling down inside the transmission, insert a clean metal rod or wooden dowel of the same diameter as the driveshaft into the aperture until the gear is securely supported.

11　Prise out the seal, taking care not to scratch the seal housing (photo); if difficulty is experienced, use an internally-expanding claw-type puller to extract the seal.

12　Dip the new seal in clean oil, fit it to the transmission aperture and drive it squarely into place, until it seats on its locating shoulder, using a piece of tubing (such as a socket) which bears only on the seal's hard outer edge as a drift (photo).

13　Before refitting the driveshaft check its seal rubbing surface for signs of burrs, scratches or other damage which may have caused the seal to fail in the first place. It may be possible to polish away faults of this sort using fine abrasive paper.

14　Thoroughly clean the driveshaft and the aperture in the transmission to prevent the entry of dirt during reassembly. Apply a thin film of grease to the oil seal lips and to the driveshaft shoulder.

15　Ensure that the circlip fitted to the inboard end of each driveshaft is in good condition and is located securely in its groove. Remove the sun gear support.

16　Taking care not to damage the oil seal lips, insert the driveshaft into the transmission and engage its splines with those of the sun gear. Press the driveshaft firmly into place until the circlip engages correctly behind (inboard of) the sun gear. If it is necessary to use tools to tap the driveshaft into place, be very careful not to damage the rubber gaiter.

17　Check that the circlip is properly engaged by grasping the inner joint body firmly and trying to pull the driveshaft out of the sun gear.

18　Refit the lower balljoint to the hub carrier, tightening the pinch-bolt and nut to the specified torque wrench setting (Chapter 10).

19　Refit the upper balljoint to the suspension upper arm, fit a new lockwasher and tighten the balljoint-to-upper arm nut to the specified torque wrench setting (Chapter 10). Secure the nut by bending the washer tab up against one of its flats.

20　Connect the track rod balljoint to the hub carrier steering arm and tighten the balljoint nut to the specified torque wrench setting (Chapter 10).

21　Refit the brake caliper, tightening its bolts to the specified torque wrench setting (Chapter 9).

22　Jack up the suspension, remove the spacer and lower the suspension again, then refit the underwing shield and the roadwheel.

23　Refill the transmission with oil and check the level (Chapter 1 and Sec 2), then wash off any spilt oil.

Input shaft (clutch) oil seal

Note: *On later transmissions, the clutch release bearing guide sleeve and the input shaft oil seal are an assembly and must be renewed as one unit*

24　Remove the transmission from the car (Sec 8) and remove the clutch release fork (Chapter 6).

25　Unbolt the clutch release bearing guide sleeve and remove it, with the oil seal, from the bellhousing. Discard the bolts; they must be renewed whenever disturbed. Clean any locking material from the bellhousing threads using Loctite Chisel and a suitable tap, then degrease thoroughly.

26　Before fitting a new seal, check the input shaft's seal rubbing surface for signs of burrs, scratches or other damage which may have caused the seal to fail in the first place. It may be possible to polish away faults of this sort using fine abrasive paper. Ensure that the input shaft is clean and greased to protect the seal lips on refitting.

27　Dip the new seal in clean oil and (where separate) fit it to the guide sleeve, then refit the guide sleeve, tightening the **new** bolts to the specified torque wrench setting (Chapter 6).

28　Reassemble and lubricate the clutch release mechanism (Chapter 6), wipe off any surplus oil or grease, then refit the transmission to the car (Sec 8).

Gear selector lower lever oil seal

29　Disconnect the gearchange linkage link rod from the transmission lower selector lever (Sec 4).

30　Using a hammer and a parallel punch, drive out the roll pin securing the lever to its shaft and remove the lever.

31　Prise out the seal, taking care not to scratch the seal housing.

32　Clean and check both housing and shaft for signs of wear or damage which might have caused the seal to fail in the first place.

33　Dip the new seal in clean oil and drive it into the housing, using a piece of tubing (such as a socket) which bears only on the seal's hard outer edge as a drift, until it seats on its locating shoulder.

34　Reassemble the gearchange linkage (Sec 4), check the transmission oil level and top up if necessary (Chapter 1), then wash off any spilt oil.

7　Reversing lamp switch – testing, removal and refitting

Testing

1　The reversing lamp circuit is controlled by a plunger-type switch that is screwed into the transmission casing (photo). The circuit feed is protected by fuse number 9.

2　To test the switch disconnect its wires and use a multimeter (set to the resistance function) or a battery and bulb test circuit to check that there is continuity between the switch terminals only when reverse gear is selected. If this is not the case and there are no obvious breaks or other damage to the wires, the switch is faulty and must be renewed.

Removal

3　To remove the switch, disconnect its wires and unscrew it.

7.1 Disconnecting reversing lamp switch wires

Refitting

4   On refitting, apply a smear of sealant to the switch threads and tighten it securely, but do not overtighten it. Re-connect its wires and test the circuit.

8   Transmission – removal and refitting

Note: *To carry out this task an engine hoist or similar will be required to lift out the transmission and a second, similar, piece of equipment must be available to take the weight of the engine while it is moved sideways and raised or lowered. A strong trolley jack would be useful in the latter case, provided that a wooden spacer is available to spread the load and prevent the risk of damage to the sump*

Removal

1   Park the car on firm, level ground, apply the handbrake and remove the bonnet (Chapter 11).
2   Drain the transmission oil; clean and refit the drain plug, tightening it to its specified torque wrench setting (Sec 2).
3   Remove the battery and its tray (Chapter 12).
4   Remove, where fitted, the charcoal canister (Chapter 4).
5   On carburettor engines, remove the distributor (Chapter 5). Remove its clamp and undo the two screws securing the cold air duct to the body front panel, then withdraw it (Chapter 4).
6   On fuel-injected engines, disconnect the ignition HT coil spark plug (HT) lead from the distributor cap. Disconnect the vacuum pipe from the intake air temperature control valve, release the two clips securing the

air intake duct to the air cleaner assembly and undo the screw or release the two quarter-turn fasteners, as appropriate, securing the duct to its support bracket. Unfasten the rubber strap (where fitted) and remove the two screws securing the cold air intake duct to the body front panel, then withdraw the assembly, taking care not to lose the hot air intake connector hose (Chapter 4).
7   On all models, disconnect the clutch cable and secure it clear of the engine/transmission unit (Chapter 6).
8   Disconnect the reversing lamp switch (Sec 7).
9   Disconnect the speedometer drive upper cable from the lower cable, release the upper cable from any securing clips and secure it clear of the engine/transmission (Chapter 12).
10   Disconnect the gearchange linkage link rods from the transmission upper and lower selector levers (Sec 4).
11   Either remove the engine/transmission rear mounting (Chapter 2) or unbolt the mounting bracket from the transmission and slacken the tie-rod-to-body bolt and nut so that the mounting can be swung down clear of the transmission.
12   Remove the starter motor (Chapter 12).
13   Unbolt the flywheel front, lower and rear cover plates, disconnecting the clips (where fitted) securing the engine wiring harness (photos).
14   Dismantle the front suspension and remove both driveshafts (see Chapter 8 for full details, but for simplicity follow the abbreviated procedure given in Section 6, paragraphs 1 to 10).
15   Attaching the lifting equipment to the lifting eye formed in the transmission casing flange (photo), take the weight of the transmission and support the weight of the engine using a trolley jack, with a wooden spacer to prevent damage to the sump.
16   Release the engine wiring harness from the clip on the engine/transmission left-hand mounting, unbolt the mounting bracket from the mounting, then unbolt the support member from the front subframe. Remove the support member (Chapter 2).
17   Lever forwards the engine/transmission by approximately 25 mm and insert a wooden block (measuring 150 x 80 mm) lengthways between the front subframe and the rear of the cylinder block/crankcase to hold it forwards (photo).
18   Make a final check that all components have been removed or disconnected that will prevent the removal of the transmission from the car and ensure that components such as the gearchange linkage link rods are secured so that they cannot be damaged on removal.
19   Unscrew the four bolts securing the transmission to the engine (noting that the top two are shorter) and gently prise the transmission off the two locating dowels (at the front and rear of the main bearing ladder). Move the transmission squarely away from the engine, ensuring that the clutch components are not damaged.
20   Lift the transmission out of the car, ensuring that nothing is trapped or damaged (photo).
21   Whenever the transmission is removed, check the mountings and renew them if necessary (Chapter 2). Overhaul the clutch components (Chapter 6); if the transmission is to be overhauled or renewed, unbolt the mounting bracket and remove the clutch release mechanism and speedometer drive assembly.

Refitting

22   Check that the mating surfaces of the engine and transmission are

8.13A Removing the flywheel front cover plate

8.13B Remove large bolt and nut as well as mounting screws ...

8.13C ... to release flywheel rear cover plate

8.15 Attach lifting equipment using lifting eye provided in casing flange

8.17 Lever engine forwards and use wooden block to hold it in place

8.20 Lifting the transmission out of the car

completely clean and dry, that all clutch components are in good condition and correctly installed and that the locating dowels are clean and lubricated with a smear of anti-seize compound (eg Holts Copaslip).

23   Apply a thin smear of molybdenum disulphide grease to the splines of the clutch friction plate and the transmission input shaft, also to the release fork shaft's bearing surfaces, the release bearing bore and the guide sleeve. Push the release bearing as far towards the transmission as possible, then hold the release fork's lever in that position by locking it with a spanner applied to the nearest transmission casing-to-bellhousing bolt head.

24   Offer up the transmission to the engine and engage the input shaft with the clutch friction plate; ensure that the transmission is absolutely square to the engine.

25   Push the transmission into full engagement with the engine, ensuring that it seats correctly on the dowels. If the transmission proves reluctant to mate with the engine, try swivelling it slightly, or have an assistant rotate the crankshaft via the alternator drive pulley bolt, until the input shaft splines engage with those of the friction plate.

26   Once the transmission is fully engaged, refit the bolts securing it to the engine, remove the wooden block and refit the engine/transmission mountings; tighten all nuts and bolts to their specified torque wrench settings. Unlock the release fork's lever.

27   The remainder of the refitting procedure is the reverse of removal, noting the following points.

(a)   Tighten all nuts and bolts to their specified torque wrench settings.

(b)   Ensuring that they are clean and greased, refit the driveshafts as described in Section 6, paragraphs 14 to 23.

(c)   For full details of refitting all ancillary components, refer to the relevant Sections of this Chapter or of the other Chapters mentioned during removal.

(d)   On carburettor engines, check the ignition timing (Chapter 1).

9   Transmission overhaul – general notes and precautions

The overhaul of a complete transmission is a demanding task that requires considerable previous experience. Owners are advised to remove the transmission themselves, if they so wish (Sec 8), but then to renew it or have it overhauled by a Rover dealer or transmission specialist.

The dismantling of a transmission into its major assemblies is reasonably straightforward and can be carried out without using the manufacturer's special tools (although a comprehensive standard tool kit will be required). This will enable an initial assessment of any wear or damage to be made, and a decision whether or not to proceed with an overhaul; an exploded view of the transmission's components is provided to assist owners who wish to undertake this. Note, however, that any further overhaul work will require the dismantling and rebuilding of many small and intricate assemblies as well as the measurement of any worn components; this will require more sophisticated equipment and a far greater level of skill to assess whether an item is worn or not. As a minimum, you will require internal and external circlip pliers (flat-bladed, as well as the normal end fitting), a selection of pin punches and Torx bits, a bearing puller, a slide hammer and a hydraulic press.

While the 'Fault diagnosis' section at the beginning of this manual should help to isolate most transmission faults so that you can decide in advance what course of action to follow, remember that economic considerations may rule out an apparently simple repair. For example, a common reason for transmission overhaul is to renew the synchro-mesh units; wear or faults in these assemblies being indicated by noise when changing gear, or by the synchro-mesh being easily beaten. Jumping out of gear or similar gear selection faults may mean the renewal of the selector mechanism, forks, or synchro-sleeves. General noise during operation on the road, however, may be due to worn bearings, shafts or gears; the cumulative cost of renewing all worn components may well make it more economical to renew the transmission complete.

To establish whether transmission overhaul is economically viable or not, first establish the cost of a complete replacement transmission, comparing the price of a new unit with that of an exchange reconditioned unit (if available) or even a good secondhand unit (with a guarantee) from a breaker. Compare this with the likely cost of the replacement parts that will be required if the existing transmission is overhauled; do not forget to include all items that must be renewed whenever they are disturbed, such as all oil seals and sealing O-rings, roll or drive pins, Belleville washers, circlips and snap rings. Owners of cars with early five-speed transmissions (transmission serial number below 2104300) should note that the output shaft left-hand end nut is welded to the shaft to secure it; this means that the weld must be chiselled off before the nut can be unfastened and the transmission dismantled, also that the nut, the output shaft and both its bearings **must** be renewed as a matter of course.

Fig. 7.4 Exploded view of the transmission (Sec 9)

1 Nut*
2 Stop plate*
3 Synchro-hub*
4 Finger*
5 Spring*
6 Steel ball*
7 5th gear synchro-sleeve*
8 5th gear selector fork
9 Roll pin
10 Baulk ring*
11 Output shaft 5th gear
    pinion*
12 Needle roller bearing*
13 Spacer
14 Output shaft ball-bearing
15 Bearing retainer and Torx
    screws
16 Output shaft 4th gear
    pinion
17 Circlip – four-speed
    transmission only
18 Belleville washer –
    four-speed transmission,
    Spacer – five-speed
    transmission
19 3rd/4th gear synchro-sleeve
20 Segment ring
21 Output shaft 3rd gear
    pinion
22 Output shaft 2nd gear
    pinion
23 Baulk ring
24 1st/2nd gear synchro-hub
25 1st/2nd gear
    synchro-sleeve – with
    reverse gear
26 Finger
27 Output shaft 1st gear
    pinion
28 Output shaft roller bearing
29 Output shaft
30 Plastic lubrication insert
31 Bolt
32 Left-hand end cover
33 Rubber gasket
34 Transmission casing
35 Oil seal
36 Oil filler/level plug
37 Sealing washer
38 Bolt
39 Bolt
40 Breather body
41 Breather cap
42 Reversing lamp switch
43 Sealing washer
44 Reverse lockout cable insert
    – see note below
45 1st/2nd gear selector fork
46 5th, 1st/2nd and reverse
    selector fork shaft
47 3rd/4th gear selector fork
48 3rd/4th selector fork shaft
49 Reverse idler gear shaft
50 Thrust bearing
51 Reverse idler gear pinion
52 Needle roller bearing

53 Reverse gear selector fork
54 Pivot pin
55 Reverse gear locking
    plunger
56 Spring
57 Locking ring
58 Belleville washer
59 Input shaft 5th gear pinion*
60 Bearing retainer and Torx
    screws
61 Input shaft ball-bearing
62 Input shaft
63 Input shaft ball-bearing
64 Thrustwasher
65 Planetary gear pinion
66 Centre tube
67 Thrustwasher
68 Sun gear pinion

69 Planetary gear shaft
70 Differential side taper roller
    bearing
71 Differential case and
    crownwheel assembly
72 Roll pin
73 Retaining ring
74 Speedometer drivegear
75 Speedometer drive pinion
76 Speedometer lower cable
    retaining rubber dowel
77 Sealing O-ring
78 Speedometer drive housing
79 Oil seal
80 Screw
81 Oil seal
82 Roll pin
83 Transmission gear selector
    lower lever and shaft
    assembly

84 Bellhousing and
    intermediate plate
    assembly
85 Torx screw
86 Bolt
87 Roll pin
88 Combined interlock and
    detent assembly
89 Plastic cup
90 Bias spring
91 Dowel
92 Oil seal
93 Clutch release bearing
    guide sleeve
94 Bolt
95 Transmission gear selector
    upper lever
96 Reverse gear lever
    assembly
97 Oil drain plug
98 Oil seal
99 Control fork – later
    four-speed transmissions
    only

Notes:
*fitted to five-speed transmission only
Item 44 (if fitted) will be sealed by a blanking plug; if not fitted, it will be replaced by a blanking plug
Items 92 and 93 are a single assembly on later transmissions
Item 99 (where applicable) replaces item 8

Chapter 8 Driveshafts

Contents

Specifications

Type .... Unequal-length solid steel shafts, splined to inner and outer constant velocity joints, dynamic damper on right-hand shaft

Lubrication (overhaul only – see text)

Lubricant type/specification .... Use only special grease supplied in sachets with gaiter kits – joints are otherwise pre-packed with grease and sealed

Torque wrench settings

	Nm	lbf ft
Driveshaft nut	210	155

1 General information

Drive is transmitted from the differential sun gears to the front roadwheels by two unequal-length steel driveshaft assemblies; the (longer) right-hand driveshaft is fitted with a dynamic damper to reduce harmonic vibrations and resonance.

Both driveshafts are splined at their outer ends to accept the wheel hubs and are threaded so that each hub can be fastened by a large nut. The inner end of each driveshaft is splined to accept the differential sun gear and has a groove to accept the circlip which secures the driveshaft to the sun gear.

Two constant velocity joints are fitted to each driveshaft to ensure the smooth and efficient transmission of drive at all the angles possible as the roadwheels move up and down with the suspension, and as they turn from side to side under steering. Each outer joint is of the Birfield-Rzeppa ball-and-cage type, but the inner joint is of the tripod type and is plunge-accepting, to allow for the differences in driveshaft effective length at the extremes of suspension travel.

Note: *The only replacement parts listed are the inner constant velocity joint and shaft assemblies, the outer constant velocity joint assemblies and the rubber gaiters; the gaiters are supplied in a kit with the necessary sachets of grease and their clips. If any joint is worn or damaged it cannot be reconditioned but must be renewed; in the case of the inner joints, this means that the complete joint/shaft assembly must be renewed.*

2 Driveshaft – removal and refitting

Removal

1 With the car standing on its wheels apply the handbrake firmly and select first or reverse gear.

2 Remove the roadwheel trim or centre cap (as appropriate) (photo). Relieve the staking of the driveshaft nut using a hammer and punch or (if necessary) an electric drill, then use a suitable socket, a strong T-bar and a long extension tube to slacken the nut; do not unscrew it yet. If the nut is particularly tight, have an assistant apply the brakes hard.

3 Slacken the roadwheel nuts, then jack up the front of the car and support it securely on axle stands (see *'Jacking, towing and wheel changing'*). Remove the roadwheel, then unscrew the driveshaft nut and discard it; it must be renewed as a matter of course whenever disturbed.

4 Drain the transmission oil (Chapter 7).

5 Remove the underwing shield (Chapter 11).

6 Relieve the pressure of the Hydragas system from the components by using a trolley jack or similar (with a block of wood interposed to prevent damage) to jack up the suspension via the lower balljoint until it is just beginning to take the weight of the car, then slip a wooden spacer between the suspension upper arm and the front subframe and lower the jack.

7 Unscrew the brake caliper mounting bolts, remove the caliper from the hub carrier and slip a clean spacer (of the same thickness as the brake disc) between the pads, then secure the caliper clear of the working area without stretching or kinking the brake flexible hose.

8 Disconnect the track rod balljoint from the hub carrier steering arm (Chapter 10).

9 Disconnect the suspension upper balljoint from the upper suspension arm (Chapter 10); discard the lockwasher.

10 Sharply tug the hub carrier outwards off the driveshaft splines; it may be necessary to use a soft-faced mallet (having first refitted the driveshaft nut to protect the shaft's threaded end) to tap the driveshaft out of the hub.

11 Use a suitable lever to prise out the driveshaft until the circlip compresses into its groove and is released from the differential sun gear (photo).

12 Withdraw the driveshaft assembly. Check the circlip at the driveshaft's inboard end carefully, renewing it if there is any doubt about its condition. To prevent the risk of the sun gear falling down

**Fig. 8.1 Exploded view of
driveshaft assembly (Sec 1)**

1   Circlip
2   Inner joint and shaft
    assembly
3   Large gaiter clip
4   Gaiter
5   Small gaiter clip
6   Damper clip
7   Dynamic damper –
    right-hand driveshaft
    only
8   Small gaiter clip
9   Gaiter
10 Large gaiter clip
11 Stopper ring
12 Circlip
13 Outer joint assembly
14 Driveshaft nut

**2.2 On cars fitted with alloy roadwheels, remove the centre cap to
expose driveshaft nut**

inside the transmission, insert a clean metal rod or wooden dowel of the
same diameter as the driveshaft into the transmission aperture until the
gear is securely supported.

Refitting

13   On refitting, proceed as follows.
14   Thoroughly clean the driveshaft itself and the apertures in the
transmission and hub carrier to prevent the entry of dirt during
reassembly. Apply a thin film of grease to the oil seal lips and to the
driveshaft splines and shoulders. Check that all gaiter clips are securely
fastened.
15   Ensure that the circlip fitted to the inboard end of each driveshaft is
in good condition and is located securely in its groove. Remove the sun
gear support.
16   Taking care not to damage the oil seal lips, insert the driveshaft

into the transmission and engage its splines with those of the sun gear.
Press the driveshaft firmly into place until the circlip engages correctly
behind (inboard of) the sun gear. If it is necessary to use tools to tap the
driveshaft into place, be very careful not to damage the rubber gaiter.
17   Check that the circlip is properly engaged by grasping the inner
joint body firmly and trying to pull the driveshaft out of the sun gear.
18   Refit the driveshaft to the hub carrier and fit a new driveshaft nut.
19   Refit the upper balljoint to the suspension upper arm, fit a new
lockwasher and tighten the balljoint-to-upper suspension arm nut to the
specified torque wrench setting, then secure the nut by bending the
washer tab up against one of its flats (Chapter 10).
20   Connect the track rod balljoint to the hub carrier steering arm and
tighten the balljoint nut to the specified torque wrench setting (Chapter 10).
21   Refit the brake caliper, tightening its bolts to the specified torque
wrench setting (Chapter 9).
22   Jack up the suspension, remove the spacer and lower the
suspension again, then refit the underwing shield and the roadwheel.
23   Lower the car to the ground and tighten the driveshaft nut and
roadwheel nuts to their specified torque settings. Using a hammer and
punch, secure the driveshaft nut by staking its collar into the driveshaft
groove (photos).
24   Refit the roadwheel trim or centre cap.
25   Refill the transmission with oil (Chapter 7).

3   Driveshaft rubber gaiters – renewal

Outer joint

Note: *This operation is a great deal easier if the driveshaft is removed
from the car, as described below; however, it is possible to dismantle an
outer joint without removing the driveshaft from the transmission,
provided that care is taken to hold the driveshaft into the transmission
while the hub carrier and outer joint are removed. If this approach is to be
used, refer to Section 2, paragraphs 1 to 3, then 5 to 10*

1   Remove the driveshaft (Sec 2).

2.11 Levering driveshaft out of
transmission

2.23A Tighten driveshaft nut to specified
torque wrench setting ...

2.23B ... and stake into driveshaft groove to
secure it

3.2 It may be necessary to cut gaiter clips to
release gaiters

3.4 Driving outer constant velocity joint off
driveshaft end

3.9 Refitting outer constant velocity joint to
driveshaft

Fig. 8.2 Position the dynamic damper the specified distance from
the outer joint flange, then secure the clip (Sec 3)

A = 393.25 to 399.25 mm

2   Cut the gaiter clips and peel back the gaiter from the joint (photo).
3   Clamp the driveshaft in a soft-jawed vice.
4   Using a sharply-pointed punch or scribing tool, mark the
relationship of the joint body to the driveshaft itself, then use a hammer
and a drift (applied to the joint inner race only) to tap the joint off the
shaft splines until the circlip compresses into its groove and is released
from the inner race (photo).
5   Withdraw the joint from the driveshaft and slide off the gaiter; if it is
to be re-used, wrap insulating tape around the shaft to protect the gaiter
from any sharp edges. Check the gaiter for splits, cracking or other signs
of damage and renew it if necessary. Renew both clips.
6   Remove and discard the circlip from the driveshaft end.
7   On refitting, proceed as follows.
8   Wind a thin layer of insulating tape around the shaft to protect the
gaiter from the shaft splines and other sharp edges. Fit the small gaiter
clip, then slide on the gaiter and check that it is seated correctly before
removing the tape.

9   Ensuring that the stopper ring is securely located in its groove, fit a
new circlip to the groove nearest the driveshaft's end, apply a smear of
grease and press the outer joint into place so that the driveshaft end, the
circlip and the joint inner race are all aligned. Using a soft-faced mallet
and protecting the joint's threaded end by refitting temporarily the
driveshaft nut, tap the outer joint onto the driveshaft until the circlip
compresses into its groove and passes through the inner race (photo).
10   Check that the circlip is correctly engaged by trying to pull the joint
off the shaft.
11   Fill the joint with the grease provided in sachets in the gaiter kit
(photo); pack any surplus into the gaiter.
12   Position the gaiter on the joint groove, fasten the large gaiter clip
and expel all air from the gaiter before fastening the small gaiter clip.

Inner joint
13   Remove the outer joint as described above.
14   On right-hand shafts only, remove the clip and withdraw the
dynamic damper; use liquid soap if necessary to aid damper removal
and clean off any rust deposits or similar using emery cloth.
15   Cut the clips (photo) and withdraw the gaiter; if it is to be re-used,
wrap insulating tape around the shaft to protect the gaiter from any
sharp edges. Check the gaiter for splits, cracking or other signs of
damage and renew it if necessary. Renew both clips.
16   Clean the shaft (using emery cloth to polish away any rust or sharp
edges which might damage the new gaiter's sealing lip) and joint,
renewing any worn or damaged items.
17   On reassembly, pack the joint with the grease provided in sachets
in the gaiter kit (photo) then slide the new gaiter onto the shaft, taking
care not to damage the gaiter lip.
18   Position the gaiter on the joint groove, fasten the large gaiter clip
and expel all air from the gaiter before fastening the small gaiter clip
(photo).
19   On left-hand shafts, refit the outer joint. On right-hand shafts,
lubricate the shaft and refit the dynamic damper (with a new clip) so that
its clip flange is inboard, towards the inner joint. Reassemble the outer
joint, then position the damper as shown in Fig. 8.2 and secure its clip;
clean off any surplus lubricant.

3.11 Components of driveshaft (outer) constant velocity joint gaiter kit

3.15 Cutting inner constant velocity joint gaiter clip to release it

3.17 Using sachets supplied with gaiter kit to fill inner joint with grease

3.18 Using correct tool to tighten gaiter clip – end cutters can be used instead, if care is exercised

4 Driveshaft overhaul – general information

1   If any of the checks described in Chapter 1 reveal wear in any driveshaft joint, first remove the roadwheel trim or centre cap (as appropriate). If the staking is still effective, the driveshaft nut should be correctly tightened; if in doubt use a torque wrench to check that the nut is securely fastened and re-stake it (Sec 2), then refit the centre cap or trim. Repeat this check on the remaining driveshaft nut.

2   Road test the vehicle and listen for a metallic clicking from the front as the vehicle is driven slowly in a circle on full lock. If a clicking noise is heard this indicates wear in the outer constant velocity joint. This means that the joint must be renewed; reconditioning is not possible.

3   If the outer joint is worn it can be renewed separately (see note, Section 1); the procedure is as described in Section 3, paragraphs 1 to 12.

4   If vibration, consistent with road speed, is felt through the car when accelerating, there is a possibility of wear in the inner constant velocity joints.

5   Remove the driveshafts (Sec 2), then dismantle them (Sec 3) and check the joints; if any wear or free play is found, the inner joints are worn and must be renewed, complete with the shaft assembly (see note, Section 1).

Chapter 9 Braking system

Contents

Specifications

System type .... Hydraulically-operated diagonally split dual circuit with pressure regulating valves to rear brakes, vacuum servo-assisted, discs front, drums rear. Handbrake cable-operated on rear drums

Front brakes
Type.. Disc, with single-piston sliding caliper
Disc diameter .... 238 mm
Disc thickness:
   New... 12.76 mm
   Minimum .... 10.80 mm
   Maximum thickness variation .... 0.015 mm
Disc maximum run-out .... 0.150 mm
Brake pad friction material minimum thickness .... 3.0 mm

Rear brakes
Type.. Single leading shoe drum
Drum diameter:
   New... 177.90 mm
   Maximum .... 179.0 mm
Drum maximum ovality... 0.050 mm
Brake shoe friction material minimum thickness .... 1.5 mm

Handbrake
Roadwheels bind at:
   Up to VIN 661301 .... 2 to 3 notches
   VIN 661301 on.. 1 notch
Roadwheels lock at:
   Up to VIN 661301 .... 3 to 4 notches
   VIN 661301 on.. 1 to 2 notches

Hydraulic system
Recommended fluid.. Duckhams Universal Brake and Clutch Fluid

Torque wrench settings

	Nm	lbf ft
Vacuum servo unit mounting nuts	13	10
Master cylinder-to-vacuum servo unit mounting nuts	13	10
Vacuum servo unit vacuum hose banjo union bolt – at inlet manifold	50	37
Brake pipe union nuts	15	11
Rear brake pressure regulating valve mounting bolt	25	19
Front brake caliper:		
Bleed nipple	13	10
Brake flexible hose banjo union bolt	35	26
Guide pin bolts	30	22
Caliper-to-hub carrier mounting bolts	85	63
Front brake disc securing screws	7	5
Front brake disc shield mounting bolts	10	8
Rear brake drum securing screw	7	5
Rear brake (wheel cylinder) bleed nipple	7	5
Rear brake backplate-to-suspension trailing arm nuts and bolts	25	19
Handbrake lever assembly-to-body mounting nuts and bolts	25	19

1 General information

The braking system is hydraulically-operated and incorporates a vacuum servo unit and master cylinder mounted on the right-hand side of the engine compartment bulkhead, with disc brakes at the front wheels and drums at the rear.

The master cylinder is of the tandem type and, with the connecting metal pipes and flexible hoses, provides a diagonally-split dual circuit system. The primary circuit operates the right-hand front and left-hand rear brakes while the secondary operates the left-hand front and right-hand rear. Under normal conditions both circuits operate in unison, but in the event of hydraulic failure of one of the circuits full brake pressure will still be available at two of the brakes, thus allowing the car to be stopped in a stable manner, albeit with increased pedal movement.

To prevent the rear wheels locking under heavy braking, a pressure-sensitive regulating valve is fitted into each circuit to control the amount of hydraulic pressure at the rear brakes.

The handbrake operates the rear brakes through a lever assembly bolted to the floor and a cable to the brake backplates.

In addition to the stop-lamps, there is a brake warning lamp in the instrument panel; this is activated by a plunger switch mounted at the base of the handbrake lever, so that the lamp lights whenever the handbrake is applied, and also by a float-type sender unit in the master cylinder reservoir filler cap, so that the lamp lights whenever the fluid level falls to a dangerously low level.

The vacuum servo unit uses inlet manifold depression (generated only while the engine is running) to boost the effort applied by the driver at the brake pedal and transmits this increased effort to the master cylinder pistons. It is direct-acting, with its input rod connected directly to the brake pedal and is of the suspended-vacuum type. Basically it consists of a sealed metal chamber divided into two by a diaphragm, passages between the two being controlled by the input rod. Under normal running conditions both chambers are at less than atmospheric pressure, but when the brake pedal is applied a valve opens the rear chamber to atmospheric pressure; the pressure difference forces the diaphragm forwards, causing the pushrod to apply increased effort to the master cylinder.

The front brake calipers are of the single-piston sliding type in which the main caliper body slides on a mounting bracket rigidly attached to the hub carrier. Full braking efficiency relies on the ability of the caliper body to slide easily on its mounting bracket, as well as on the condition of the pads and the caliper bore, piston and seals.

The rear brakes consist of the drum, which is of cast iron and is fastened to the hub and roadwheel, as well as the backplate which is mounted on the rear suspension trailing arm to carry the shoes and wheel cylinder.

Note: *When servicing any part of the system, work carefully and methodically; also observe scrupulous cleanliness when overhauling any part of the hydraulic system. Always renew components (in axle sets, where applicable) if in doubt about their condition and use only genuine Rover replacement parts, or at least those of known good quality. Note the warnings given in 'Safety first' and at relevant points in this Chapter concerning the dangers of asbestos dust and hydraulic fluid.*

2 Brake pedal – removal, inspection and refitting

Removal

1   Release the retaining fasteners and remove the fusebox cover.
2   Remove its retaining screw and bolt and withdraw the steering column cover, then unfasten the column from its remaining mountings and lower it as far as possible without stretching the wiring (Chapter 10).
3   Remove its split pin and withdraw the pedal-to-vacuum servo unit fork clevis pin, then unhook the pedal return spring from the pedal (photo).
4   Undo the nuts and bolt securing the pedal pivot bracket (and the vacuum servo unit) to the bulkhead, then unbolt the pedal pivot bracket from the steering column lower mounting bracket (photo).
5   Unscrew the nut securing the bracket to the pedal pivot shaft and withdraw the bracket far enough to permit the pedal to be removed; disconnect or release the wiring as necessary.

Inspection

6   Carefully clean all components and renew any that are worn or damaged; check the return spring and the bearing surfaces of the pivot bushes and shaft with particular care; the bushes can be renewed separately if required.

2.3 Brake pedal-to-vacuum servo unit fork clevis pin 'A', pedal pivot bracket mounting bolt 'B'

Fig. 9.2 Brake pedal assembly – see also Fig. 6.3 (Sec 2)

1	Pivot bracket	7	Pedal pivot bush – 2 off
2	Washer	8	Pedal rubber
3	Spring washer	9	Clevis pin
4	Nut	10	Circlip
5	Pedal	11	Return spring
6	Stop-lamp switch adjuster	12	Bolt
	nut – 2 off	13	Spring washer

Fig. 9.1 Layout of braking system components (Sec 1)

1	Secondary hydraulic circuit	8	Brake pipe – left-hand rear brake
2	Primary hydraulic circuit	9	Master cylinder assembly
3	Brake pipe – right-hand valve-to-right-hand front hose	10	Vacuum servo unit
		11	Brake flexible hose – right-hand front brake
4	Brake pipe – left-hand valve-to-left-hand front hose	12	Brake flexible hose – left-hand front brake
5	Brake pipe – right-hand valve-to-left-hand rear hose	13	Brake flexible hose – rear brake
		14	Brake pedal
6	Brake pipe – left-hand valve-to-right-hand rear hose	15	Rear brake pressure regulating valve assembly
		16	Bolt
7	Brake pipe – right-hand rear brake	17	Spacer

Refitting

7 Refitting is the reverse of the removal procedure, but apply a thin smear of Molykote 44 lubricant to the pedal-to-vacuum servo unit fork clevis pin and multi-purpose grease to all other pivots and bearing surfaces.

3   Vacuum servo unit – checking

1 In normal use any failure of the vacuum servo unit will be evident to the driver due to the increased pedal effort required to achieve normal braking. To test the unit, park the car on level ground and release the handbrake, then proceed as follows.

2 Switch off the engine and destroy the vacuum in the unit by depressing the brake pedal five to six times; check that there is no significant change in pedal travel after the first two or three strokes.

3 Apply normal pressure to the brake pedal and maintain it while the engine is started. If the unit is operating correctly the pedal should move down slightly as vacuum is restored in the unit.

4 To check whether the unit is completely airtight, start the engine and run it for one or two minutes, then switch off the ignition. Depress the brake pedal slowly several times using the same, normal, pressure at each stroke. If the unit is airtight the pedal should go down to the normal depressed height on the first one or two strokes, but after that the depressed height should gradually rise as the vacuum is destroyed and the level of assistance decreases.

5 Finally start the engine again, apply normal pressure to the brake pedal and maintain it while the engine is switched off; there should be no change in pedal height for at least thirty seconds.

6 If the vacuum servo unit proves faulty as a result of the above tests it must be renewed, although it is worth checking first that the non-return check valve is not faulty (Sec 5) or that the vacuum hose from the inlet manifold is not kinked, blocked or leaking. While a repair kit is available from Rover dealers, no details are available of how to overhaul the unit, so this task **must** be left to a Rover dealer or similar expert; always check first the cost of a replacement unit against that of a kit and labour charges to establish whether repairs are economically viable.

2.4 Remaining pedal pivot bracket mountings and pivot shaft nut (arrows)

6.2 Always renew sealing washers whenever vacuum hose banjo union is disturbed. Ensure that locating pin is correctly positioned

4 Vacuum servo unit – removal and refitting

Removal

1 Open the bonnet. If the extra clearance is required, remove the air cleaner assembly (Chapter 4).

2 Unscrew the two nuts securing the master cylinder to the vacuum servo unit and very carefully lift the master cylinder upwards clear of the servo unit studs and pushrod, taking great care not to kink or damage the metal brake pipes. If there is any risk of kinking or damaging either of the pipes, either unclip them from the bulkhead or disconnect them (Sec 8) until the master cylinder can be moved clear or removed, as required (photo).

3 Carefully unplug the vacuum hose adaptor from the vacuum servo unit.

4 Working inside the car, release the retaining fasteners and remove the fusebox cover.

5 Remove its retaining screw and bolt and withdraw the steering column cover, then unfasten the column from its remaining mountings and lower it as far as possible without stretching the wiring (Chapter 10).

6 Remove its split pin and withdraw the brake pedal-to-vacuum servo unit fork clevis pin.

7 Unscrew the four nuts securing the vacuum servo unit (and the

4.2 Master cylinder mounting nuts 'A', vacuum hose adaptor 'B', non-return check valve 'C'

brake pedal pivot bracket) to its mounting plate and the bulkhead; while three of the nuts are unscrewed from inside the car, immediately above the brake pedal pivot, the fourth is reached from beneath the front edge of the mounting plate, inside the engine compartment.

8 Withdraw the vacuum servo unit and discard the gasket.

9 If the vacuum servo unit is faulty it must be renewed (Sec 3, paragraph 6). Renew the gasket as a matter of course.

Refitting

10 Refitting is the reverse of the removal procedure, noting the following points.

(a) Tighten all nuts and bolts securely, to the specified torque wrench settings, where given.

(b) Lubricate the pedal-to-servo unit fork clevis pin as described in Section 2.

(c) If any brake pipes were disconnected, bleed any air from the system (Sec 7) and wash off any spilt hydraulic fluid.

(d) When refitting the vacuum hose adaptor, take note of the comments made in Section 6.

(e) Check the operation of the brakes in general and of the vacuum servo unit in particular.

5 Vacuum servo unit non-return check valve – testing

1 When testing the valve, remember that its function is to allow air to flow in one direction only, out of the vacuum servo unit. If it allows air to flow in both directions, or in neither, it is faulty and must be renewed.

2 To test the valve, carefully unplug the vacuum hose adaptor from the vacuum servo unit and blow through the hose from the adaptor; air should pass freely through the valve. Now disconnect the hose from the inlet manifold (Sec 6), block the manifold banjo union holes and suck hard on the adaptor end; there should be no leakage at all back through the valve.

3 If the valve is faulty it must be renewed; do not try to separate it from its hose (see note, Section 6).

6 Vacuum servo unit non-return check valve – removal and refitting

Note: *The valve is only available as part of the vacuum hose assembly; do not try to remove it, the adaptor, or the banjo union from the hose or air leaks may ensue, necessitating the renewal of the assembly*

Removal

1   The valve is set in the vacuum hose from the inlet manifold which is plugged into the top of the vacuum servo unit (see photo 4.2).
2   To remove the valve, carefully unplug the hose adaptor from the vacuum servo unit, then unscrew the banjo union bolt from the inlet manifold and withdraw the hose assembly (photo). Discard the sealing washers; they must be renewed whenever disturbed.

Refitting

3   Refitting is the reverse of the removal procedure, noting the following points.

  (a) Use new sealing washers when refitting the inlet manifold banjo union (one on each side of the hose union) and tighten the bolt to its specified torque wrench setting, ensuring that the union's locating pin is correctly engaged between the manifold lugs and that the union does not twist as the bolt is tightened.
  (b) When plugging the hose adaptor into the vacuum servo unit, take care not to distort or displace the sealing grommet. Note that if the grommet is displaced into the vacuum servo unit, the unit must be renewed.
  (c) As soon as the engine is restarted check that there are no signs of air leaks.

7   Hydraulic system – bleeding

Note: *Hydraulic fluid is poisonous; wash off immediately and thoroughly in the case of skin contact and seek immediate medical advice if any fluid is swallowed or gets into the eyes. Certain types of hydraulic fluid are inflammable and may ignite when allowed into contact with hot components; when servicing any hydraulic system it is safest to assume that the fluid is inflammable and to take precautions against the risk of fire as though it is petrol that is being handled. Hydraulic fluid is also an effective paint stripper and will attack plastics; if any is spilt, it should be washed off immediately using copious quantities of fresh water. Finally, it is hygroscopic (it absorbs moisture from the air) – old fluid may be contaminated and unfit for further use. When topping-up or renewing the fluid, always use the recommended type and ensure that it comes from a freshly-opened sealed container*

General

1   The correct operation of any hydraulic system is only possible after removing all air from the components and circuit; this is achieved by bleeding the system.
2   During the bleeding procedure, add only clean, unused hydraulic fluid of the recommended type; never re-use fluid that has already been bled from the system. Ensure that sufficient fluid is available before starting work.
3   If there is any possibility of incorrect fluid being already in the system, the brake components and circuit must be flushed completely with uncontaminated, correct fluid and new seals should be fitted to the various components.
4   If hydraulic fluid has been lost from the system, or air has entered, because of a leak ensure that the fault is cured before proceeding further.
5   Park the car on level ground, switch off the engine and select first or reverse gear, then chock the wheels and release the handbrake.
6   Check that all pipes and hoses are secure, unions tight and bleed nipples closed. Clean any dirt from around the bleed nipples.
7   Top the master cylinder reservoir up to the 'Max' level line; refit the cap loosely and remember to maintain the fluid level at least above the 'Min' level line throughout the procedure or there is a risk of further air entering the system.
8   There are a number of one-man, do-it-yourself brake bleeding kits currently available from motor accessory shops. It is recommended that one of these kits is used whenever possible as they greatly simplify the bleeding operation and also reduce the risk of expelled air and fluid being drawn back into the system. If such a kit is not available the basic (two-man) method must be used which is described in detail below.
9   If a kit is to be used, prepare the car as described previously and follow the kit manufacturer's instructions as the procedure may vary slightly according to the type being used; generally they are as outlined below in the relevant sub-section.

10   Whichever method is used, the same sequence must be followed (paras 11 and 12) to ensure the removal of all air from the system.

Bleeding sequence

11   If the system has been only partially disconnected and suitable precautions were taken to minimise fluid loss, it should be necessary only to bleed that part of the system (ie the primary or secondary circuit).
12   If the complete system is to be bled, then it should be done working in the following sequence.

  (a) Left-hand rear brake.
  (b) Right-hand front brake.
  (c) Right-hand rear brake.
  (d) Left-hand front brake.

Bleeding – basic (two-man) method

13   Collect a clean glass jar, a suitable length of plastic or rubber tubing which is a tight fit over the bleed nipple and a ring spanner to fit the nipple. The help of an assistant will also be required.
14   Remove the dust cap from the first nipple in the sequence. Fit the spanner and tube to the nipple, place the other end of the tube in the jar and pour in sufficient fluid to cover the end of the tube.
15   Ensure that the master cylinder reservoir fluid level is maintained at least above the 'Min' level line throughout the procedure.
16   Have the assistant fully depress the brake pedal several times to build up pressure, then maintain it on the final stroke.
17   While pedal pressure is maintained, unscrew the bleed nipple (approximately one turn) and allow the compressed fluid and air to flow into the jar. The assistant should maintain pedal pressure, following it down to the floor if necessary and should not release it until instructed to do so. When the flow stops, tighten the bleed nipple again, release the pedal slowly and recheck the reservoir fluid level.
18   Repeat the steps given in paragraphs 16 and 17 until the fluid emerging from the bleed nipple is free from air bubbles. If the master cylinder has been drained and refilled and air is being bled from the first nipple in the sequence, allow approximately five seconds between cycles for the master cylinder passages to refill (see also Sec 9).
19   When no more air bubbles appear, tighten the bleed nipple securely, remove the tube and spanner and refit the dust cap. Do not overtighten the bleed nipple; note the specified torque wrench settings.
20   Repeat the procedure on the remaining nipples in the sequence until all air is removed from the system and the brake pedal feels firm again.

Bleeding – using a one-way valve kit

21   As their name implies, these kits consist of a length of tubing with a one-way valve fitted to prevent expelled air and fluid being drawn back into the system; some kits include a translucent container which can be

7.21 Bleeding the brake hydraulic system using a typical one-way valve kit

8.1 Using a brake hose clamp will minimise fluid loss when brake flexible hoses are disconnected

positioned so that the air bubbles can be more easily seen flowing from the end of the tube (photo).

22   The kit is connected to the bleed nipple, which is then opened. The user returns to the driver's seat and depresses the brake pedal with a smooth, steady stroke and slowly releases it; this is repeated until the expelled fluid is clear of air bubbles.

23   Note that these kits simplify work so much that it is easy to forget the master cylinder reservoir fluid level; ensure that this is maintained at least above the 'Min' level line at all times.

Bleeding – using a pressure bleeding kit

24   These kits are usually operated by the reservoir of pressurised air contained in the spare tyre, although note that it will probably be necessary to reduce the pressure to a lower limit than normal; refer to the instructions supplied with the kit.

25   By connecting a pressurised, fluid-filled container to the master cylinder reservoir, bleeding can be carried out simply by opening each nipple in turn (in the specified sequence) and allowing the fluid to flow out until no more air bubbles can be seen in the expelled fluid.

26   This method has the advantage that the large reservoir of fluid provides an additional safeguard against air being drawn into the system during bleeding.

27   Pressure bleeding is particularly effective when bleeding 'difficult' systems or when bleeding the complete system at the time of routine fluid renewal.

All methods

28   When bleeding is complete and firm pedal feel is restored, wash off any spilt fluid, tighten the bleed nipples securely and refit their dust caps. Do not overtighten the bleed nipples; note their specified torque wrench settings.

29   Check the hydraulic fluid level and top up if necessary (Chapter 1).

30   Discard any hydraulic fluid that has been bled from the system; it will not be fit for re-use.

31   Check the feel of the brake pedal. If it feels at all spongy, air must still be present in the system and further bleeding is required. Failure to bleed satisfactorily after a reasonable repetition of the bleeding procedure may be due to worn master cylinder seals.

8   Hydraulic pipes and hoses – renewal

Note: *Before starting work, refer to the note at the beginning of Section 7 concerning the dangers of hydraulic fluid*

1   If any pipe or hose is to be renewed, minimise fluid loss by removing the master cylinder reservoir cap and then tightening it down onto a piece of polythene (taking care not to damage the sender unit) to obtain an airtight seal. Alternatively flexible hoses can be sealed, if required, using a proprietary brake hose clamp (photo), while metal brake pipe unions can be plugged (if care is taken not to allow dirt into the system) or capped immediately they are disconnected. Place a wad of rag under any union that is to be disconnected to catch any spilt fluid.

2   If a flexible hose is to be disconnected, unscrew the brake pipe union nut before removing the spring clip which secures the hose to its mounting bracket.

3   To unscrew the union nuts it is preferable to obtain a brake pipe spanner of the correct size; these are available from most large motor accessory shops. Failing this a close-fitting open-ended spanner will be required, though if the nuts are tight or corroded their flats may be rounded-off if the spanner slips. In such a case a self-locking wrench is often the only way to unscrew a stubborn union, but it follows that the pipe and the damaged nuts must be renewed on reassembly. Always clean a union and surrounding area before disconnecting it. If disconnecting a component with more than one union make a careful note of the connections before disturbing any of them.

4   If a brake pipe is to be renewed it can be obtained, cut to length and with the union nuts and end flares in place, from Rover dealers. All that is then necessary is to bend it to shape, following the line of the original, before fitting it to the car. Alternatively, most motor accessory shops can make up brake pipes from kits, but this requires very careful measurement of the original to ensure that the replacement is of the correct length. The safest answer is usually to take the original to the shop as a pattern.

5   On refitting, do not overtighten the union nuts. The specified torque wrench settings are not high and it is not necessary to exercise brute force to obtain a sound joint. When refitting flexible hoses, always renew any sealing washers used; again, note the torque settings specified.

6   Ensure that the pipes and hoses are correctly routed with no kinks and that they are secured in the clips or brackets provided. After fitting remove the polythene from the reservoir and bleed the hydraulic system (Sec 7). Wash off any spilt fluid and check carefully for fluid leaks.

9   Master cylinder – removal, overhaul and refitting

Note: *Before starting work, refer to the note at the beginning of Section 7 concerning the dangers of hydraulic fluid*

Removal

1   Remove the master cylinder reservoir cap, having disconnected the sender unit wires, and syphon the hydraulic fluid from the reservoir. **Note:** *Do not syphon the fluid by mouth, as it is poisonous; use a syringe or an old poultry baster.* Alternatively, open any convenient bleed nipple in the system and gently pump the brake pedal to expel the fluid through a plastic tube connected to the nipple (Sec 7).

2   Release their clips and secure the clutch and speedometer drive cables and the wiring clear of the master cylinder.

3   Unscrew the union nuts and disconnect the metal brake pipes (Sec 8). Try to keep fluid spillage to a minimum and wash off any spilt fluid as soon as possible.

4   Unscrew the two nuts securing the master cylinder to the vacuum servo unit and withdraw it; remove and discard the sealing O-ring.

Overhaul

Note: *Before attempting to overhaul the unit, check the price and availability of individual components and compare this with the price of a new or reconditioned unit, as overhaul may not be viable on economic grounds alone. Also, read through the procedure and check that the special tools and facilities required are available*

5   Remove the master cylinder from the car and clean it thoroughly.

6   Extract the roll pin, then prise the reservoir from the master cylinder body and remove the two seals and their baffle plates from the body ports.

7   Press the primary piston in as far as possible and extract the secondary piston stop pin from the reservoir inlet port, then remove the retaining circlip.

Fig. 9.3 Master cylinder – cutaway and exploded views (Sec 9)

1   Master cylinder body
2   Secondary piston stop pin
3   Fluid reservoir
4   Seals
5   Baffle plates
6   Sealing O-ring
7   Roll pin
8   Secondary piston seal and washer
9   Secondary piston and spring
10 Secondary piston seal
11 Screw
12 Spring retainer
13 Circlip
14 Spring seat
15 Primary piston seal and washer
16 Primary piston and spring
17 Spacer
18 Primary piston vacuum seals and washers
19 Circlip

8   Noting the order of removal and the direction of fitting of each component, withdraw the piston assemblies with their springs and seals, tapping the body on to a clean wooden surface to dislodge them. If necessary, clamp the master cylinder body in a vice (fitted with soft jaw covers) and use compressed air (applied through the secondary circuit fluid port) to assist the removal of the secondary piston assembly.

9   Undo the retaining screw to separate the spring retainer and spring from the primary piston and remove the circlip to release the spring seat, the piston seal and its washer.

10 Thoroughly clean all components using only methylated spirit, isopropyl alcohol or clean hydraulic fluid as a cleaning medium. Never use mineral-based solvents such as petrol or paraffin which will attack the hydraulic system's rubber components. Dry the components immediately using compressed air or a clean, lint-free cloth.

11 Check all components and renew any that are worn or damaged. Check particularly the cylinder bores and pistons; the complete assembly should be renewed if these are scratched, worn or corroded. If

there is any doubt about the condition of the assembly or of any of its components, renew it. Check that the body's inlet and bypass ports are clear.

12 If the assembly is fit for further use, obtain a repair kit. Renew all seals and sealing O-rings disturbed on dismantling as a matter of course; these should never be re-used. Renew also any other items included in the repair kit.

13 On reassembly, soak the pistons and the new seals in clean hydraulic fluid. Smear clean fluid into the cylinder bore.

14 Fit the new seals to their pistons using only the fingers to manipulate them into the grooves.

15 Insert the pistons into the bore using a twisting motion to avoid trapping the seal lips. Ensure that all components are refitted in the correct order and the right way round.

16 Press the secondary piston assembly fully up into the bore using a clean metal rod, then refit the stop pin.

17 Refit the primary piston assembly, then secure it with a new circlip.

18 Refit the baffle plates and press new seals into the body ports,

10.4 Unscrew caliper bottom guide pin bolt and swing up caliper body ...

10.5 ... note location of anti-rattle springs before removing brake pads

10.6 Measuring thickness of brake pad friction material

then refit the reservoir and secure it with the roll pin.

19 Refit the master cylinder to the car, using a new sealing O-ring.

Refitting

20 Refitting is the reverse of the removal procedure, noting the following points.

(a) Refit the master cylinder to the vacuum servo unit, aligning the servo's pushrod with the master cylinder primary piston.

(b) Fit a new sealing O-ring and tighten the mounting nuts to their specified torque wrench setting.

(c) Refill the reservoir with new fluid and bleed the system (Sec 7).

(d) If a new master cylinder has been fitted (or the original was fully drained) start the bleeding procedure by disconnecting each metal brake pipe in turn (top first) and gently pumping the brake pedal until only clear hydraulic fluid emerges. Catch the ejected fluid with a rag wrapped around the master cylinder.

(e) In very difficult cases, disconnect both pipes, plug their ports with the fingers, then uncover each one in turn as the brake pedal is depressed and plug it again as the pedal is released, so that fluid is forcibly drawn in from the reservoir. Refit and tighten securely all pipe unions as soon as the master cylinder is cleared of air and is pumping correctly, then proceed with the normal bleeding procedure.

(f) Ensure the disturbed cables and wiring are correctly re-routed, check the hydraulic fluid level and top up if necessary, then reconnect the sender unit wires (Chapter 1).

---

10 Front brake pads – renewal

Warning: *Renew both sets of front brake pads at the same time – never renew the pads on only one wheel as uneven braking may result. Note that the dust created by wear of the pads may contain asbestos, which is a health hazard. Never blow it out with compressed air and don't inhale any of it. An approved filtering mask should be worn when working on the brakes. DO NOT use petroleum-based solvents to clean brake parts. Use brake cleaner or methylated spirit only*

1 Jack up the front of the car and support it securely on axle stands, then remove the roadwheel (see *'Jacking, towing and wheel changing'*).

2 If the quick check described in Chapter 1 has shown the condition of the brake pads to be doubtful, they must be removed and checked, as follows.

3 Pull the caliper body outwards to compress the piston into the cylinder, then check that the caliper body slides smoothly and easily in the mounting bracket. If not, the guide pins must be cleaned, checked for wear and lubricated before reassembly.

4 Unscrew the caliper bottom guide pin bolt, if necessary using a slim open-ended spanner to counterhold the head of the guide pin itself (photo). Pivot the caliper body upwards to expose the brake pads. Do not depress the brake pedal until the caliper is reassembled.

5 Noting the exact location of the anti-rattle springs, withdraw the brake pads (photo). Mark them so that they will be refitted in their

10.9 Remove, clean and lubricate guide pins if caliper body is not free to slide on mounting bracket

original locations; do not be tempted to interchange pads to compensate for uneven wear.

6 First measure the thickness of friction material remaining on each brake pad (photo). If either pad is worn at any point to the specified minimum thickness or less, all four pads must be renewed (see the warning above and note that replacement pads are available from Rover dealers only as an axle set). Also, the pads should be renewed if any are fouled with oil or grease; there is no satisfactory way of degreasing friction material once contaminated.

7 If any of the brake pads are worn unevenly or fouled with oil or grease, trace and rectify the cause before reassembly.

8 If the brake pads are still serviceable, carefully clean them using a clean, fine wire brush or similar, paying particular attention to the sides and back of the metal backing. Clean out the grooves in the friction material (where applicable) and pick out any large embedded particles of dirt or debris. Carefully clean the anti-rattle springs and the pad locations in the caliper body and mounting bracket.

9 If there is any doubt about the ability of the caliper to slide in the mounting bracket, dismantle, clean and lubricate the guide pins as described in Section 12 (photo). Check the brake disc (Sec 13).

10 On reassembly, fit the anti-rattle springs to the brake pads and apply a thin smear of high-temperature brake grease (silicone- or PBC/Poly Butyl Cuprysil-based) or anti-seize compound (eg Holts Copaslip) to the sides and back of each pad's metal backing and to those surfaces of the caliper body and mounting bracket which bear on the pads. Do not allow the lubricant to foul the friction material.

11 Refit the brake pads, ensuring that the friction material is against the disc.

12 If new brake pads have been fitted, the caliper piston must be pushed back into the cylinder to make room for them. Either use a G-clamp or similar tool, or use suitable pieces of wood as levers.

Provided that the master cylinder reservoir has not been overfilled with hydraulic fluid there should be no spillage, but keep a careful watch on the fluid level while retracting the piston. If the fluid level rises above the 'Max' level line at any time the surplus should be syphoned off or ejected via a plastic tube connected to the bleed nipple (see Section 9, paragraph 1).

13   Pivot the caliper body down over the brake pads, refit the bottom guide pin bolt and tighten it to the specified torque wrench setting.

14   Check that the caliper body slides smoothly in the mounting bracket, then depress the brake pedal repeatedly until the pads are pressed into firm contact with the brake disc and normal (non-assisted) pedal pressure is restored. Refit the roadwheel.

15   Repeat the full procedure on the opposite brake caliper, then lower the car to the ground and tighten the roadwheel nuts to the specified torque wrench setting (Chapter 10).

16   Check the hydraulic fluid level (Chapter 1).

11   Front brake caliper – removal and refitting

Note: *Before starting work, refer to the note at the beginning of Section 7 concerning the dangers of hydraulic fluid and to the warning at the beginning of Section 10 concerning the dangers of asbestos dust*

Removal

1   Jack up the front of the car and support it securely on axle stands, then remove the roadwheel (see *'Jacking, towing and wheel changing'*).

2   Minimise fluid loss either by removing the master cylinder reservoir cap and then tightening it down onto a piece of polythene to obtain an airtight seal (taking care not to damage the sender unit), or by using a brake hose clamp, a G-clamp or a similar tool to clamp the flexible hose.

3   Clean the area around the union, then unscrew the flexible hose banjo union bolt. Discard the sealing washers; they must be renewed whenever disturbed. If the caliper is not to be dismantled, plug the fluid orifice to prevent the entry of dirt; similarly, plug or wrap the flexible hose banjo union tightly with polythene.

4   Unscrew the two caliper mounting bracket-to-hub carrier bolts (photo).

5   Withdraw the brake caliper assembly and slip a clean wooden spacer (of the same thickness as the brake disc) between the brake pads to retain them.

Refitting

6 Refitting is the reverse of the removal procedure, noting the following points.

11.4 Caliper mounting bracket-to-hub carrier bolts 'A', guide pin bolts 'B', flexible hose banjo union bolt 'C'

(a)   *Tighten all nuts and bolts to the specified torque wrench settings.*

(b)   *Renew the flexible hose union sealing washers as a matter of course.*

(c)   *Ensure that the flexible hose is correctly routed and secured by the clamp provided, without being twisted.*

(d)   *Bleed any air from the system (Sec 7).*

(e)   *Check the hydraulic fluid level (Chapter 1).*

12   Front brake caliper – overhaul

Note: *Before starting work, refer to the note at the beginning of Section 7 concerning the dangers of hydraulic fluid and to the warning at the beginning of Section 10 concerning the dangers of asbestos dust*

1   Jack up the front of the car and support it securely on axle stands, then remove the roadwheel (see *'Jacking, towing and wheel changing'*).

2   Minimise fluid loss either by removing the master cylinder reservoir cap and then tightening it down onto a piece of polythene to obtain an airtight seal (taking care not to damage the sender unit), or by using a brake hose clamp, a G-clamp or a similar tool to clamp the flexible hose.

3   Clean the area around the union, then unscrew the flexible hose banjo union bolt. Discard the sealing washers; they must be renewed whenever disturbed. Wrap polythene tightly around the flexible hose banjo union to prevent the entry of dirt.

4   Unscrew the caliper guide pin bolts, if necessary using a slim open-ended spanner to counterhold the head of each guide pin. Withdraw the caliper body.

5   Remove and check the brake pads (Sec 10).

6   Extract the guide pins, if necessary by screwing their bolts into them and pulling on the head of each bolt using a self-locking wrench or similar. Peel off the rubber dust cover from each guide pin and check it for cracks, splits or other damage; these can be renewed separately if required.

7   Unbolt the caliper mounting bracket from the hub carrier.

8   Prise off the piston dust seal lip from the caliper body. Place a small block of wood in the jaws of the caliper body and remove the piston, including dust seal, by applying a jet of low-pressure compressed air (such as that from a tyre pump) to the fluid entry port.

9   Peel the dust seal off the piston and use a blunt instrument such as a knitting needle to extract the piston (fluid) seal from the caliper cylinder bore.

10   Thoroughly clean all components using only methylated spirit, isopropyl alcohol or clean hydraulic fluid as a cleaning medium. Never use mineral-based solvents such as petrol or paraffin which will attack the hydraulic system's rubber components. Dry the components immediately using compressed air or a clean, lint-free cloth. Use compressed air to blow clear the fluid passages.

11   Check all components and renew any that are worn or damaged. Check particularly the cylinder bore and piston; these should be renewed (note that this means the renewal of the complete body assembly) if they are scratched, worn or corroded in any way. Similarly check the condition of the guide pins and their bores in the mounting bracket; both guide pins should be undamaged and (when cleaned) a reasonably tight sliding fit in the mounting bracket bores. If there is any doubt about the condition of any components, renew it.

12   If the assembly is fit for further use, obtain the appropriate repair kit; the components are available from Rover dealers in various combinations.

13   Renew all rubber seals, dust covers and caps, and also the sealing washers disturbed on dismantling as a matter of course; these should never be re-used.

14   On reassembly, ensure that all components are absolutely clean and dry.

15   Soak the piston and the new piston (fluid) seal in clean hydraulic fluid. Smear clean fluid on the cylinder bore surface.

16   Fit the new piston (fluid) seal using only the fingers to manipulate it into the cylinder bore groove. Fit the new dust seal to the piston and refit it to the cylinder bore using a twisting motion, and ensure that the piston enters squarely into the bore. Press the piston fully into the bore, then secure the dust seal to the caliper body.

17   Refit the caliper mounting bracket to the hub carrier, tightening the two bolts to the specified torque wrench setting.

Fig. 9.4 Exploded view of front brake caliper (Sec 12)

1   Guide pins
2   Rubber dust covers
3   Caliper mounting bracket
4   Brake pads
5   Piston (fluid) seal
6   Piston
7   Piston (dust) seal
8   Caliper body
9   Guide pin bolts
10 Bleed nipple
11 Sealing washers
12 Flexible hose banjo union bolt

18   Fit a new rubber dust cover to each guide pin and apply a thin smear of grease to the guide pins before refitting them to their bores. Rover recommend Molykote 111 for this purpose; a sachet is included in all appropriate repair kits. If it is not available, any good quality silicone- or PBC/Poly Butyl Cuprysil-based high-temperature brake grease or anti-seize compound (eg Holts Copaslip) can be used.
19   Refit the brake pads (Sec 10).
20   Fit the caliper body over the mounting bracket and brake pads, refit the guide pin bolts and tighten them to the torque wrench setting specified. Check that the caliper body slides smoothly in the mounting bracket.
21   Ensuring that the flexible hose is correctly routed and secured by the clamp provided without being twisted, refit the hose banjo union to the caliper body so that the union's locating peg is between the two body lugs, fit two new sealing washers (one on each side of the hose union), then refit the banjo union bolt and tighten it to its specified torque wrench setting, ensuring that the union does not twist as the bolt is tightened.
22   Bleed any air from the system (Sec 7), then depress the brake pedal repeatedly until the pads are pressed into firm contact with the brake disc and normal (non-assisted) pedal pressure is restored.
23   Wash off any spilt fluid and check for any fluid leaks while an assistant applies full pressure to the brake pedal. Refit the roadwheel.
24   Repeat the full procedure on the opposite brake caliper, then lower the car to the ground and tighten the roadwheel nuts to the specified torque wrench setting (Chapter 10).
25   Check the hydraulic fluid level (Chapter 1). Check for any fluid leaks which might subsequently appear.

13   Front brake disc – inspection, removal and refitting

Note: *Before starting work, refer to the warning at the beginning of Section 10 concerning the dangers of asbestos dust*

Inspection

Note: *To ensure even and consistent braking, both discs should be renewed at the same time, even if only one is faulty*

1   Jack up the front of the car and support it securely on axle stands, then remove the roadwheel (see 'Jacking, towing and wheel changing').
2   Slowly rotate the brake disc so that the full area of both sides can be checked; remove the brake pads (Sec 10) if better access is required to the inboard surface. Light scoring is normal in the area swept by the brake pads, but if heavy scoring is found the disc must be renewed. The only alternative to this is to have the disc surface-ground until it is flat again, but this must not reduce the disc to less than the minimum thickness specified.
3   It is normal to find a lip of rust and brake dust around the disc's perimeter; this can be scraped off if required. If, however, a lip has formed due to excessive wear of the brake pad swept area then the disc's thickness must be measured using a micrometer. Take measurements at four places around the disc at the inside and outside of the pad swept area; if the disc has worn at any point to the specified minimum thickness or less, or if any measurement differs from the

others by more than the maximum specified variation, the disc must be renewed.

4   If the disc is thought to be warped it can be checked for run-out (6 mm in from the disc's outer edge) either using a dial gauge mounted on any convenient fixed point, while the disc is slowly rotated, or by using feeler gauges to measure (at several points all around the disc) the clearance between the disc and a fixed point such as the caliper mounting bracket. If the measurements obtained are at the specified maximum or beyond, the disc is excessively warped and must be renewed; however it is worth checking first that the hub bearing is in good condition (Chapters 1 and/or 10). Also try the effect of removing the disc and turning it through 180° to reposition it on the hub; if run-out is still excessive the disc must be renewed.

5   Check the disc for cracks, especially around the stud holes, and any other wear or damage. Renew it if any of these are found.

Removal

6   Jack up the front of the car and support it securely on axle stands, then remove the roadwheel (see 'Jacking, towing and wheel changing').

7   Unscrew the two brake caliper mounting bracket-to-hub carrier bolts, then withdraw the caliper assembly and secure it out of harm's way without stretching or kinking the brake hose. Place a clean spacer (of the same thickness as the brake disc) between the pads to prevent them being dislodged.

8   Use chalk or paint to mark the relationship of the disc to the hub, then undo the disc securing screws (photo) and withdraw the disc.

Refitting

9   Refitting is the reverse of the removal procedure, noting the following points.

    (a)   Ensure that the mating surfaces of the disc and hub are clean and flat.
    (b)   Align (if applicable) the marks made on removal.
    (c)   If a new disc has been fitted, use a suitable solvent to wipe any preservative coating from the disc before refitting the caliper.
    (d)   Tighten the screws, bolts and roadwheel nuts to their specified torque wrench settings.

14   Front brake disc shield – removal and refitting

Note: *Before starting work, refer to the warning at the beginning of Section 10 concerning the dangers of asbestos dust*

Removal

1   Remove the brake disc (Sec 13).
2   Unbolt the brake disc shield from the hub carrier and withdraw it.

Refitting

3   Refitting is the reverse of the removal procedure; tighten the shield mounting bolts to the specified torque wrench setting.

15   Pressure regulating valve – general, removal and refitting

General

1   If one or both rear roadwheels lock repeatedly under heavy braking, first check that this is not due to adverse road conditions or to incorrectly inflated or badly-worn tyres, then check the condition of all four brake assemblies before suspecting a pressure regulating valve fault. Note that the right-hand valve serves only the primary circuit, which includes the left-hand rear brake, while the left-hand valve serves the secondary circuit and the right-hand rear brake; if a fault appears, this may help to isolate the cause.

2   If either valve is thought to be faulty, it must be renewed; the valves are available only as complete units and must **not** be dismantled.

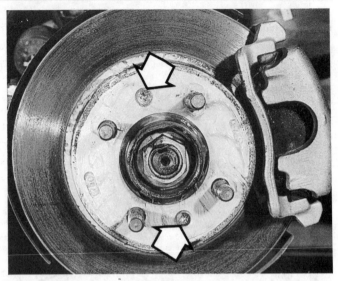

13.8 Front brake disc securing screws (arrows)

15.3 Rear brake pressure regulating valves on engine compartment bulkhead

Removal

Note: *Before starting work, refer to the note at the beginning of Section 7 concerning the dangers of hydraulic fluid*

3   The two pressure regulating valves are bolted to the engine compartment bulkhead (photo); remove the air cleaner assembly, if required, to gain better working space (Chapter 4).

4   Minimise fluid loss either by removing the master cylinder reservoir cap and then tightening it down onto a piece of polythene to obtain an airtight seal (taking care not to damage the sender unit), or by capping or plugging each metal brake pipe as it is disconnected from the valve (Sec 8). Also plug the valve orifices, whilst taking great care not to allow dirt into the system.

5   Unbolt the valve from the bulkhead, noting the spacer and withdraw it.

Refitting

6   Refitting is the reverse of the removal procedure, noting the following points.

    (a)   Prevent the valve from rotating while tightening the bolt to its specified torque wrench setting.
    (b)   When the metal brake pipe unions are secured (Sec 8), bleed any air from the system (Sec 7) and wash off any spilt fluid.
    (c)   Check the hydraulic fluid level (Chapter 1).

16 Rear brake drum – removal, inspection and refitting

Note: *Before starting work, refer to the warning at the beginning of Section 17 concerning the dangers of asbestos dust*

Removal

1   Jack up the rear of the car and support it securely on axle stands, then remove the roadwheel (see *'Jacking, towing and wheel changing'*).
2   Use chalk or paint to mark the relationship of the drum to the hub.
3   With the handbrake firmly applied to prevent drum rotation, unscrew the drum securing screw (photo). Fully release the handbrake and withdraw the drum.
4   If the drum will not pull away, first check that the handbrake is fully released, then slacken off the brake shoe adjustment until the drum can be removed (Chapter 1). If the drum still will not move, it is probably stuck to the hub flange with corrosion; use a soft-faced mallet to gently tap the drum off the hub. Discard the drum gasket; this must be renewed whenever the drum is disturbed.

Inspection

Note: *If either drum requires renewal, both should be renewed at the same time to ensure even and consistent braking*

5   Working carefully (see warning, Section 17) remove all traces of brake dust from the drum.
6   Scrub clean the outside of the drum and check it for obvious signs of wear or damage such as cracks around the roadwheel stud holes; renew the drum if necessary.
7   Examine the inside of the drum. Light scoring of the friction surface is normal, but if heavy scoring is found the drum must be renewed. It is usual to find a lip on the drum's inboard edge which consists of a mixture of rust and brake dust; this should be scraped away to leave a smooth surface which can be polished with fine (120 to 150 grade) emery paper. If, however, the lip is due to the friction surface being recessed by excessive wear, then the drum must be renewed.
8   If the drum is thought to be excessively worn, or oval, its internal diameter must be measured at several points using an internal micrometer. Take measurements in pairs, the second at right angles to the first, and compare the two to check for signs of ovality. Provided that it does not enlarge the drum to beyond the specified maximum diameter, it may be possible to have the drum refinished by skimming or grinding; if this is not possible, the drums on both sides must be renewed.

16.3 Removing the rear brake drum securing screw

Refitting

9   Refitting is the reverse of the removal procedure, noting the following points.

(a)   On fitting a new brake drum, use a suitable solvent to remove any preservative coating that may have been applied to its interior.
(b)   Use a clean wire brush to remove all traces of dirt, brake dust and corrosion from the mating surfaces of the drum and the hub flange; always fit a new gasket to the hub flange.
(c)   Align (if applicable) the marks made on removal.
(d)   Tighten the drum securing screw and the roadwheel nuts to their specified torque wrench settings.
(e)   Depress the brake pedal several times until the wheel cylinder(s) and brake shoes have taken up their correct working positions and normal (non-assisted) pedal pressure is restored.
(f)   Check, and correct if necessary, the brake shoe adjustment (Chapter 1).
(g)   Check, and correct if necessary, the handbrake adjustment (Chapter 1); ensure that the roadwheels rotate easily, with no (or very slight) sound of brake shoe-to-drum contact.

17 Rear brake shoes – renewal

Warning: *Brake shoes must be renewed on both rear wheels at the same time – never renew the shoes on only one wheel as uneven braking may result. Also, the dust created by wear of the shoes may contain asbestos, which is a health hazard. Never blow it out with compressed air and don't inhale any of it. An approved filtering mask should be worn when working on the brakes. DO NOT use petroleum based solvents to clean brake parts. Use brake cleaner or methylated spirit only*

1   Remove and check the brake drum (Sec 16).
2   Working carefully (see warning above) remove all traces of brake dust from the brake drum, backplate and shoes.
3   Measure the thickness of friction material remaining on each brake shoe at several points; if either shoe is worn at any point to the specified minimum thickness or less, all four shoes must be renewed (see the warning above and note that replacement shoes from Rover dealers are only available as an axle set). Also, the shoes should be renewed if any are fouled with oil or grease; there is no satisfactory way of degreasing friction material once contaminated.
4   If any of the brake shoes are worn unevenly or fouled with oil or grease, trace and rectify the cause before reassembly.
5   To remove the brake shoes, first remove the shoe retainer springs and pins, using a pair of pliers to press in each retainer washer until it can be rotated through 90° and released. Release the shoes one at a time from the adjuster, then from the wheel cylinder and handbrake lever assembly, unhook the bottom return spring and withdraw the shoes from the backplate (photos). Do not depress the brake pedal until the brakes are reassembled; wrap a strong elastic band around the wheel cylinder pistons to retain them.
6   Clean the backplate and apply a thin smear of high-temperature brake grease (silicone- or PBC/Poly Butyl Cuprysil-based) or anti-seize compound (eg Holts Copaslip) to all those surfaces of the backplate which bear on the shoes, particularly the adjuster and the wheel cylinder pistons. Do not allow the lubricant to foul the friction material.
7   Check the adjuster for wear or damage; it can be unbolted and renewed separately if necessary (photos).
8   Peel back the rubber protective caps and check the wheel cylinder for fluid leaks or other damage (Sec 18).
9   Check the handbrake lever assembly for wear or damage and renew it if necessary. Apply a smear of lubricant to its bearing surfaces.
10   Fit the shoe assembly to the backplate, being careful not to get grease onto the friction material. Ensure that the shoe ends engage properly with the wheel cylinder piston and adjuster grooves, then hook on the bottom return spring and engage the shoes on the handbrake lever assembly (photo).
11   Tap the shoes to centralise them on the backplate, then refit the shoe retainer pins, springs and washers. If new shoes have been fitted, slacken off the adjuster to provide sufficient clearance for them.
12   Refit the brake drum (Sec 16).
13   Repeat the procedure on the opposite brake.

Fig. 9.5 Exploded view of a rear brake assembly (Sec 17)

1   Brake backplate
2   Adjuster assembly
3   Shoe return springs
4   Brake shoe
5   Brake drum
6   Shoe retainer spring and washer
7   Wheel cylinder
8   Gasket
9   Handbrake lever assembly
10 Wheel cylinder circlip
11 Shoe retainer pin
12 Shoe inspection grommet
13 Backplate mounting bolt
14 Adjuster mounting nut and washer – 2 off
15 Drum securing screw

17.5A Releasing brake shoe retainer components

17.5B Removing brake shoes

17.7A Rear brake shoe adjuster assembly ...

17.7B ... is secured by two nuts (arrows)

17.10 Showing brake shoes and handbrake lever assembly correctly refitted

18   Rear wheel cylinder – removal, overhaul and refitting

Note: *Before starting work, refer to the note at the beginning of Section 7 concerning the dangers of hydraulic fluid and to the warning at the beginning of Section 17 concerning the dangers of asbestos dust*

Removal

1   Remove the brake drum (Sec 16).
2   Remove the brake shoes (Section 17, paragraphs 2 to 5).
3   Minimise fluid loss by removing the master cylinder reservoir cap and then tightening it down onto a piece of polythene to obtain an airtight seal (taking care not to damage the sender unit), or by using a brake hose clamp, a G-clamp or a similar tool to clamp the flexible hose, or by capping or plugging the metal brake pipe as it is disconnected from the cylinder (Sec 8); unscrew the bleed nipple. Plug the cylinder orifices, taking great care not to allow dirt into the system.
4   Noting how it is fitted, prise out the circlip securing the cylinder to the backplate. Withdraw the cylinder and its gasket.

Overhaul

Note: *Before attempting to overhaul the unit, check the price and availability of individual components and the price of a new or reconditioned unit, as overhaul may not be viable on economic grounds alone. Also, read through the procedure and check that the special tools and facilities required are available*

5   Remove the wheel cylinder from the car and clean it thoroughly.
6   Mount the wheel cylinder in a soft-jawed vice and remove the rubber protective caps. Extract the piston assemblies.
7   Thoroughly clean all components using only methylated spirit, isopropyl alcohol or clean hydraulic fluid as a cleaning medium. Never use mineral-based solvents such as petrol or paraffin which will attack the hydraulic system's rubber components. Dry the components immediately using compressed air or a clean, lint-free cloth.
8   Check all components and renew any that are worn or damaged. Check particularly the cylinder bore and pistons; the complete assembly must be renewed if these are scratched, worn or corroded. If there is any doubt about the condition of the assembly or of any of its components, renew it. Check that the fluid entry port and bleed nipple passage are clear.
9   If the assembly is fit for further use, obtain a repair kit. Renew the rubber protective caps, dust caps and seals disturbed on dismantling as a matter of course; these should never be re-used. Renew also any other items included in the repair kit.
10   On reassembly, soak the pistons and the new seals in clean hydraulic fluid. Smear clean fluid on the cylinder bore surface.
11   Fit the new seals to their pistons using only the fingers to manipulate them into the grooves. Ensure that all components are refitted in the correct order and the right way round.

12   Insert the pistons into the bore using a twisting motion to avoid trapping the seal lips. Apply a smear of rubber lubricant to each piston before fitting the new rubber protective caps.
13   Refit the wheel cylinder to the car.

Refitting

14   Refitting is the reverse of the removal procedure, noting the following points.

(a)   Fit the gasket to the cylinder and refit the cylinder, ensuring that the circlip is fitted correctly.
(b)   Refit the bleed nipple, then connect the metal brake pipe to the cylinder (Sec 8) and refit the brake shoes and drum (Secs 17 and 16).
(c)   Bleed any air from the system (Sec 7) and check for leaks while an assistant applies full pressure to the brake pedal, then wash off any spilt fluid.
(d)   Check the brake hydraulic fluid level (Chapter 1). Check for any fluid leaks which might subsequently appear.

19   Rear brake backplate – removal and refitting

Note: *Before starting work, refer to the note at the beginning of Section 7 concerning the dangers of hydraulic fluid and to the warning at the beginning of Section 17 concerning the dangers of asbestos dust*

Removal

1   Remove the rear hub (Chapter 10).
2   Remove the brake shoes (Section 17, paragraphs 2 to 5).
3   Minimise fluid loss by removing the master cylinder reservoir cap and then tightening it down onto a piece of polythene to obtain an airtight seal (taking care not to damage the sender unit), or by using a brake hose clamp, a G-clamp or a similar tool to clamp the flexible hose, or by capping or plugging the metal brake pipe as it is disconnected from the wheel cylinder (Sec 8). Also plug the cylinder orifices, taking great care not to allow dirt into the hydraulic system.
4   Disconnect the handbrake cable from the lever assembly (Sec 21).
5   Unbolt the backplate from the rear suspension trailing arm and withdraw it, noting the arrangement of the handbrake cable bracket and, where fitted, the anti-roll bar link bracket (photo).

Refitting

6   Refitting is the reverse of the removal procedure, but apply a smear of sealant to the backplate/trailing arm mating surfaces. Tighten all nuts and bolts to their specified torque wrench settings. Refer to the relevant Sections of Chapter 10 as well as this Chapter for detailed instructions.

20   Handbrake lever – removal and refitting

Removal

1   With the car parked on level ground, switch off the ignition, select first or reverse gear and chock the roadwheels so that the car cannot move.
2   Referring to the relevant Sections of Chapter 11, carry out the following (photo).

(a)   Remove the front seats and the front seat rear mounting bar.
(b)   Unscrew the rear seat mountings; remove the seats if required.
(c)   Remove all door sill trim panels.
(d)   Unbolt the front seat belt bottom anchorages and the stalks.

3   Withdraw the two covering plastic mouldings from the floor front crossmember, lift the carpet and peel it forwards, clear of the handbrake lever.
4   Either disconnect the handbrake switch wires or remove its retaining screws and withdraw the switch from the lever (Sec 23).
5   Remove its split pin and withdraw the clevis pin securing the cable yoke to the handbrake lever (photo).
6   Unbolt the handbrake lever from the floor.

19.5 Brake backplate mounting bolts/nuts (arrows)

20.2 Remove front seat rear mounting bar (1), rear seat mountings (2), door sill trim panels (3), seat belt anchorages and stalks (4) and front crossmember covers (5) to lift carpet for access to handbrake

20.5 Handbrake lever-to-cable clevis pin (1), switch mounting screws (2), lever mounting nuts and bolts (3)

Refitting

7   Refitting is the reverse of the removal procedure. Apply a smear of grease (Rover recommend Molykote 44) to all pivots, the cable yoke fittings and the adjuster threads. Adjust the handbrake (Chapter 1).

---

21   Handbrake cable – removal, inspection and refitting

Removal

1   Gain access to the cable assembly by carrying out the preliminary

dismantling described in Section 20, paragraphs 1 to 3.
2   Remove its split pin and withdraw the clevis pin securing the cable yoke to the handbrake lever; unscrew the cable adjuster nuts and remove the yoke and nuts from the cable (photo).
3   Drill out the pop rivet securing the cable cover plate to the floor, then remove the cover and withdraw the seal from the cable.
4   Jack up the rear of the car and support it securely on axle stands (see 'Jacking, towing and wheel changing').
5   Release the cable from the clips securing it to the fuel tank left-hand end.
6   Remove the clip securing the front end of the cable outer to the underbody bracket (immediately above the exhaust intermediate pipe rubber mounting), release the cable from the bracket and pull it down clear of the car.
7   Disconnect the cable from both rear brake handbrake lever

Fig. 9.6 Handbrake mechanism (Sec 21)

1   Handbrake lever
2   Switch
3   Rear brake handbrake lever assembly
4   Compensator
5   Rear brake drum
6   Location of cable securing clips
7   Handbrake cable
8   Cover plate
9   Cable yoke
10   Adjuster assembly

21.2 Lift floor carpet to expose handbrake cable yoke and adjuster

21.7 Handbrake cable-to-lever assembly clevis pin and trailing arm bracket clip (arrows)

21.9 Handbrake cable and compensator clips (arrows)

assemblies by removing its split pin and withdrawing the clevis pin securing each cable yoke (photo).

8   Remove the clip securing each rear end of the cable outer to its respective suspension trailing arm bracket, release each cable seal and the cable tie securing the cable to the trailing arm, then release the cable from the trailing arm.

9   Remove the clip securing the cable outer to each end of the rear suspension subframe (photo), release each cable seal and move the cable into the larger subframe aperture, then remove both cable ends from the subframe.

10   Release the compensator assembly from the subframe clip and withdraw the cable assembly from the car, noting carefully how it is routed.

Inspection

11   Check the cable for wear or damage and renew it if necessary.

12   Clean the adjuster threads thoroughly and apply a smear of grease to the yokes. Check and lubricate the compensator and, if required, the rear brake lever assembly (Sec 17).

Refitting

13   Refitting is the reverse of the removal procedure, noting the following points.

(a)   Lay out the cable under the car so that it is in its correct relative position, then pass the front end over the subframe.

(b)   Feed each cable rear end through the subframe and route it along the trailing arm, then clip the compensator into place, push each cable outer into the subframe smaller aperture, refit the clips to secure them and position the cable seals.

(c)   Refit each cable rear end to its trailing arm bracket, refit the clip to secure it and position the cable seal.

(d)   Lubricate the clevis pins (Rover recommend Molykote 44) before connecting each cable rear end to its respective rear brake lever assembly.

(e)   Pass the cable's front end into the car, secure the cable outer with the clip and fasten the clips securing the cable to the fuel tank.

(f)   Check the cable seal and renew it if necessary, then connect the cable to the handbrake lever and pop-rivet the cover plate to the floor.

(g)   Adjust the handbrake (Chapter 1).

(h)   Use new cable ties to secure the cables to the trailing arms, then lower the car to the ground.

(i)   Refit the carpet, the seat belts and the seats (Chapter 11).

22   Stop-lamp switch – adjustment

1   The stop-lamp switch should be set so that the lamps light whenever the brake pedal is depressed to the point where the pedal free play is taken up.

2   To adjust the switch setting, first release the retaining fasteners and remove the fusebox cover.

3   Remove its retaining screw and bolt and withdraw the steering column cover, then unfasten the column from its remaining mountings and lower it as far as possible without stretching the wiring (Chapter 10). Peel back the carpet if better access is required.

4   Slacken the two nuts securing the switch and reposition the switch until the lamps light at the correct moment; either have an assistant check the stop-lamps for you or disconnect the switch wires and use a multimeter set to the resistance scale to check when the switch contacts close, allowing current to flow. Tighten the two nuts securely, then switch on the ignition and check the operation of the stop-lamps.

5   Refit the steering column, its cover and the fusebox cover.

23   Brake system warning lamps – general

Stop-lamp

1   The stop-lamp circuit is controlled by a plunger-type switch mounted on the brake pedal bracket (photo).

2   Check and adjust the switch setting as described in Section 22 of this Chapter.

3   If the switch is thought to be faulty it can be tested by disconnecting its wires and connecting either a multimeter (set to the resistance function) or a battery and bulb test circuit across the switch terminals. The switch should allow current to flow only when it is extended; if the switch is faulty it must be renewed.

4   To remove the switch, disconnect its wires and unscrew the adjuster locknut to remove it from its bracket.

5   Refitting is the reverse of the removal procedure; adjust the switch setting (Sec 22).

23.1 Location of stop-lamp switch (arrow)

23.6 Location of handbrake switch (arrow)

Brake warning lamp

6   The handbrake circuit of the instrument panel brake warning lamp is activated by a plunger switch mounted at the base of the handbrake lever. The lamp lights whenever the handbrake is applied or whenever the brake fluid level in the master cylinder reaches a dangerously low level (photo).

7   Unless the switch, its mounting screws and connector can be reached by (carefully) lifting the handbrake lever gaiter and peeling back the carpet, the switch can be reached only by lifting the carpet, as outlined in Section 20, paragraphs 1 to 3.

8   The switch is not adjustable and is secured by two screws; to remove it, undo the screws and unplug the wiring connector.

9   To test the switch, remove it and use the equipment described in paragraph 3 to check that continuity exists between the switch's terminal and its earth only when the plunger is extended; if the switch is faulty it must be renewed.

10   Refitting is the reverse of the removal procedure.

11   The brake fluid level circuit of the instrument panel brake warning lamp is activated by a float-type sender unit in the master cylinder reservoir filler cap. The lamp lights whenever the fluid level falls to a dangerously low level or the handbrake is applied.

12   The sender unit is a only available with the master cylinder reservoir filler cap; if faulty, the complete sender/cap assembly must be renewed.

13   To test the sender unit, remove it and use the equipment described in paragraph 3 to check that continuity exists between the unit's terminals only when the float is at the bottom of its travel.

Chapter 10 Suspension and steering

Contents

Specifications

Front suspension

Type.. Fully independent, with unequal-length upper (T-shaped) and
lower (wishbone-type) transverse arms, Hydragas units providing
(nitrogen) gas springing and fluid damping. Anti-roll bar on GTa and
GTi 16v models. Telescopic, hydraulic dampers additional on
GTi 16v models. Complete assembly rubber-mounted on subframe

Rear suspension

Type.. Fully independent, with trailing arms, Hydragas units with helper
springs providing (nitrogen) gas springing and fluid damping. Anti-
roll bar on GTi 16v models. Complete assembly rubber mounted on
subframe

Hydragas suspension

System description... Front units mounted vertically, rear units horizontally. Units on each
side connected front to rear through a plastic pipe; each side
independent of the other

Nitrogen gas nominal pressure.. $2172 \text{ kN/m}^2 \pm 3\%$ ($315 \text{ lbf/in}^2 \pm 3\%$)
Ride height – measured vertically from front hub centre to wheel arch
underside, car at kerb weight (see *'General dimensions and weights'*),
engine cold .... 341 ± 10 mm
Ride height maximum permissible side-to-side difference....................... 10 mm
Note: *Ride heights correct at nominal ambient temperature of 17°C – above this temperature add 0.6 mm for every 1°C temperature difference,
below it subtract 0.6 mm for every 1°C temperature difference*

Steering

Type.. Rack and pinion
Turns lock-to-lock:
    GTa, GTi 16v 3.3
    All other models 3.7

Wheel alignment and steering angles

Note: *All measurements are with car at kerb weight (see 'General dimensions and weights') and at (exactly) correct ride heights*

Toe-out in turns:
    GTa, GTi 16v .... Inside roadwheel 31° 34′, Outside roadwheel 28° 21′
    All other models .... Inside roadwheel 35° 18′, Outside roadwheel 30° 40′
Camber angle:
    Front – GTa, GTi 16v.. 0° 10′ ± 0° 37′ positive
    Front – all other models .... 0° 18′ ± 0° 37′ positive
    Rear – all models .... 0° 0′ ± 0° 30′ negative
Castor angle:
    GTa, GTi 16v .... 2° 00′ ± 0° 55′ positive
    All other models .... 0° 23′ ± 0° 55′ positive
Steering axis inclination/SAI – also known as kingpin inclination/KPI ...... 10° 52′
Toe setting:
    Front .... 0° 00′/Parallel to 0° 50′ (inclusive) toe-out
    Rear .... 0° 10′ to 0° 50′ toe-in

Roadwheels

Type:
    1.1C, 1.1L, 1.1S, 1.4SL, 1.4GS .... Steel
    GTa .... Steel (Alloy optional)
    GTi 16v .... Alloy
Size:
    1.1C, 1.1L, 1.1S, 1.4SL, 1.4GS .... 4.5J x 13
    GTa – standard.. 5.5J x 13
    GTa – optional, GTi 16v .... 5.5J x 13 x CH-52

Tyres

Type.. Tubeless, steel-braced radial
Size:
    1.1C, 1.1L, 1.1S, 1.4SL, 1.4GS .... 155/65 R 13 73T
    GTa, GTi 16v .... 185/55 R 13 77H

Pressures (cold) – 1.1C, 1.1L, 1.1S, 1.4SL, 1.4GS:

	Front	Rear
Up to and including four persons	2.1 bar (31 psi)	2.1 bar (31 psi)
Four persons up to maximum permissible gross vehicle weight	2.1 bar (31 psi)	

Pressures (cold) – GTa, GTi 16v:

	Front	Rear
All loads – up to 100 mph	2.0 bar (29 psi)	2.0 bar (29 psi)
All loads – over 100 mph	2.3 bar (33 psi)	2.3 bar (33 psi)

Note: *Pressures apply only to original equipment tyres and may vary if any other make or type is fitted; check with the tyre manufacturer or supplier for correct pressures if necessary*

Torque wrench settings

	Nm	lbf ft
Front suspension		
Lower arm pivot bolts	85	63
Lower balljoint:		
Balljoint-to-lower arm nuts and bolts – applicable to replacement parts only	40	30
Balljoint-to-hub carrier pinch-bolt and nut	60	44
Damper top mounting nut – GTi 16v	37	27
Upper balljoint:		
Balljoint-to-upper arm nut	55	40.5
Balljoint-to-hub carrier	105	78
Upper arm:		
Pivot shaft nuts	75	55
Pivot shaft retaining plate mounting bolts and nut	10	8
Damper bottom mounting/brake hose bracket bolt – GTi 16v	50	37
Brake hose bracket bolt – all other models	35	26
Anti-roll bar:		
Bar-to-suspension lower arm bolt and nut	25	19
Clamp bolts	45	33
Hydragas connecting pipe unions	20	15
Hydragas unit clamp plate bolts and nuts	25	19
Subframe fasteners:		
Mounting-to-body bolts or nuts	45	33
Engine/transmission support members-to-subframe bolts	45	33
Rear suspension		
Rear hub nut	90	66
Trailing arm:		
Pivot shaft nuts	75	55
Grease nipple	4	3
Pivot shaft retaining plate mounting bolts and nuts	25	19
Rear brake backplate nuts and bolts	25	19

Torque wrench settings (continued)

	Nm	lbf ft
Anti-roll bar:		
Clamp bolts	25	19
Bar-to-link bolts and nuts	25	19
Link-to-bracket bolts	25	19
Hydragas connecting pipe unions	20	15
Hydragas unit clamp plate bolts	25	19
Hydragas unit retaining strap nuts	7	5
Subframe fasteners:		
Mounting-to-body bolts	45	33
Mounting-to-subframe bolts	45	33
Steering		
Steering wheel nut	33	24
Steering column:		
Mounting bolts and nut	25	19
Column cover clamp bolt	11	8
Universal joint pinch-bolt	30	22
Bulkhead aperture cover bolts or nuts	11	8
Steering lock/ignition switch shear-head bolts	Tighten until heads shear off – at least 19 Nm (14 lbf ft)	
Steering gear mounting nuts	25	19
Track rod:		
Balljoint locknuts	48	36
Balljoint-to-steering arm nuts	30	22
Roadwheels		
Roadwheel nuts	70	52

1 General information

The suspension is fully independent at front and rear, with the principal suspension components being mounted on separate subframes. The subframes are rubber-mounted to the body.

The Hydragas system is employed, using four suspension units (also known as displacers) each of which is connected by a knuckle joint to its respective upper arm (at the front) or trailing arm (at the rear). **Note:** *Unlike previous Metros, the Hydragas units are connected front-to-rear on each side; each side's units are independent of the other.* The units are basically sealed metal containers, divided into two chambers by a rubber diaphragm; the upper chamber contains dry nitrogen gas under pressure and thus forms a gas spring, while the lower contains a fluid (water-based, with alcohol to prevent freezing) and is further sub-divided by a damper valve through which the fluid must pass in either direction. The knuckle joints act on a tapered piston to bear against a second rubber diaphragm that seals the fluid in the unit's lower chamber. Thus when a roadwheel hits a bump, pressure is transmitted by the fluid to the gas spring formed in the upper chamber and also (through the fluid in the pipe connecting the pair of units on each side) to the remaining unit, thus levelling the car and providing a smooth ride. When both units on one side are compressed together, as during cornering, the effect of the units acting together is to minimise roll. The damper valve orifices, the restrictor in each connecting pipe and the suspension lower arm pivot bushes are all carefully matched to provide the characteristics required; a helper spring is fitted to the rear unit to assist it in coping with various loads. The car's ride heights are set and can be adjusted by pressurising the fluid in the system, via a Schrader-type valve located next to each rear unit.

The front suspension on each side consists of the hub carrier which is located, via upper and lower balljoints, by two transverse arms; the upper (T-shaped) arm pivots on needle roller bearings while the lower (wishbone-type) arm pivots on rubber bushes. The GTa and GTi 16v models are fitted with an anti-roll bar that is clamped to the underbody via rubber bushes and is attached at each end to the lower arms. The GTi 16v models are also fitted with a pair of telescopic, hydraulic dampers; one being mounted between each upper arm and the body. The hub rotates on a sealed, pre-adjusted and pre-lubricated, double-row tapered-roller bearing.

The rear suspension consists of two trailing arms that are pivoted on needle roller bearings and have the roadwheel stub axles pressed into their rear ends; each hub rotates on two ball-journal bearings. The GTi 16v models are fitted with an anti-roll bar clamped to the underbody via rubber bushes and attached at each end via links and brackets to the trailing arms.

The steering wheel is of the energy-absorbing type to protect the driver in the event of an accident and is attached by a deeply-recessed nut to the steering column, which is collapsible and is also of the energy-absorbing type. The steering column incorporates a rubber coupling to damp out road shocks and has a universal joint at its bottom end which is clamped to the steering gear pinion. The steering gear is clamped to the front subframe and is connected by two track rods, with balljoints at their outer ends, to the steering arms projecting rearwards from the hub carriers. The track rods ends are threaded to facilitate adjustment.

Note: *On those models with 4.5J roadwheels and 155-section tyres (see Specifications), various suspension components differ from their counterparts fitted to GTa and GTi 16v models (5.5J roadwheels and 185-section tyres); the wider wheels and tyres must not be fitted to any of the other models.*

General notes and warnings concerning the Hydragas suspension

For the average DIY owner, most suspension removal, refitting and servicing procedures are complicated by the need to depressurise the Hydragas suspension before work starts and to evacuate air from it and to pressurise it (thus setting the ride heights) on completion. This can be done only by an experienced mechanic using the Hydragas Service Unit (Rover Service Tool Number 18G 703 V); obviously, the most likely source of such facilities is at your local Rover dealer, but some non-franchised dealers also have such equipment. **Warning:** *Do not attempt to depressurise the suspension yourself.*

Rover state that if the suspension is depressurised the car can be driven for repair at no more than 20 mph to the nearest dealer; while obviously this is a 'get-you-home' procedure for use in emergency only and is not intended as permission to drive the car in such a state at any other time, it does indicate a possible solution if you wish to carry out suspension repair work yourself. Before any work is attempted on the relevant parts of the suspension, you should check whether your local dealer is prepared to depressurise the suspension so that you can drive the car home, carry out the work yourself and then drive the car back to them for the suspension to be pressurised.

Warning: *If the car is to be driven with the suspension depressurised (even if a leak is only suspected, or if either side's ride height is low), it must be loaded as lightly as possible and must be driven slowly and carefully over smooth roads for the minimum possible distance. Even apart from the effect on the car's handling and ride, driving it normally with the suspension depressurised will overload the Hydragas units and damage them.*

Fig. 10.1 Exploded view of the front suspension (Sec 1)

1   Hydragas unit
2   Return spring
3   Spacer – if fitted
4   Knuckle joint and socket assembly
5   Upper arm pivot shaft
6   Bump stop
7   Rubber gaiter
8   Damper top mounting bushes*
9   Damper*
10 Pivot shaft retaining plate

11 Thrust collar
12 Sealing ring
13 Needle roller bearing
14 Upper arm
15 Anti-roll bar clamp bush*
16 Anti-roll bar*
17 Anti-roll bar clamp*
18 Bolt – bar-to-lower arm*
19 Rubber bush and metal washer*
20 Bolt*
21 Spacer*

22 Rebound rubber buffer
23 Upper balljoint
24 Lockwasher
25 Lockwasher
26 Steering arm
27 Locating dowel
28 Lockwasher
29 Circlip
30 Hub carrier
31 Nut
32 Hub bearing
33 Hub

34 Lower arm pivot bolt
35 Lower arm pivot bush
36 Lower arm
37 Spacer*
38 Rivet – replaced by bolt and nut when balljoint is renewed
39 Lower balljoint
40 Pinch-bolt
41 Thrustwasher
*   Not fitted to all models

Fig. 10.2 Exploded view of the rear suspension (Sec 1)

1 Anti-roll bar clamp bush*
2 Anti-roll bar clamp*
3 Anti-roll bar*
4 Mounting pad
5 Hydragas unit
6 Helper spring
7 Hydragas unit retaining
   strap
8 Strut
9 Return spring
10 Spacer

11 Knuckle joint
12 Bump stop
13 Circlip
14 Stub axle
15 Anti-roll bar link*
16 Handbrake cable bracket
17 Anti-roll bar link bracket*
18 Thrustwasher
19 Seal
20 Needle roller bearing

21 Trailing arm
22 Rebound rubber buffer
23 Thrustwasher
24 Rubber sleeve
25 Oil seal
26 Hub inboard bearing
27 Hub
28 Trailing arm pivot shaft
29 Thrustwasher

30 Pivot shaft retaining plate
31 Grease nipple
32 Hub outboard bearing
33 Roadwheel stud
34 Washer
35 Hub nut
36 Hub cap
* Not fitted to all models

Fig. 10.3 Exploded view of the steering column (Sec 1)

1   Nut
2   Steering wheel
3   Spring ring
4   Nacelle upper half
5   Steering column assembly
6   Column upper mounting
7   Extendable energy strap
8   Column lower mounting
9   Rubber coupling
10 Bolt
11 Nut
12 Intermediate shaft and universal joint
13 Direction indicator cancelling cam
14 Multi-function switch assembly
15 Steering lock/ignition switch assembly
16 Nacelle lower half
17 Screw
18 Steering column and bulkhead aperture covers
19 Steering wheel centre cover(s)
Note: Items 5 to 12 inclusive are available only as a complete assembly

Fig. 10.4 Steering gear components (Sec 1)

1   Steering gear
2   Track rod balljoint
3   Steering gear rubber gaiter
4   Clip
5   Clip
6   Balljoint locknut
7   Mounting clamp
8   Mounting spacer
9   Bolts
10 U-bolt
11 Nuts

Fig. 10.5 Pressing out hub from hub carrier (Sec 3)

Fig. 10.6 Pressing hub bearing out of hub carrier (Sec 3)

Fig. 10.7 Pressing new hub bearing into hub carrier (Sec 3)

Fig. 10.8 Pressing hub into hub carrier – note support for bearing inner race (Sec 3)

2 Front hub carrier – removal and refitting

Removal

1 Separate the hub carrier from the driveshaft as described in Chapter 8, Section 2, paragraphs 1 to 3, then 5 to 10.

2 Unscrew the nut and fully remove the pinch-bolt securing the suspension lower balljoint to the hub carrier, then pull the hub carrier off the balljoint.

3 If the hub carrier is to be dismantled, remove the brake disc and its shield (Chapter 9).

4 If the steering arm is removed note the two dowels locating the arm on the hub carrier, ensure that the lockwasher is renewed and that the bolts are tightened securely and locked by bending up the lockwasher tabs against their flats on refitting.

Refitting

5 Refitting is the reverse of the removal procedure, referring for full details where necessary to the relevant Sections of this Chapter and of Chapters 8 and 9; tighten all nuts and bolts to their specified torque wrench settings.

3 Front hub and bearing – removal and refitting

Note: *The bearing is sealed, of the pre-adjusted and pre-lubricated, double-row tapered-roller type and is intended to last the car's entire service life without maintenance or attention. Do not attempt to remove the bearing unless absolutely necessary, as it will probably be damaged during the removal operation, and never overtighten the driveshaft nut beyond the specified torque wrench setting in an attempt to 'adjust' the bearing*

Note: *A press will be required to dismantle and rebuild the assembly; if such a tool is not available, a large bench vice and suitable spacers (such as large sockets) will serve as an adequate substitute. Also, the bearing's inner races are an interference fit on the hub; if the outboard inner race remains on the hub when it is pressed out of the hub carrier, a proprietary knife-edged bearing puller will be required to remove it*

Removal

1 Remove the hub carrier from the car (Sec 2) and remove the brake disc and its shield (Chapter 9).

4.2 Front anti-roll bar-to-body clamp bolts (arrows)

4.9 Note location of metal washers on anti-roll bar-to-suspension lower arm mounting

5.2 Washer system reservoir must be moved to expose right-hand damper top mounting

2   Press the hub out of the hub carrier (Fig. 10.5). If the bearing's outboard inner race remains on the hub, remove it using the appropriate equipment (see note above).
3   Extract both circlips from the hub carrier and discard them; they should be renewed whenever they are disturbed.
4   Press the bearing out of the hub carrier (Fig. 10.6).
5   Thoroughly clean the hub and hub carrier, removing all traces of dirt and grease and polishing away any burrs or raised edges which might hinder reassembly. Check both for cracks or any other signs of wear or damage and renew them if necessary. As noted above, the bearing and its circlips must be renewed whenever they are disturbed.
6   Note that replacement bearings are available from Rover dealers either as separate items or as part of a bearing kit which includes both circlips and the driveshaft nut. The purchase of the kit is advised because it will ensure that all replacement parts required are ready to hand on reassembly.
7   Check the condition of the roadwheel studs in the hub flange. If any are sheared off, stretched or have damaged threads, they can be pressed out of the hub providing that its flange is fully supported; on refitting, support the hub flange and press in the new stud until it seats fully.

Refitting

8   On reassembly, check (as far as is possible) that the new bearing is packed with grease and fit the new circlip to the hub carrier outboard groove. Apply a light film of oil to the bearing inner and outer races and to their matching surfaces in the hub and hub carrier to aid installation of the bearing.
9   Supporting the hub carrier outboard face and applying pressure only to the bearing's outer race, press in the new bearing until it seats against the circlip (Fig. 10.7), then fit the second new circlip to the hub carrier's inboard groove.
10   Supporting the bearing's inner race fully, press the hub into the bearing and hub carrier until the hub shoulder seats against the bearing's inner race (Fig. 10.8). Wipe off any surplus oil or grease.
11   Refit the brake disc shield and brake disc (Chapter 9).
12   Refit the hub carrier assembly (Sec 2).

4   Front suspension anti-roll bar and mountings – removal, overhaul and refitting

Removal

1   Jack up the front of the car and support it securely on axle stands (see 'Jacking, towing and wheel changing').
2   Unscrew the nut securing the bar to each suspension lower arm and slacken the bolts securing the bar clamps to the underbody (photo).
3   Disconnect the bar from the suspension lower arms, collecting the rubber bushes, their washers and the metal spacers.
4   Mark the location of the clamp bushes on the bar, then unbolt the clamps and withdraw the bar, manoeuvring it clear of the exhaust system.

Overhaul

5   Thoroughly clean all components and the underbody areas around the mountings, removing all traces of dirt and, if necessary, of underseal, then check all components for wear or damage and renew them if necessary.
6   Check the rubber bushes and renew them if they are cracked, worn, split or perished.

Refitting

7   Manoeuvre the bar into position and apply soft soap to the clamp bush locations to act as a lubricant.
8   Fit the clamp bushes to the bar, noting that the bush split must be at the front and aligning the bushes with the marks made on removal, engage the clamps in the underbody and lightly tighten the clamp bolts.
9   Ensuring that a metal washer is fitted between each rubber bush and the bolt head, the nut or the metal spacer, reassemble the bar-to-suspension lower arm mountings; again tighten the nuts only by enough to secure the assembly (photo).
10   With all bar mountings correctly installed, check that the bar is centred on the body and that all rubber bushes are seated without distortion.
11   Lower the car to the ground. When all the car's weight is back on its wheels, rock it to settle the suspension, then tighten the bolts and nuts to their specified torque wrench settings.

5   Front suspension damper and mountings – removal, overhaul and refitting

Removal

1   Jack up the front of the car and support it securely on axle stands (see 'Jacking, towing and wheel changing'), then turn the steering to full lock so that the damper bottom mounting can be reached; if better access is required, the roadwheel should be removed.
2   Open the bonnet and unscrew the nut securing the damper top mounting; on the right-hand side this will first require the removal of the washer system reservoir (Chapter 12). Remove the nut, the metal washer and the top rubber bush (photo).
3   Unscrew the nut and bolt securing the damper bottom mounting to the suspension upper arm and withdraw the damper, collecting the metal spacer and washers from the bottom mounting and the rubber bush and metal washer from the top mounting. Always store the damper in an upright position.

Overhaul

4   Check the damper's action by clamping it, by its bottom mounting eye, upright in a soft-jawed vice and moving the piston rod fully up and down. Firm, even resistance should be felt in both directions; if the damping is weak, if the unit shows signs of oil leaks at any point or if the piston rod is bent, scored or damaged, the damper must be renewed. Note that it is good practice, if either damper requires renewal, to renew both together as a matched pair.

5.8 Note metal washer on each side of damper bottom mounting eye (arrows)

5   Check the damper's bottom mounting bush and renew it as follows if it is cracked, worn, split or perished.
6   Removal and refitting are easiest if a press is used, but if not available a strong bench vice and appropriately-sized sockets or pieces of tubing will serve as an adequate substitute. Extract the bush's metal sleeve, then cut the rubber with a hacksaw or similar and remove it. Polish any burrs or raised edges from the damper bottom mounting eye, then lubricate the new bush components with liquid soap or petroleum jelly before pressing them into place; ensure that both are located centrally in the mounting eye.

Refitting

7   If a new damper is being fitted, or if the original has been out of service for some time, the damper must be primed by clamping it, by its bottom mounting eye, upright in a soft-jawed vice and moving the piston rod fully up and down (through at least three full strokes) until full damping action is restored and there is no free play when changing direction at the end of each stroke.
8   First reassemble the top mounting, tightening the nut loosely, then align the damper bottom mounting eye with the upper arm and brake flexible hose bracket and refit the bolt with the spacer and washers, tightening the nut loosely (photo).
9   Lower the car to the ground. When all the car's weight is back on its wheels, rock it to settle the suspension, then tighten the damper top mounting nut, followed by the bottom mounting nut and bolt, both to the specified torque wrench settings. Turn the steering to the full lock position required to reach the damper bottom mounting.
10   Refit the washer system reservoir if working on the right-hand damper.

6   Front suspension lower arm and pivot bushes – removal, overhaul and refitting

Removal

1   Jack up the front of the car and support the body securely on axle stands then remove the roadwheel (see 'Jacking, towing and wheel changing').
2   Relieve the pressure of the Hydragas system from the lower arm by using a trolley jack or similar (with a block of wood interposed to prevent damage) to jack up the suspension via the lower balljoint until it is just beginning to take the weight of the car, then slip a wooden spacer between the suspension upper arm and the subframe and lower the jack (photos).
3   Where fitted, disconnect the anti-roll bar from the lower arm (Sec 4).
4   Unscrew the nut and fully remove the pinch-bolt securing the suspension lower balljoint to the hub carrier. Note that if the original balljoint has been replaced so that it is now secured by nuts and bolts rather than rivets, the balljoint can be unbolted from the lower arm instead, if required.
5   Unscrew the lower arm front and rear pivot bolts. Prise out the sealing grommet from the front of the subframe to reach the front bolt. Note that it may be necessary to unscrew the front outboard mounting bolt from the subframe rear mounting to allow the rear pivot bolt to be removed (photos).
6   Withdraw the lower arm.

Overhaul

Note: *The suspension lower arm front and rear pivot bushes are different; if they are to be renewed, ensure that only the correct bush is fitted to each arm location*

7   Check the arm pivot bushes; if they are worn, cracked, split or perished they must be renewed. *The renewal of these bushes is best left to a Rover dealer as a press is required with a bush removal/refitting mandrel, a support, a front bush fitting guide and a rear bush fitting guide (Rover Service Tool Numbers 18G 1612-1, 1612-4, 1612-3 and 1612-2 respectively). While the old bushes can be extracted using a strong bench vice and suitable sockets it is unlikely that new bushes can be installed successfully without the shaped mandrels.*

For those owners with access to the required equipment, note that the rear bush must be fitted with its rounded flange to the rear of the arm and with the arrows on that face pointing outboard, to the lower balljoint; the front bush must be fitted with its flat flange to the front. Rover recommend the use of Marlene 148 rubber lubricant to aid installation.
8   Thoroughly clean the lower arm and the subframe around the arm mountings, removing all traces of dirt and of underseal if necessary, then check carefully for cracks, distortion or any other signs of wear or damage. Do not forget to check the pivot bolts.

Refitting

9   Refitting is the reverse of the removal procedure, noting the following points.

(a)   *Tighten only lightly at first the various nuts and bolts.*

6.2A Jack up suspension under lower balljoint (arrow) ...

6.2B ... and wedge wooden spacer (arrow) between upper arm and subframe to relieve pressure of Hydragas system from suspension components

6.5A Remove sealing grommet from subframe to reach lower arm front pivot bolt

6.5B It may be necessary to remove bolt 'A' to allow removal of lower arm rear pivot bolt 'B'

7.6A Fully remove pinch-bolt ...

7.6B ... to allow separation of lower balljoint from hub carrier

(b) Jack up the suspension, remove the spacer, then lower the jack and refit the roadwheel. Lower the car to the ground.
(c) When all the car's weight is back on its wheels, rock it to settle the suspension, then tighten all disturbed nuts and bolts to their specified torque wrench settings; refit the subframe sealing grommet.
(d) Depending on the reason for the work, it may be advisable to check the wheel alignment (Sec 31) on completion.

7   Front suspension lower balljoint – removal and refitting

Note: The original balljoint is riveted to the suspension lower arm; when it is renewed the rivets are replaced by nuts and bolts. Proceed as described in the relevant sub-section below

Removal

Riveted (original) balljoint

1   Remove the suspension lower arm (Sec 6).
2   Extract the rivets; Rover recommend the use of a pedestal drill (for accuracy) to drill out the rivet heads so that a press can be used to remove the rivet studs.
3   Remove the old balljoint from the lower arm.

Bolted (replacement) balljoint

4   Jack up the front of the car and support the body securely on axle stands then remove the roadwheel (see 'Jacking, towing and wheel changing').
5   Relieve the pressure of the Hydragas system from the lower balljoint by using a trolley jack or similar (with a block of wood interposed to prevent damage) to jack up the suspension via the balljoint until it is just beginning to take the weight of the car, then slip a wooden spacer between the suspension upper arm and the subframe and lower the jack.
6   Unscrew the nut and fully remove the pinch-bolt securing the lower balljoint to the hub carrier (photos).
7   Unbolt the balljoint from the lower arm and remove it. Note that it may be necessary to slacken the suspension lower arm pivot bolts (Sec 6, paragraph 5) and to disconnect the anti-roll bar (where fitted) from the lower arm so that the arm can be swung down far enough for the balljoint to be removed.

Refitting

8   Refitting is the reverse of the removal procedure, noting the following points.

(a) Tighten all disturbed nuts and bolts to their specified torque wrench settings; if the suspension lower arm pivot bolts and anti-roll bar mountings were slackened, tighten them when the weight of the car is back on its wheels and the car has been rocked to settle the suspension components.
(b) Depending on the reason for the work, it may be advisable to check the wheel alignment (Sec 31) on completion.

8.3 Flatten back lockwasher raised tab to unlock upper balljoint-to-upper arm nut – note also balljoint lockwasher tab (arrow)

8   Front suspension upper balljoint – removal and refitting

Note: The upper balljoint is screwed into the hub carrier and will require a large spanner or socket to remove and refit it. The recommended Rover Service Tool is Number 18G 1341, but proprietary Metro balljoint sockets are available from any good motor accessory shop; these tools will make the job easier and will permit the balljoint to be tightened using a torque wrench. In addition, a universal balljoint separator tool may be required; have one available in case

Removal

1   Jack up the front of the car and support the body securely on axle stands then remove the roadwheel (see 'Jacking, towing and wheel changing').
2   Relieve the pressure of the Hydragas system from the upper balljoint by using a trolley jack or similar (with a block of wood interposed to prevent damage) to jack up the suspension via the lower balljoint until it is just beginning to take the weight of the car, then slip a wooden spacer between the suspension upper arm and the subframe to hold the suspension in that position.
3   Flatten back the lockwasher raised tabs from the balljoint-to-upper arm nut (photo) and from the balljoint itself. If a suitably-sized open-ended spanner is available, the balljoint can be slackened (or even unscrewed from the hub carrier) at this stage.
4   Unscrew the balljoint-to-upper arm nut and remove the lockwasher. Refit the nut so that it is flush with the end of the balljoint stud thread

and disconnect the balljoint from the upper arm, if necessary using a universal balljoint separator tool (photo).

5 Lower the hub carrier/suspension lower arm assembly on the jack, taking care that the brake flexible hose is not stretched or damaged, until the balljoint stud is clear of the upper arm; if necessary, unbolt the brake hose bracket (and damper bottom mounting, where fitted) from the upper arm.

6 Unscrew the balljoint from the hub carrier (see note above), if necessary, having an assistant hold the hub carrier steady. Discard the lockwashers; they must be renewed whenever disturbed.

Refitting

7 On reassembly, check that the threads of the balljoint and of the hub carrier are clean, dry and undamaged and that the balljoint pin and upper arm tapers are undamaged and degreased. **Always** fit new lockwashers; note that these are included in the balljoint kit available from Rover dealers.

8 Screw the balljoint into the hub carrier and tighten it to the specified torque wrench setting, then secure it by bending a portion of the lockwasher up against one of its flats. If the lockwasher is not already secured to the hub carrier by a small tab, bend a portion of the lockwasher (opposite to that securing the balljoint) down against the hub carrier to secure the assembly.

9 Jack up the hub carrier/suspension lower arm assembly until the balljoint taper is fully engaged with that of the upper arm, fit a new lockwasher and tighten the balljoint-to-upper arm nut to its specified torque wrench setting. Secure the nut by bending one of the lockwasher tabs up against one of its flats. If the lockwasher is not already secured to the upper arm by a small tab, bend down the lockwasher's other tab against the arm to secure the assembly.

10 Refit, if removed, the brake hose bracket bolt (and damper bottom mounting, where fitted). Tighten the bolt and nut to the specified torque wrench setting; where a damper is fitted, the bolt and nut should be finally tightened only when the car's weight is back on its wheels and the suspension components are settled in their normal working positions.

11 Jack up the suspension, remove the spacer, then lower the jack and refit the roadwheel. Lower the car to the ground.

9 Front suspension upper arm and pivot bearings – removal, overhaul and refitting

Note: *This procedure requires the depressurisation of (the appropriate side of) the Hydragas suspension system – refer to the remarks in Section 1 of this Chapter before starting work*

Removal

1 Remove the Hydragas unit (Sec 10).
2 Remove the underwing shield (Chapter 11).
3 Unbolt the brake hose bracket from the upper arm.
4 Support the weight of the hub carrier/suspension lower arm assembly using a block of wood or similar, then disconnect the upper balljoint from the arm end (Sec 8, paragraphs 3 and 4).
5 Remove the upper arm pivot shaft rear nut and washer, then undo the pivot shaft retaining plate bolts and nut. Withdraw the pivot shaft and retaining plate forwards.
6 Withdraw the upper arm, collecting the front and rear sealing rings and the rear thrustwasher.

Overhaul

7 Clamp the pivot shaft in a soft-jawed vice and unscrew the front nut and washer; collect the retaining plate and thrust collar, noting which way round the collar is fitted.
8 Dismantle and check the knuckle joint (Sec 11).
9 Thoroughly clean all components and the subframe around the upper arm mountings. Check the subframe for signs of wear or damage to the upper arm pivot points and to the various threads, then check the rebound rubber buffer. Renew any component that shows signs of wear or damage.
10 If the pivot bearings are to be renewed, unscrew the grease nipple from the upper arm and extract the bearings using an internally-expanding bearing puller, or drive them out from the inside using a hammer and a slim metal drift passed through the arm pivot from the opposite end.

8.4 Using a universal balljoint separator tool to release upper balljoint from upper arm

11 Carefully clean the pivot bore, polish away any burrs or raised edges that might damage the new bearings on installation and check that the grease nipple and the lubricant passage in the arm are clear.
12 Ensuring that they are fitted with their marked surfaces outwards and that they enter exactly squarely into the pivot bore, install the new bearings using either a press, a large bench vice or a length of studding, two large plain washers and nuts. Check that the bearings are installed correctly by passing the pivot shaft through them.
13 Pack the bearings with multi-purpose grease, refit the grease nipple and lubricate all other pivot components. Fit the rear thrustwasher to the arm (noting that its grooved surface must be against the bearing), grease it and fit the rear sealing ring to retain it. Fit the front sealing ring.
14 Refit the knuckle joint to the arm (Sec 11).
15 Clamp the pivot shaft in a soft-jawed vice and fit the thrust collar (noting that its grooved surface must be against the bearing), the retaining plate, the washer and the nut, tightening the nut to its specified torque wrench setting. Check that the shaft is clean and unmarked, then smear it with grease.

Refitting

16 Taking care not to displace the sealing rings or thrustwasher, refit the upper arm to the subframe, followed by the pivot shaft assembly. Tighten the retaining plate bolts and nut and the pivot shaft rear nut to their specified torque wrench settings, then check that the arm pivots smoothly but without free play.
17 Use a grease gun to pack the bearings until grease can be seen exuding from both ends of the pivot, then wipe off all surplus grease.
18 For the remainder of the refitting procedure, work as follows.

   (a) Refit the Hydragas unit (Sec 10).
   (b) Refit the underwing shield (Chapter 11).
   (c) Refit the brake hose bracket bolt (and damper bottom mounting, where fitted). Tighten the bolt and nut to the specified torque wrench setting; where a damper is fitted, the bolt and nut should be finally tightened only when the car's weight is back on its wheels and the suspension components are settled in their normal working positions.
   (d) Connect the upper balljoint to the upper arm (Sec 8).
   (e) Refit the roadwheel and lower the car to the ground.
   (f) Have any air evacuated from the Hydragas suspension and have it pressurised to the correct ride height.

10 Front suspension Hydragas unit – removal and refitting

Note: *This procedure requires the depressurisation of (the appropriate side of) the Hydragas suspension system – refer to the remarks in Section 1 of this Chapter before starting work*

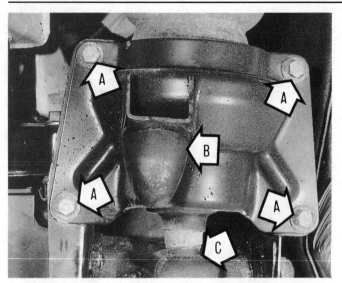

10.5 Front Hydragas unit clamp plate bolts 'A', bump stop 'B', knuckle joint 'C'

Removal

1   Have the Hydragas suspension depressurised on the relevant side.
2   Jack up the front of the car and support it securely on axle stands then remove the roadwheel (see *'Jacking, towing and wheel changing'*).
3   Uncouple the plastic connecting pipe from the Hydragas unit; plug or cap the orifices immediately to prevent the entry of dirt (Sec 14).
4   Where a damper is fitted, unbolt the bottom mounting and slacken the top mounting so that the damper can be moved out of the way (Sec 5); do not force it or its top mounting might be damaged.
5   Unbolt the unit's clamp plate from the subframe and withdraw the plate. Check the condition of the bump stop and renew it if worn or damaged (photo).
6   Withdraw the Hydragas unit, lifting it off the knuckle joint; note the presence of the return spring and (where fitted) the spacer.
7   Whenever the unit is removed, the knuckle joint should be dismantled, checked for wear and greased (Sec 11).

Refitting

8   Clean carefully the mating surfaces of the unit and of the knuckle joint, then apply a smear of the recommended grease (Sec 11); ensure that the spacer (if fitted) and return spring are in place.
9   Offer up the Hydragas unit, aligning it carefully on the knuckle joint, then refit the clamp plate and tighten the bolts and nuts to the specified torque wrench setting.
10   For the remainder of the refitting procedure, work as follows.

    (a)   Connect the plastic connecting pipe to the unit (Sec 14).
    (b)   If applicable, reassemble the damper bottom mounting; the mounting bolt and nuts should be finally tightened (to their specified torque wrench settings) when the car's weight is back on its wheels and the suspension components are settled in their normal working positions.
    (c)   Refit the roadwheel and lower the car to the ground.
    (d)   Have any air evacuated from the Hydragas suspension and have it pressurised to the correct ride height.

11   Front suspension knuckle joint – removal and refitting

Note: *This procedure requires the depressurisation of (the appropriate side of) the Hydragas suspension system – refer to the remarks in Section 1 of this Chapter before starting work*

Removal

1   Remove the Hydragas unit (Sec 10).

2   Withdraw the return spring and, where fitted, the spacer from the knuckle joint.
3   Carefully lift the rubber boot and remove the knuckle joint from the upper arm, then prise out the joint socket.
4   Thoroughly clean all components and check them for signs of wear or damage; check particularly that the ball end of the knuckle joint is not corroded, worn or pitted and that the socket is not cracked or split.
5   Renew any worn or damaged components; note that if the knuckle joint is to be renewed it is available only as an assembly with the socket and the rubber boot, otherwise only the return spring, the spacer and the socket are available separately.

Refitting

6   On reassembly, clean the upper arm socket location and tap in the socket.
7   The recommended lubricant for the knuckle joint is Dextragrease Super GP (available from Rover dealers); apply a smear of this grease to all knuckle joint components before refitting.
8   Pack the socket with grease and press in the knuckle joint, then fill the space above the joint ball with grease and ensure that the rubber boot is correctly located over the socket lip so that no dirt or water can enter the joint.
9   Refit the spacer (if fitted) and the return spring, then wipe off any surplus grease.
10   Refit the Hydragas unit (Sec 10).

12   Front suspension subframe mountings – renewal

Note: *The subframe is secured at its four corners to the body; each mounting being secured by a bolt and nut (front) or three bolts (rear) to the body and by a through-bolt to the subframe. Removal and refitting is essentially the same for all mountings; note that great care will be required in supporting the body securely while the subframe is disturbed*

1   Jack up the front of the car and support the body securely on axle stands (see *'Jacking, towing and wheel changing'*).
2   To dismantle one of the front mountings, first unscrew the through-bolt nut, then the mounting-to-body bolt and nut, then withdraw the mounting; it may be necessary carefully to prise down the subframe to allow the mounting to be removed (photo).
3   The procedure is the same on the rear mountings, but where an

12.2 Front subframe front mounting through-bolt nut 'A' and mountings 'B'

Fig. 10.9 Front suspension subframe and mountings (Sec 12)

1 Subframe
2 Hydragas unit clamp plate
3 Bolt
4 Nut
5 Subframe front mounting
6 Subframe rear mounting
7 Bolt – support member-to-subframe
8 Nut
9 Through-bolt – front mounting-to-subframe
10 Bolt – rear mounting-to-body
11 Sealing grommet
12 Through-bolt – rear mounting-to-subframe
13 Engine/transmission right-hand support member
14 Engine/transmission left-hand support member
15 Bolt – support member-to-subframe
16 Bolt – support member-to-subframe

anti-roll bar is fitted the bar-to-body clamps must be unbolted and the bar must be lowered so that the mounting can be removed (see photos 4.2 and 6.5B).

4 Refitting is the reverse of the removal procedure; tighten all disturbed nuts and bolts to their specified torque wrench settings (where given).

13 Front suspension subframe – removal and refitting

Note: *This procedure requires the depressurisation of both sides of the Hydragas suspension system – refer to the remarks in Section 1 of this Chapter before starting work*

Removal

1 Remove the engine/transmission unit (Chapter 2).
2 Remove the exhaust system front pipe (Chapter 4).
3 Remove the gearchange linkage components from the subframe (Chapter 7).
4 Either disconnect the plastic connecting pipes from the front Hydragas units (Sec 14) or remove the units completely (Sec 10).
5 Remove the steering gear (Sec 29).
6 Disconnecting the brake flexible hoses from the metal hydraulic pipes if required, ensure that both front brake calipers are separated from the subframe and suspension components (Chapter 9).
7 Either completely remove the suspension damper and anti-roll bar (where fitted) and the upper and lower arms, or disconnect them from the body so that they can be removed with the subframe and subsequently dismantled; refer to the relevant Sections of this Chapter.
8 Make a final check that all components have been removed or disconnected that are attached to the subframe or might prevent its removal.

9 Support the subframe, unbolt its mountings (Sec 12), then lower the subframe to the ground and remove it.

Refitting

10 Refitting is the reverse of the removal procedure; tighten all disturbed nuts and bolts to their specified torque wrench settings (where given).

14 Hydragas suspension connecting pipes – renewal

Note: *This procedure requires the depressurisation of (the appropriate side of) the Hydragas suspension system – refer to the remarks in Section 1 of this Chapter before starting work*

1 Have the Hydragas suspension depressurised on the relevant side.
2 Jack the car up first at the front and support the body securely on an axle stand, then jack up the rear side and support the body securely on an axle stand (see *'Jacking, towing and wheel changing'*).
3 Unscrew the union nut connecting each end of the pipe to the Hydragas front and rear units (photo). To prevent the entry of dirt or other foreign matter into the system, **immediately** plug or cap both the pipe end and the unit orifice whenever they are disconnected.
4 Work from front to rear along the length of the (large-bore, plastic) pipe and release it from the retainers securing it to the underbody.
5 Carefully pull the pipe clear of the front suspension subframe. On models so equipped, it may be necessary to disconnect the anti-roll bar from the suspension lower arms and to unbolt the bar clamps from the underbody so that the pipe can be removed (Sec 4).
6 Release the pipe from around the rear suspension and withdraw it from the car.

14.3 Hydragas connecting pipe union nut (arrowed) – at front left-hand unit

7   Refitting is the reverse of the removal procedure, noting the following points.

(a)   Route the pipe carefully from the front unit to the rear and check that it is free from sharp bends or kinks and clear of any moving or hot component, then secure it to the body with the retainers.

(b)   Remove the plugs or caps from the pipe and unit union orifices, wipe them clean and connect them; tighten the union nuts securely, to the specified torque wrench setting if the tools are available.

(c)   If applicable, refit the anti-roll bar mountings (Sec 4).

(d)   Lower the car to the ground.

(e)   Have any air evacuated from the Hydragas suspension and have it pressurised to the correct ride height.

15   Suspension ride heights – checking and adjusting

General

1   The car's ride heights are set initially, and adjusted if necessary afterwards, by pressurising the fluid in each side of the Hydragas suspension system using the equipment mentioned in Section 1 of this Chapter; there are no alternatives to using this equipment.

2   It is essential that the ride heights are checked at regular intervals and maintained at **exactly** the specified value. While a permissible tolerance is given, the suspension and steering are designed to perform best with the ride heights as specified and the same on each side of the car.

3   If the car is used with incorrect ride heights, one or more of the following will happen.

(a)   The car's ride and handling will deteriorate; the greater the variation from the specified value, the more marked will be the effect on the car's comfort and stability.

(b)   The front suspension and steering geometry will alter, affecting the steering and causing exaggerated and uneven tyre wear.

(c)   As with cars with conventional suspension, braking performance will be affected and stopping distances increased if the suspension does not perform as the manufacturer intended.

(d)   If the ride heights are low (suspension pressure low) and the car is driven over rough roads, heavily laden, or at high speeds, the Hydragas units may be overloaded and damaged.

4   If any of the above symptoms are experienced, **always** check the ride heights first before investigating further; have them set exactly if they are incorrect, then drive the car (for as long as necessary) to check whether the fault still exists.

5   Note that incorrect ride heights can be an MOT test failure point.

15.7 Measuring suspension ride height

Checking

6   To check the ride heights, prepare the car as follows.

(a)   With the car at kerb weight (ie, unladen, but with a full fuel tank, spare wheel and tools and all lubricants and fluids), park it on smooth, level ground with the steering and front roadwheels in the straight-ahead position, then rock and bounce it several times at both ends to settle the suspension components.

(b)   Do not apply the handbrake, but ensure that the car does not move.

(c)   Remove the front roadwheel trims or centre caps (as appropriate).

(d)   Roll the car forwards 1 metre to relieve any suspension stresses.

(e)   Push down with your full body weight on the front of the car and allow it to rise naturally.

(f)   Leave the car standing undisturbed for at least two hours to allow the temperature of its components to equalise with the ambient air temperature – as a guide, the engine should be cold before a measurement is made.

(g)   To be absolutely accurate, record the ambient air temperature; if it is significantly above or below 17°C, calculate a corrected ride height value according to the correction factor given in the Specifications Section of this Chapter.

7   Ensuring that the measurement is made exactly vertically (seen

15.11 Suspension ride height adjustment valve – right-hand side (arrow)

from the front of the car, as well as from the side), use a straight-edged ruler to measure the distance from the front hub centre to the underside of the wheel arch (photo).

8   Repeat the measurement on the opposite side of the car; record both measurements and compare them with those specified.

9   If the ride heights recorded are outside the specified tolerances, or if one side differs significantly from the other, they must be adjusted as soon as possible.

10   If, for example, you are trying to establish the cause of uneven tyre wear it will be necessary to have the ride heights set to **exactly** the specified value; an experienced Rover mechanic should be able to do this without difficulty.

Adjusting

11   If the ride heights need adjustment, take the car to a Rover dealer; see paragraph 1 of this Section. Adjustment is made via a Schrader-type valve located next to each rear unit (photo).

Fig. 10.10 Driving outboard rear hub bearing out of hub (Sec 17)

16   Hydragas suspension system – testing

1   If either suspension ride height is repeatedly found to be low, there is evidence of a leak in that side of the system.

2   Working from the front unit along the connecting pipe to the rear unit on the side affected, check carefully for any signs of fluid leakage. Raise and support the car (see *'Jacking, towing and wheel changing'*) if better access is required.

3   If the leak is serious, it may be revealed by damp patches, but in most cases all that will be visible is a slight residue left after the fluid has evaporated. If a leak is very difficult to spot, clean all Hydragas system components carefully, including those around them, and dust the suspect area with talcum powder; this should help to make the source of the leak more obvious.

4   If the leak is found to be from one of the connecting pipe unions, tighten the union carefully (but do not overtighten it) and have the ride heights adjusted. Check carefully that the leak is not from the Hydragas unit's valve.

5   If the leak is found to be in the connecting pipe or in one of the Hydragas units, renew the component concerned as described in the relevant Section of this Chapter.

6   If either ride height is low and there is no sign of a fluid leak from the system, it is possible that one of the Hydragas units is leaking nitrogen. If this is thought to be the case, the fault should be investigated by a Rover dealer.

Fig. 10.11 Driving inboard rear hub bearing out of hub (Sec 17)

17   Rear hub and bearings – removal and refitting

Note: *Do not attempt to remove either bearing unless absolutely necessary; it will probably be damaged during the removal operation. Never overtighten the hub nut beyond the specified torque wrench setting in an attempt to 'adjust' the bearings*

Note: *A press will be required to rebuild the assembly; if such is not available a large bench vice and suitable spacers (such as large sockets) will serve as an adequate substitute*

Note: *Depending on the equipment available, it may be easier for some owners to slacken and tighten the hub nut (see paragraph 4 below) when the car's weight is on its wheels; the nut is accessible once the roadwheel trim or centre cap (as appropriate) and the hub cap have been removed*

Removal

1   Remove and check the brake drum (Chapter 9).

2   Prise off the hub cap (photo).

3   Relieve the staking of the hub nut using a hammer and punch or (if necessary) an electric drill, then unscrew the hub nut and remove the washer.

4   Note that the **left-hand** side stub axle and nut have a **left-hand** thread; the nut is therefore unscrewed **clockwise**. The right-hand side components have a conventional right-hand thread and are unscrewed in the usual anti-clockwise direction. It is good practice to renew the hub nuts whenever they are disturbed.

Fig. 10.12 Pressing new inboard rear hub bearing into hub (Sec 17)

17.2 Prising off rear hub cap

17.5 Remove hub nut to permit removal of hub from stub axle

17.18 Securing hub nut by staking its collar into stub axle groove

Fig. 10.13 Pressing new outboard rear hub bearing into hub (Sec 17)

5　Withdraw the hub from the stub axle (photo).
6　If the stub axle is worn or damaged it must be renewed using a press (Sec 18).
7　Taking care not to scratch or damage the seal housing, prise the oil seal out of the hub inboard end and discard it; the seal must be renewed whenever it is disturbed.
8　Drive the outboard bearing out of the hub, using a hammer and a suitable punch (Fig. 10.10).
9　Drive the inboard bearing out of the hub (Fig. 10.11).
10　Thoroughly clean the hub, removing all traces of dirt and grease and polishing away any burrs or raised edges which might hinder reassembly. Check it for cracks or any other signs of wear or damage and renew if necessary.
11　Note that replacement bearings are available from Rover dealers either as separate items or as part of a bearing kit which includes both bearings, the oil seal and the hub nut. The purchase of the kit is advised because it will ensure that all replacement parts required are ready to hand on reassembly.
12　Check the condition of the roadwheel studs in the hub flange. If any are sheared off, stretched or have damaged threads, they can be pressed out of the hub providing that its flange is fully supported; on refitting, support the hub flange and press in the new stud until it seats fully.

Refitting

13　On reassembly, check (as far as is possible) that the new bearings are packed with grease. Apply a light film of oil to the bearing outer races and to the hub bores to aid bearing installation. Note that both bearings must be installed with their marked faces outwards (ie so that the inner races project towards each other).
14　Supporting the hub outboard end and applying pressure only to the bearing's outer race, press in the new inboard bearing until it seats against the shoulder (Fig. 10.12).

15　Similarly, support the hub inboard end and press in the new outboard bearing (Fig. 10.13).
16　Ensuring that it is fitted with its sealing lips pointing outboard (towards the bearings), press the new oil seal into the hub and apply a thin smear of grease to the seal lips. Wipe off any surplus oil or grease.
17　Refit the hub to the stub axle, followed by the washer and the **new** nut.
18　Remembering that the left-hand nut must be tightened **anti-clockwise**, tighten the hub nut to the specified torque wrench setting, then secure it by using a hammer and punch to stake the nut's collar into the stub axle groove (photo).
19　Check that the hub rotates smoothly and easily, with no trace of free play or stiffness, then refit the hub cap.
20　Refit the brake drum (Chapter 9).

18　Rear stub axle – removal and refitting

Note: *A press is required to remove and install the rear stub axle; this operation will therefore require the removal of the relevant trailing arm which in turn involves the depressurisation of (the appropriate side of) the Hydragas suspension system – refer to the remarks in Section 1 of this Chapter before starting work*

Removal

1　Remove the trailing arm (Sec 20).
2　Remove the brake drum and backplate (Chapter 9).
3　Press out the stub axle.

Refitting

4　Fitting a new circlip to locate it, press the new stub axle into the trailing arm, from the inboard side outwards.
5　Refit the brake components (Chapter 9).
6　Refit the trailing arm (Sec 20).

19　Rear suspension anti-roll bar and mountings – removal, overhaul and refitting

Removal

1　Jack up the rear of the car and support it securely on axle stands (see 'Jacking, towing and wheel changing').
2　Unscrew the bolt and nut securing the bar to each link and slacken the bolts securing the bar clamps to the underbody. Unbolt the links from their brackets if required (photos).
3　Unhook the exhaust system from its rubber mountings and lower it onto a support to take its weight without damaging or distorting it at the front (Chapter 4).
4　Mark the location of the clamp bushes on the bar, then unbolt the clamps and withdraw the bar.

19.2A Anti-roll bar-to-suspension trailing arm link mounting bolts (arrows)

19.2B Rear anti-roll bar-to-body clamp

Overhaul

5   Thoroughly clean all components and the underbody areas around the mountings, removing all traces of dirt and, if necessary, of underseal, then check all components for wear or damage and renew them if necessary.

6   Check the rubber bushes and renew them if they are cracked, worn, split or perished.

Refitting

7   Manoeuvre the bar into position and apply soft soap to the clamp bush locations to act as a lubricant.

8   Fit the clamp bushes to the bar, noting that the bush split must face downwards. Align the bushes with the marks made on removal, then refit the clamps and tighten the clamp bolts lightly.

9   Reassemble the bar-to-suspension trailing arm mountings; again tighten the bolts and nuts only by enough to secure the assembly.

10   With all bar mountings correctly installed, check that the bar is centred on the body and that all rubber bushes are seated without distortion, then hook the exhaust system on its mountings again.

11   Lower the car to the ground. When all the car's weight is back on its wheels, rock it to settle the suspension, then tighten all the disturbed bolts and nuts to their specified torque wrench settings.

20   Rear suspension trailing arm and pivot bearings – removal, overhaul and refitting

Note: *This procedure requires the depressurisation of (the appropriate side of) the Hydragas suspension system – refer to the remarks in Section 1 of this Chapter before starting work*

Removal

1   Remove the Hydragas unit (Sec 21). Support the weight of the trailing arm, using a wooden block or similar.

2   Disconnect the handbrake cable from the rear brake lever assembly and release the cable from the cable ties and bracket securing it to the trailing arm (Chapter 9).

3   Minimise fluid loss by removing the master cylinder reservoir cap and then tightening it down onto a piece of polythene to obtain an airtight seal (taking care not to damage the sender unit), or by using a brake hose clamp, a G-clamp or a similar tool to clamp the flexible hose, or by capping or plugging the metal brake pipe as it is disconnected (Chapter 9). Try to keep fluid spillage to a minimum and wash off any spilt fluid as soon as possible.

4   Unscrew the union nut to disconnect the metal brake pipe from the hose, then unscrew the nut to release the hose from the trailing arm bracket. Take great care not to allow dirt into the hydraulic system.

5   Unscrew the trailing arm pivot shaft inboard nut and washer, then undo the pivot shaft retaining plate bolts and nuts (photos).

6   Extract the pivot shaft with the retaining plate. If the pivot has been regularly greased the shaft will slide out easily. If, as is more likely, the shaft is stuck with corrosion, it must be driven out from its inboard end outwards using a hammer and a suitable drift; the only alternative is to grip the outboard nut with a self-locking wrench and to hammer the shaft out. In extreme cases, apply a liberal quantity of penetrating fluid to both ends of the pivot and allow time for it to 'work', then break the shaft free by rotating it before attempting to remove it.

7   When the pivot shaft is removed, withdraw the trailing arm, collecting the inboard and outboard seals and the thrustwasher(s). Check the condition of the rebound rubber buffer and renew it if worn or damaged.

8   Remove and check the helper spring, strut and knuckle joint (Section 22).

9   Remove the rear brake drum and backplate, if required, as described in Chapter 9, removing the rear hub as described in Section 17 of this Chapter. If the stub axle is worn or damaged it must be renewed using a press (Sec 18), but note that if the trailing arm is to be renewed, a stub axle will be supplied fitted to the new arm.

Overhaul

Note: *The trailing arm pivot needle roller bearings, the pivot shaft and the associated thrustwashers are available only as part of a repair kit and cannot be purchased separately. The pivot shaft nuts, washers, grease nipple and seal can be purchased separately if required, but are also part of the repair kit*

10   Clamp the pivot shaft in a soft-jawed vice and unscrew the grease nipple, the outboard nut and its washer; collect the retaining plate and thrustwasher, noting which way round the thrustwasher is fitted.

11   Thoroughly clean all components and the subframe around the trailing arm mountings. Check the subframe for signs of wear or damage to the trailing arm pivot points and to the various threads, then check the rebound rubber buffer and the bump stop (photo). Renew any component that shows signs of wear or damage.

12   If the pivot bearings are to be renewed, first note the exact position of each in the arm pivot, measuring carefully the depth of each bearing's outer race from the arm's outer end. Extract them using an internally-expanding bearing puller or drive them out from the inside using a hammer and a slim metal drift passed through the arm pivot from the opposite end.

13   Carefully clean the pivot bore, polish away any burrs or raised edges that might damage the new bearings on installation and check that the grease nipple is clear.

14   Ensuring that they are fitted with their marked surfaces outwards and that they enter exactly squarely into the pivot bore, install the new bearings using either a press, or a large bench vice or a length of studding, two large plain washers and nuts. Press the bearings into the positions noted on removal, then check that they are installed correctly

20.5A Rear suspension right-hand trailing arm inboard pivot shaft nut – seen from rear of subframe (arrow)

20.5B Trailing arm pivot shaft retaining plate bolts 'A', outboard pivot shaft nut 'B', and grease nipple 'C'

20.11 Rear suspension bump stop mounting bolt (arrow)

21.4A Rear Hydragas unit retaining strap nut (arrow) – in spare wheel compartment ...

21.4B ... and underneath body (arrow)

21.6 Rear Hydragas unit clamp plate bolts (arrows)

by passing the pivot shaft through them.

15   Pack the bearings with multi-purpose grease and lubricate all other pivot components. Fit the thrustwashers and seals to the arm (noting that the thrustwasher grooved surfaces must be against their respective bearings), grease each as it is installed.

16   Clamp the pivot shaft in a soft-jawed vice and fit the thrustwasher (noting that the grooved surface must be against the bearing), the retaining plate, the washer and outboard nut and the grease nipple, tightening the nut and grease nipple to their respective specified torque wrench settings. Check that the shaft is clean and unmarked, then smear it with grease.

Refitting

17   Taking care not to displace the seals or thrustwashers, refit the trailing arm to the subframe, then use a wooden block or similar to support the weight of its rear end. Align the arm's pivot with the subframe holes and refit the pivot shaft assembly, taking care not to damage the shaft or the bearings. Tighten the retaining plate bolts and nuts and the pivot shaft inboard nut to their specified torque wrench settings, then check that the arm pivots smoothly but without free play.

18   Use a grease gun to pack the bearings until grease can be seen exuding from both ends of the pivot, then wipe off all surplus grease.

19   For the remainder of the refitting procedure, work as follows.

    (a) Refit the helper spring, strut and knuckle joint to the arm (Sec 22).
    (b) Refit the Hydragas unit (Sec 21).
    (c) If they were removed, refit the brake backplate (Chapter 9), the rear hub (Sec 17) and the brake drum (Chapter 9).
    (d) Connect the handbrake cable to the rear brake lever assembly, connect the brake flexible hose to the trailing arm bracket and the metal brake pipe, then bleed any air from the system (Chapter 9). Adjust the rear brake shoes and the handbrake cable (Chapter 1).
    (e) Refit the roadwheel and lower the car to the ground.
    (f) Have any air evacuated from the Hydragas suspension and have it pressurised to the correct ride height.

21 Rear suspension Hydragas unit – removal and refitting

Note: *This procedure requires the depressurisation of (the appropriate side of) the Hydragas suspension system – refer to the remarks in Section 1 of this Chapter before starting work*

Removal

1   Have the Hydragas suspension depressurised on the relevant side.

2   Jack up the rear of the car and support it securely on axle stands then remove the roadwheel (see 'Jacking, towing and wheel changing').

3   Uncouple the plastic connecting pipe from the Hydragas unit; plug or cap the orifices immediately to prevent the entry of dirt (Sec 14).

4   Open the tailgate and lift the luggage compartment floor covering and the spare wheel cover, then unscrew the retaining strap nut inside the car. Working outside and underneath the car, unscrew the second retaining strap nut, then withdraw the strap and its rubber sleeve (photos).

5   On models so equipped, unbolt the anti-roll bar from the link (Sec 19).

6   Unbolt the Hydragas unit's clamp plate from the subframe and withdraw the plate (photo).

7   Withdraw the Hydragas unit, lifting it off the helper spring, strut and knuckle joint; if these components come away with the unit, note how each is located and note the presence of the return spring and the spacer between the strut and knuckle joint.

8   Collect the unit's mounting pad; check its condition, also that of the bump stop and renew either if worn or damaged.

9   Whenever the unit is removed, the strut and knuckle joint should be dismantled, checked for wear and greased (Sec 22).

Refitting

10   Clean carefully the mating surfaces of the unit and of the strut and knuckle joint, then apply a smear of the recommended grease (Sec 22); ensure that the spacer and return spring are in place between the

Fig. 10.14 Rear suspension subframe and mountings (Sec 23)

1   Subframe
2   Hydragas unit clamp plate
3   Bolt – clamp plate
4   Subframe (front) mounting
5   Mounting-to-body bolt – 3 off
6   Mounting-to-subframe bolt – 2 off

knuckle joint and strut and that the helper spring is correctly located on the trailing arm.
11   Offer up the Hydragas unit, aligning it carefully on the helper spring and ensuring that the strut fits into the centre hole in the unit, then refit the unit's mounting pad and its clamp plate, tightening the clamp plate bolts to the specified torque wrench setting.
12   Refit the retaining strap and its rubber sleeve, tightening the strap nuts to the specified torque wrench setting.
13   For the remainder of the refitting procedure, work as follows.

(a)   Connect the plastic connecting pipe to the unit (Sec 14).
(b)   Where fitted, connect the anti-roll bar to the link (Sec 19).
(c)   Refit the roadwheel and lower the car to the ground.
(d)   Have any air evacuated from the Hydragas suspension and have it pressurised to the correct ride height.

22   Rear suspension strut and knuckle joint – removal and refitting

Note: *This procedure requires the depressurisation of (the appropriate side of) the Hydragas suspension system – refer to the remarks in Section 1 of this Chapter before starting work*

Removal

1   Remove the Hydragas unit (Sec 21).
2   Withdraw the helper spring, noting how it is located on the trailing arm, then remove the strut, return spring and spacer from the knuckle joint.
3   Carefully lift the rubber boot and remove the knuckle joint from the trailing arm, then prise out the joint socket.
4   Thoroughly clean all components and check them for any signs of wear or damage; check particularly that the ball end of the knuckle joint is not corroded, worn or pitted and that the socket is not cracked or split.
5   Renew any worn or damaged components; note that if the knuckle joint is to be renewed it is available only as an assembly with the socket and the rubber boot, otherwise only the return spring, the spacer and the strut are available separately.

Refitting

6   On reassembly, clean the trailing arm socket location and tap in the socket.

7   The recommended lubricant for the knuckle joint is Dextragrease Super GP (available from Rover dealers); apply a smear of this grease to all knuckle joint components before refitting.
8   Pack the socket with grease and press in the knuckle joint, then fill the space above the joint ball with grease and ensure that the rubber boot is correctly located over the socket lip so that no dirt or water can enter the joint.
9   Refit the spacer and return spring to the knuckle joint, then refit the strut; apply a smear of grease to all these components as they are refitted, then wipe off any surplus grease. Locate the helper spring on its trailing arm seat.
10   Refit the Hydragas unit (Sec 21).

23   Rear suspension subframe (front) mountings – renewal

Note: *The subframe is fastened positively to the body only at its front corners; the rear ends being secured by the Hydragas units via their retaining straps and mounting pads. Each (front) mounting is secured by three bolts to the body and by two bolts to the subframe and consists of two metal plates sandwiching a bonded rubber layer; a 'safety' through-bolt is provided to ensure that the rear suspension remains attached to the car if the bonding should shear. Great care will be required in supporting the body and subframe securely while the subframe is disturbed*

1   Jack up the rear of the car and support the body securely on axle stands, then remove the roadwheel (see *'Jacking, towing and wheel changing'*). Where fitted, if better access is required to the various bolts, remove the side skirts/sill extensions (Chapter 11).
2   Use a wooden block or similar to support the subframe securely in its correct position relative to the body, so that there is no strain on the mounting.
3   Unscrew the two mounting-to-subframe bolts, followed by the three mounting-to-body bolts. There is no need to disturb the 'safety' through-bolt or its nut (photo).
4   Withdraw the mounting. It may be necessary to prise down the subframe to allow the mounting to be removed; if so, take care not to stretch the brake flexible hose.
5   While the mounting is removed, check the condition of the threads in the body and of the body itself around the mounting points; any signs

23.3 Rear suspension subframe mounting-to-body bolts 'A', mounting-to-subframe bolts 'B', 'safety' through-bolt and nut 'C'

of corrosion, wear or damage will mean that repairs must be carried out by an expert as soon as possible.
6   On reassembly, secure the mounting first to the body, then to the subframe; tighten the bolts and roadwheel nuts to their specified torque wrench settings.

24 Rear suspension subframe – removal and refitting

Note: *This procedure requires the depressurisation of both sides of the Hydragas suspension system – refer to the remarks in Section 1 of this Chapter before starting work*

Removal

1   Jack up the rear of the car and support the body securely on axle stands, then remove the roadwheels (see *'Jacking, towing and wheel changing'*).
2   Disconnect the handbrake cable from the rear brake lever assemblies and release the cable from the cable ties and bracket securing it to each trailing arm, then remove the cable from the subframe (Chapter 9).
3   Minimise fluid loss by removing the master cylinder reservoir cap and then tightening it down onto a piece of polythene to obtain an airtight seal (taking care not to damage the sender unit), or by using brake hose clamps, G-clamps or similar tools to clamp the flexible hoses, or by capping or plugging the metal brake pipes as they are disconnected (Chapter 9). Try to keep fluid spillage to a minimum and wash off any spilt fluid as soon as possible.
4   Unscrew the union nuts to disconnect the metal brake pipes from the hoses, then unscrew the nuts to release the hoses from the trailing arm brackets. Take great care not to allow dirt into the hydraulic system.
5   On models so equipped, unbolt the anti-roll bar from both links (Sec 19).
6   Unhook the exhaust system mounting from the subframe hook.
7   Uncouple the plastic connecting pipes from the Hydragas units; plug or cap the orifices immediately to prevent the entry of dirt (Sec 14).
8   Make a final check that all components have been removed or disconnected that are attached to the subframe or might prevent its removal.
9   Support the subframe, unbolt its (front) mountings (Sec 23) and remove the Hydragas unit retaining straps (Sec 21), then lower the subframe to the ground and remove it. The Hydragas units and trailing arms can then be removed, if required (Secs 20 and 21).
10   Thoroughly clean the subframe and the underbody areas around its mountings, removing all traces of dirt, and of underseal if necessary, then check it carefully for excessive corrosion, cracks, distortion or any

other signs of wear or damage; do not forget the pivot holes and the threads and check the (front) mountings for signs of the rubber deteriorating or separating from the metal outer plates. Renew any worn or damaged component.
11   If either the subframe or the underbody show signs of rusting the affected area must be cleaned back to bare metal and treated before being repainted. If the underbody is seriously rusted or if any of the mounting bolt threads are damaged, seek professional advice.

Refitting

12   Refitting is the reverse of the removal procedure, noting the following points.

> (a)   *Tighten all disturbed nuts and bolts to their specified torque wrench settings.*
> (b)   *Connect the handbrake cable to the rear brake lever assemblies, connect the brake flexible hoses to the trailing arm brackets and the metal brake pipes, then bleed any air from the system (Chapter 9). Adjust the rear brake shoes and the handbrake cable (Chapter 1).*
> (c)   *Have any air evacuated from the Hydragas suspension and have it pressurised to the correct ride height.*

25 Steering wheel – removal and refitting

Removal

1   With the car parked on level ground, check that the roadwheels are in the straight-ahead position. The steering wheel spokes should be horizontal.
2   Prise off the wheel's centre cover (photo).
3   Unscrew the steering wheel nut; if the nut is fitted with a separate cover, prise this off carefully (photo).
4   Check for alignment marks between the steering wheel and the steering column; if none can be seen, make your own.
5   Grasp the steering wheel firmly and rock it to jar it free, then pull it off the steering column splines. It is permissible to thump the wheel from behind with the palms of the hands, but do not hammer the wheel or column, or use excessive force.

Refitting

6   On refitting, check that the steering column splines are clean. Refit the wheel, entering the projection on its lower surface with the direction indicator cancelling cam (photo) and aligning the marks made or noted on dismantling; this should leave the wheel positioned as described in paragraph 1 above.
7   Tighten the steering wheel nut to the specified torque wrench setting, then refit the nut cover (if fitted) and the wheel centre cover.

26 Steering column – removal and refitting

Removal

1   Check that the steering is unlocked and remove the steering wheel (Sec 25).
2   Remove the spring ring from the nacelle boss then undo the retaining screws (one into the upper half, three into the lower half) and withdraw the steering column nacelle upper and lower halves (photos).
3   Disconnect the battery negative lead (Chapter 12).
4   Disconnect the wiring of the multi-function switches and hazard warning switch by unplugging the three connectors. The switches and their centre housing need not be removed from the column unless required (Chapter 12).
5   Release the retaining fasteners and remove the fusebox cover.
6   Remove its retaining screw and bolt and withdraw the steering column cover (photo).

25.2 Prising off steering wheel centre cover

25.3 Unscrew the steering wheel nut

25.6 When refitting steering wheel, ensure projecting tab engages with cam slot (arrows)

26.2A Removing spring ring from steering column nacelle boss

26.2B Nacelle lower half retained by three screws (arrows) ...

26.2C ... upper half by one screw

26.6 Unscrewing steering column cover clamp bolt – note screw (arrow)

26.9 Steering column mountings 'A', universal joint pinch-bolt 'B'

7   Unplug the ignition switch wiring connector plug (top row, left-hand connector, marked 'IGN') from the fusebox panel, then release the wiring from any clamps or ties securing it to the facia or its mountings.

8   Using a hammer and punch, white paint or similar, mark the exact relationship of the steering column universal joint to the steering gear pinion; check first that the roadwheels are in the straight-ahead position (Sec 25). Unscrew and fully remove the pinch-bolt securing the joint to the pinion.

9   Unscrew the two remaining bolts and one nut securing the column to its mountings, then withdraw it from the car (photo).

10   Note that the steering column is available only as a complete assembly; if there is any wear or damage to the column itself, to its jacket tube or mountings, to the rubber coupling or the universal joint, the complete column assembly must be renewed.

Refitting

11   Refitting is the reverse of the removal procedure, noting the following points.

(a)   Loosely assemble the column mountings and universal joint ensuring that the joint is positioned on the steering gear pinion so that the pinch-bolt bore is aligned exactly with the pinion groove and the marks made on removal are aligned, then refit the pinch-bolt and tighten it to the specified torque wrench setting.

(b)   Check that the column is seated without stress on its mountings, then tighten the bolts and nut to the specified torque wrench setting.

(c)   When reconnecting the wiring, ensure that it is correctly routed and secured using any clamps or ties provided.

(d)   When refitting the steering wheel (Sec 25), ensure that the roadwheels are in the straight-ahead position and that the steering wheel and column are aligned as described.

(e)   Tighten the column cover clamp bolt and the steering wheel nut to their specified torque wrench settings.

(f)   When reassembly is complete, raise the front of the car and turn the steering from lock to lock to ensure that it is functioning correctly.

27   Steering lock/ignition switch – removal and refitting

Note: *The steering lock/ignition switch is secured by two shear-head bolts; although new bolts are supplied with replacement steering lock assemblies, always ensure that the bolts themselves are available before beginning work*

Removal

1   Check that the steering is unlocked and remove the steering wheel (Sec 25).
2   Remove the spring ring from the nacelle boss then undo the retaining screws (one into the upper half, three into the lower half) and withdraw the steering column nacelle upper and lower halves.
3   Release the retaining fasteners and remove the fusebox cover.
4   Remove its retaining screw and bolt and withdraw the steering column cover.
5   Disconnect the battery negative lead (Chapter 12).
6   Disconnect the wiring of the multi-function switches and hazard warning switch by unplugging the three connectors, then disconnect the ignition switch wiring by unplugging its connector plug (top row, left-hand connector, marked 'IGN') from the fusebox panel, then release the wiring from any clamps or ties securing it to the column or to the facia or its mountings.
7   Unscrew the two remaining bolts and one nut securing the column to its mountings, then lower the column onto a support such as a wooden block
8   Centre-punch the shear-head bolts, then drill off the bolt heads. New bolts will be required on refitting.
9   Withdraw the steering lock/ignition switch, then unscrew the remains of the shear-head bolts using a self-locking wrench or similar on the exposed ends.

Refitting

10   On refitting, carefully align the assembly on the steering column, lightly tighten the bolts and check that the steering lock works smoothly.
11   Tighten the shear-head bolts evenly until their heads shear off.
12   The remainder of the reassembly procedure is the reverse of removal; ensure that the wiring is correctly routed and that all disturbed fasteners are tightened to their specified torque wrench settings.

28   Steering gear rubber gaiters – renewal

1   Remove the track rod balljoint and locknut (Sec 30) and release the gaiter outboard clip.
2   Working through the aperture in the front of the front suspension subframe, cut the gaiter inboard clip and slide the gaiter off the steering gear (photos).
3   Check the gaiter for any signs of splits, tears or perishing; renew it if any such damage is found or if it is not a tight fit on the steering gear or track rod. The clips should be renewed as a matter of course whenever they are disturbed.
4   Thoroughly clean the track rod and the steering gear housing, using fine abrasive paper to polish off any corrosion, burrs or sharp edges which might damage the new gaiter's sealing lips on installation.
5   On refitting, check that the steering gear components are correctly greased, grease the gaiter's lips and slide it on, then fasten the new inboard clip to secure it.
6   Settle the gaiter evenly on the track rod and fasten the outboard clip.
7   Refit the track rod balljoint and locknut (Sec 30).
8   When checking the steering's operation, ensure that the gaiter does not snag or bulge at any point in the steering gear travel; if necessary, unfasten the clip(s) and reposition the gaiter.

29   Steering gear – removal and refitting

Note: *The steering gear is available only as a complete assembly; if there is any wear or damage to the rack or pinion, to the housing or to either*

28.2A Steering rack rubber gaiter inboard clip – left-hand side (arrow) ...

28.2B ... and right-hand side – are accessible through subframe apertures (arrow)

track rod, the complete assembly must be renewed. No information is available at the time of writing as to whether any adjustments of the rack slipper are possible

Removal

1   Working inside the car, remove the steering column (Sec 26), then unbolt the bulkhead aperture cover from the floor; remove the cover and the seal.
2   Jack up the front of the car and support the body securely on axle stands, then remove the roadwheels (see *'Jacking, towing and wheel changing'*).
3   Disconnect the track rod balljoints from the hub carrier steering arms (Sec 30).
4   On models so equipped, slacken the anti-roll bar-to-suspension lower arm bolts and nuts, then unbolt the bar clamps from the underbody (Sec 4).
5   Unscrew the steering gear mounting nuts from the front of the front suspension subframe; collect the mounting U-bolt, clamp, spacer and bolts (photos).
6   Unbolt the exhaust system front pipe from the intermediate pipe (Chapter 4) .
7   Support the subframe and engine/transmission unit on a trolley jack,

29.5A Steering gear mounting nuts – on right-hand side (arrows) ...

29.5B ... and left-hand side of front suspension subframe (arrows)

30.4 Using a universal balljoint separator tool to disconnect track rod balljoint from hub carrier steering arm

using a metal girder or strong timber baulk placed across the subframe to take the weight evenly.

8   Unbolt the engine/transmission rear mounting tie-rod from the underbody and slacken the mounting bracket-to-tie-rod through-bolt (Chapter 2). Unbolt the front suspension subframe rear mountings from the underbody (Sec 12).

9   Lower the jack until the subframe has dropped far enough to allow the removal of the steering gear; manoeuvre the steering gear out to the right of the car.

Refitting

10   On refitting, first ensure that the steering gear rack is at the exact mid-point of its travel, then refit the steering gear to the subframe, assemble the mounting components and lightly tighten the nuts.

11   Raise the subframe into position and tighten the mounting bolts to their specified torque wrench setting, then refit the engine/transmission rear mounting (Chapter 2).

12   The remainder of the reassembly procedure is the reverse of removal, noting the following points.

(a)   Tighten all disturbed nuts and bolts to their specified torque wrench settings.
(b)   Connect the exhaust system (Chapter 4).
(c)   When the steering gear is located correctly and is settled on its mountings, tighten its mounting nuts to the specified torque wrench setting, then connect the track rod balljoints to the hub carrier steering arms (Sec 30).
(d)   Reassemble the anti-roll bar (if fitted), but do not tighten its mountings until all the car's weight is back on its wheels (Sec 4).
(e)   Refit the roadwheels, lower the car to the ground and refit the steering column (Sec 26).
(f)   Have the wheel alignment checked as soon as possible (Sec 31).

30   Track rod balljoint – removal and refitting

Removal

1   Jack up the front of the car and support it securely on axle stands, then remove the roadwheel (see 'Jacking, towing and wheel changing').

2   If the balljoint is to be re-used, use a straight-edge and a scriber, or similar, to mark its relationship to the track rod.

3   Holding the balljoint, unscrew its locknut by one quarter of a turn.

4   Unscrew the balljoint-to-steering arm nut until it is flush with the end of its thread. Separate the balljoint from the hub carrier steering arm, using a universal balljoint separator tool if necessary (photo).

5   Counting the **exact** number of turns necessary to do so, unscrew the balljoint from the track rod. If the locknut is to be removed, mark its position on the track rod and count the number of turns required to remove it so that it can be returned to exactly its original position on reassembly.

6   Carefully clean the balljoint and the threads. Renew the balljoint if its movement is sloppy or if it is too stiff, if it is excessively worn or if it is

damaged in any way; carefully check the stud taper and threads. No grease leakage should be visible. Renew the retaining nut as a matter of course whenever the balljoint is renewed; otherwise check that its locking action is still effective and renew it if necessary.

Refitting

7   On refitting, screw the balljoint onto the track rod by the number of turns noted on removal. This should, of course, bring the balljoint to within a quarter of a turn from the locknut, with the alignment marks that were made (if applicable) on removal lined up.

8   Degrease the tapers of the balljoint stud and of the hub carrier steering arm, then press the balljoint firmly into the steering arm while the nut is refitted and tightened to its specified torque wrench setting.

9   If the car is to be driven elsewhere in order to have the wheel alignment checked, hold the balljoint and tighten the locknut securely; otherwise, refer to Section 31.

10   Where applicable, refit the roadwheel and lower the car to the ground.

31   Wheel alignment and steering angles – general information

Wheel alignment and steering angles – general

1   A car's steering and suspension geometry is defined in five basic settings – all angles are expressed in degrees and the steering axis is defined as an imaginary line drawn through the centres of the front suspension upper and lower balljoints, extended where necessary to contact the ground.

2   **Camber** is the angle between each roadwheel and a vertical line drawn through its centre and tyre contact patch when viewed from the front or rear of the car. Positive camber is when the roadwheels are tilted outwards from the vertical at the top; negative camber is when they are tilted inwards.

3   Camber is not adjustable and is given for reference only; while it can be checked using a camber checking gauge, if the figure obtained is significantly different from that specified the car must be taken for careful checking by a professional, as the fault can only be caused by wear or damage to the body or suspension components.

4   **Castor** is the angle between the steering axis and a vertical line drawn through each roadwheel's centre and tyre contact patch when viewed from the side of the car. Positive castor is when the steering axis is tilted so that it contacts the ground ahead of the vertical; negative castor is when it contacts the ground behind the vertical.

5   Castor is not adjustable and is given for reference only; while it can be checked using a castor checking gauge, if the figure obtained is significantly different from that specified the car must be taken for careful checking by a professional, as the fault can only be caused by wear or damage to the body or suspension components.

6   **Steering axis inclination/SAI** – also known as **kingpin inclination/KPI** – is the angle between the steering axis and a vertical line drawn through each roadwheel's centre and tyre contact patch when viewed from the front or rear of the car.

Fig. 10.15 Wheel alignment and steering angles (Sec 31)

7   SAI/KPI is not adjustable and is given for reference only.

8   **Toe** is the difference, viewed from above, between lines drawn through the roadwheel centres and the car's centre-line. 'Toe-in' is when the roadwheels point inwards, towards each other at the front, while 'toe-out' is when they splay outwards from each other at the front.

9   At the front, the toe setting is adjusted by screwing the track rods in or out of their balljoints to alter the effective length of the track rod assemblies.

10   At the rear, the toe setting is not adjustable and is given for reference only; while it can be checked as described below, if the figure obtained is significantly different from that specified the car must be taken for careful checking by a professional, as the fault can only be caused by wear or damage to the body or suspension components.

11   **Toe-out on turns** – also known as turning angles or Ackermann angles – is the difference, viewed from above, between the angles of rotation of the inside and outside front roadwheels when they have been turned through a given angle.

12   Toe-out on turns is set in production and is not adjustable as such

but can be upset by altering the length of the track rods unequally. It is essential, therefore, to ensure that the track rod lengths are exactly the same and that they are turned by the same amount whenever the toe setting is altered.

Checking – general

13   Due to the special measuring equipment necessary to check the wheel alignment and the skill required to use it properly, the checking and adjustment of these settings is best left to a Rover dealer or similar expert; note that most tyre-fitting shops now possess sophisticated checking equipment.

14   For **accurate** checking, the car **must** be.

> (a)   At kerb weight – see 'General dimensions and weights'.
> (b)   At exactly the correct ride heights – see Section 15.

15   Before starting work, always check first that the tyre sizes and types are as specified, then check the pressures and tread wear, the roadwheel run-out, the condition of the hub bearings, the steering wheel free play and the condition of the front suspension components (Chapter 1). Correct any faults found.

16   Park the car on level ground, check that the front roadwheels are in the straight-ahead position, then rock the rear and front ends to settle the suspension, release the handbrake and roll the car backwards 1 metre, then forwards again to relieve any stresses in the steering and suspension components.

Toe-out on turns – checking and adjusting

17   As far as the home mechanic is concerned, this can be checked only using a pair of scuff plates.

18   Prepare the car as described in paragraphs 14 to 16 above. Roll the car backwards, check that the front roadwheels are in the straight-ahead position, then roll it forwards on to the scuff plates until each front roadwheel is seated squarely on the centre of each plate.

19   Turn the steering wheel first one way until the outside roadwheel is at the specified angle; record the angle of the inside roadwheel. Next turn the steering wheel back through the straight-ahead position and repeat the check on that side.

20   If, in either check, the inside roadwheel is not at the angle specified, check that both track rod assemblies are exactly the same length by counting the exposed threads inboard of the locknuts. If the lengths are different this can be corrected by screwing the track rods in or out of the balljoints, but this will affect the toe setting (see below) and the steering wheel position (Sec 25, para 1).

21   If the angles are incorrect but the track rods are the same length and the steering mechanism components are known from the preliminary checks to be unworn, then there is damage to, or distortion of, part of the steering mechanism, the front suspension or the body itself. This will require careful checking, preferably by an expert such as a Rover dealer, as soon as possible.

Toe setting – checking and adjusting

22   The procedure given below refers specifically to the front toe setting; as noted in paragraph 10 above, while the rear toe setting can be checked (paragraphs 23 to 27) it is not adjustable and any variation from the specified setting must be caused by wear or damage of the suspension or body.

23   As far as the home mechanic is concerned, the toe setting can be checked only using a pair of scuff plates, in which the roadwheels are rolled across a moveable plate which records any deviation (or scuff) of the tyre relative to the straight-ahead position as it moves across the plate. While such gauges are available in relatively inexpensive form from accessory outlets, only an individual owner can decide whether the expense is justified, in view of the small amount of use such equipment would normally receive.

24   Prepare the car as described in paragraphs 14 to 16 above.

25   Roll the car backwards, check that the roadwheels are in the straight-ahead position, then roll it across the scuff plates so that each roadwheel passes squarely over the centre of its respective plate. Note the angle recorded by the scuff plates.

26   To ensure accuracy, repeat the check three times and take the average of the three readings.

27   If the roadwheels are running parallel, there will of course be no angle recorded; if a deviation value is shown on the scuff plates, add the two together and compare them with that specified. If the value

31.28 To adjust toe setting, release gaiter clip and free gaiter from track rod ...

31.30 ... then screw track rod into or out of balljoint until setting is correct

recorded is outside the set tolerance, the toe setting is incorrect and must be adjusted.

28   If adjustment is required, jack up the front of the car and support it securely on axle stands (see *'Jacking, towing and wheel changing'*). First clean the track rod threads; if they are corroded, apply penetrating fluid before starting adjustment. Release the rubber gaiter outboard clips, peel back the gaiters and apply a smear of grease so that both are free and will not be twisted or strained as their respective track rods are rotated (photo).

29   Use a straight-edge and a scriber or similar to mark the relationship of each track rod to its balljoint then, holding each balljoint in turn, unscrew its locknut fully.

30   Alter the length of both track rods (by exactly the same amount) by screwing them into or out of the balljoints one-quarter of a turn at a time and rechecking the toe setting until it is correct; shortening the track rods (screwing them into their balljoints) will reduce toe-in/increase toe-out. If the track rods are not provided with squared sections that permit the use of a spanner, they must be rotated using a self-locking wrench (photo).

31   To ensure that the track rod lengths remain equal, always rotate them in the same direction (viewed from the centre of the car).

32   When the setting is correct, hold the balljoints and tighten the locknuts securely. Check that the balljoints are seated correctly in their sockets and count the exposed threads to check the length of both track rods. If they are not the same then the adjustment has not been made equally and problems will be encountered with tyre scrubbing in turns; also, the steering wheel will no longer be in the straight-ahead position (Sec 25, para 1).

33   If the track rod lengths are the same, check that the toe setting has been correctly adjusted by lowering the car to the ground and preparing it (paragraph 16 above), then re-checking the toe setting (paragraphs 25 to 27); re-adjust if necessary. If the setting is correct, ensure that the rubber gaiters are seated correctly and are not twisted or strained, then refit their clips to secure their outboard ends.

Chapter 11 Bodywork and fittings

Contents

Specifications

Torque wrench setting

	Nm	lbf ft
Bumper fasteners:		
Nuts – rear bumper only	22	16
Bolts – front and rear bumpers	10	8
Bonnet hinge mounting bolts	10	8
Bonnet lock mounting bolts	10	8
Underwing shield screws	9	7
Tailgate handle/number plate lamp housing nuts	6	5
Sunroof roof latch mounting bolts	6	5
Sunroof safety spring-to-roof nut	10	8
Tailgate hinge nuts	10	8
Tailgate striker Torx screws	10	8
Door hinge nuts and bolts	24	18
Door exterior handle mounting nuts	6	5
Door window regulator and motor nuts and bolts	6	5
Seat mounting Torx screws	25	19
Seat belt fasteners:		
Top anchorage bolts	25	19
All other anchorage bolts, retractor and stalk mounting bolts	32 to 35	24 to 26

1 General information

The bodyshell is made of pressed-steel sections in three-door and five-door Hatchback configurations. Most components are welded together but some use is made of structural adhesives; the front wings are bolted on. Childproof locks are fitted to the rear doors.

The bonnet, door, tailgate and some other vulnerable panels are made of zinc-coated metal; once assembled, the entire body is given an eight-stage pretreatment process including a high-pressure wash before painting. The first coat of primer is applied by cathodic electro-deposition, followed by four coats of paint and two of lacquer; an anti-stone chip coating (finished in matt black, where exposed) is applied to the outer faces of the sills and the corresponding surfaces of the front and rear wings. A PVC coating is applied to the underbody, followed by a coating of protective wax; all chassis members, box-sections and sills are injected with liquid cavity wax.

Extensive use is made of plastic materials, mainly on the interior but also in exterior components such as the (ABS) bonnet air intakes and the (modified polypropylene) bumper covers; the bumper covers are each fitted over a metal reinforcing member. Features such as the plastic front wheel arch liners are fitted to improve the body's resistance to corrosion.

2 Minor body damage – repair

Note: *The photographic sequence on pages 222 and 223 illustrates the operations detailed in the following sub-sections*

Note: *For more detailed information about bodywork repair, the Haynes Publishing Group publish a book by Lindsay Porter called The Car Bodywork Repair Manual. This incorporates information on such aspects as rust treatment, painting and glass-fibre repairs, as well as details on more ambitious repairs involving welding and panel beating*

Repair of minor scratches in bodywork

If the scratch is very superficial and does not penetrate to the metal of the bodywork, repair is very simple. Lightly rub the area of the scratch with a paintwork renovator, such as Turtle Wax New Color Back, or a very fine cutting paste, like Holts Body + Plus Rubbing Compound, to remove loose paint from the scratch and to clear the surrounding bodywork of wax polish. Rinse the area with clean water.

Apply touch-up paint, such as Holts Dupli-Color Color Touch, or a paint film, such as Holts Autofilm, to the scratch using a fine paint brush; continue to apply fine layers of paint until the surface of the paint in the scratch is level with the surrounding paintwork. Allow the new paint at least two weeks to harden, then blend it into the surrounding paintwork by rubbing the scratch area with a paintwork renovator, such as Turtle Wax New Color Back, or a very fine cutting paste, like Holts Body + Plus Rubbing Compound. Finally apply wax polish from one of the Turtle Wax range of wax polishes.

Where the scratch has penetrated right through to the metal of the bodywork, causing the metal to rust, a different repair technique is required. Remove any loose rust from the bottom of the scratch with a penknife, then apply rust inhibiting paint, such as Turtle Wax Rust Master, to prevent the formation of rust in the future. Using a rubber or nylon applicator fill the scratch with bodystopper paste, such as Holts Body + Plus Knifing Putty. If required, this paste can be mixed with cellulose thinners, such as Holts Body + Plus Cellulose Thinners, to provide a very thin paste which is ideal for filling narrow scratches. Before the stopper-paste in the scratch hardens, wrap a piece of smooth cotton rag around the top of a finger. Dip the finger in cellulose thinners, such as Holts Body + Plus Cellulose Thinners, and quickly sweep it across the surface of the stopper-paste in the scratch; this will ensure that the surface of the stopper-paste is slightly hollowed. The scratch can now be painted over as described earlier in this Section.

Repair of dents in bodywork

When deep denting of the vehicle's bodywork has taken place, the first task is to pull the dent out, until the affected bodywork almost attains its original shape. There is little point in trying to restore the original shape completely, as the metal in the damaged area will have stretched on impact and cannot be reshaped fully to its original contour. It is better to bring the level of the dent up to a point which is about $\frac{1}{8}$ in (3 mm) below the level of the surrounding bodywork. In cases where the dent is very shallow anyway, it is not worth trying to pull it out at all. If the underside of the dent is accessible, it can be hammered out gently from behind, using a mallet with a wooden or plastic head. Whilst doing this, hold a suitable block of wood firmly against the outside of the panel to absorb the impact from the hammer blows and thus prevent a large area of the bodywork from being 'belled-out'.

Should the dent be in a section of the bodywork which has a double skin or some other factor making it inaccessible from behind, a different technique is called for. Drill several small holes through the metal inside the area – particularly in the deeper section. Then screw long self-tapping screws into the holes just sufficiently for them to gain a good purchase in the metal. Now the dent can be pulled out by pulling on the protruding heads of the screws with a pair of pliers.

The next stage of the repair is the removal of the paint from the damaged area and from an inch or so of the surrounding 'sound' bodywork. This is accomplished most easily by using a wire brush or abrasive pad on a power drill, although it can be done just as effectively by hand using sheets of abrasive paper. To complete the preparation for filling, score the surface of the bare metal with a screwdriver or the tang of a file, or alternatively, drill small holes in the affected area. This will provide a really good 'key' for the filler paste.

To complete the repair see the Section on filling and respraying.

Repair of rust holes or gashes in bodywork

Remove all paint from the affected area and from an inch or so of the surrounding 'sound' bodywork, using an abrasive pad or a wire brush on a power drill. If these are not available a few sheets of abrasive paper will do the job most effectively. With the paint removed you will be able to judge the severity of the corrosion and therefore decide whether to renew the whole panel (if this is possible) or to repair the affected area. New body panels are not as expensive as most people think and it is often quicker and more satisfactory to fit a new panel than to attempt to repair large areas of corrosion.

Remove all fittings from the affected area except those which will act as a guide to the original shape of the damaged bodywork (eg headlamp shells etc). Then, using tin snips or a hacksaw blade, remove all loose metal and any other metal badly affected by corrosion. Hammer the edges of the hole inwards in order to create a slight depression for the filler paste.

Wire brush the affected area to remove the powdery rust from the surface of the remaining metal. Paint the affected area with rust inhibiting paint, such as Turtle Wax Rust Master; if the back of the rusted area is accessible treat this also.

Before filling can take place it will be necessary to block the hole in some way. This can be achieved by the use of aluminium or plastic mesh, or aluminium tape.

Aluminium or plastic mesh or glass-fibre matting, such as Holts Body + Plus Glass-Fibre Matting, is probably the best material to use for a large hole. Cut a piece to the approximate size and shape of the hole to be filled, then position it in the hole so that its edges are below the level of the surrounding bodywork. It can be retained in position by several blobs of filler paste around its periphery.

Aluminium tape should be used for small or very narrow holes. Pull a piece off the roll and trim it to the approximate size and shape required, then pull off the backing paper (if used) and stick the tape over the hole; it can be overlapped if the thickness of one piece is insufficient. Burnish down the edges of the tape with the handle of a screwdriver or similar, to ensure that the tape is securely attached to the metal underneath.

Bodywork repairs – filling and respraying

Before using this Section, see the Sections on dent, deep scratch, rust holes and gash repairs.

Many types of bodyfiller are available, but generally speaking those proprietary kits are best for this type of repair which contain a tin of filler paste and a tube of resin hardener, such as Holts Body + Plus, or Holts No Mix which can be used directly from the tube. A wide, flexible plastic or nylon applicator will be found invaluable for imparting a smooth and well contoured finish to the surface of the filler.

Mix up a little filler on a clean piece of card or board – measure the hardener carefully (follow the maker's instructions on the pack) otherwise the filler will set too rapidly or too slowly. Alternatively, Holts No Mix can be used straight from the tube without mixing, but daylight is required to cure it. Using the applicator apply the filler paste to the prepared area; draw the applicator across the surface of the filler to achieve the correct contour and to level the surface. As soon as a contour that approximates to the correct one is achieved, stop working the paste – if you carry on too long the paste will become sticky and begin to 'pick-up' on the applicator. Continue to add thin layers of filler paste at twenty minute intervals until the level of the filler is just proud of the surrounding bodywork.

Once the filler has hardened, excess can be removed using a metal plane or file. From then on, progressively finer grades of abrasive paper should be used, starting with a 40 grade production paper and finishing with a 400 grade wet-and-dry paper. Always wrap the abrasive paper around a flat rubber, cork, or wooden block – otherwise the surface of the filler will not be completely flat. During the smoothing of the filler surface the wet-and-dry paper should be periodically rinsed in water. This will ensure that a very smooth finish is imparted to the filler at the final stage.

At this stage the 'dent' should be surrounded by a ring of bare metal, which in turn should be encircled by the finely 'feathered' edge of the good paintwork. Rinse the repair area with clean water, until all of the dust produced by the rubbing-down operation has gone.

Spray the whole area with a light coat of primer, either Holts Body + Plus Grey or Red Oxide Primer – this will show up any imperfections in the surface of the filler. Repair these imperfections with fresh filler paste or bodystopper and once more smooth the surface with abrasive paper. If bodystopper is used, it can be mixed with cellulose thinners to form a really thin paste which is ideal for filling small holes. Repeat this spray and repair procedure until you are satisfied that the surface of the filler and the feathered edge of the paintwork are perfect. Clean the repair area with clean water and allow to dry fully.

The repair area is now ready for final spraying. Paint spraying must be carried out in a warm, dry, windless and dust free atmosphere. This condition can be created artificially if you have access to a large indoor working area, but if you are forced to work in the open, you will have to pick your day very carefully. If you are working indoors, dousing the floor in the work area with water will help to settle the dust which would otherwise be in the atmosphere. If the repair area is confined to one body panel, mask off the surrounding panels; this will help to minimise the effects of a slight mis-match in paint colours. Bodywork fittings (eg chrome strips, door handles etc) will also need to be masked off. Use genuine masking tape and several thicknesses of newspaper for the masking operations.

Before commencing to spray, agitate the aerosol can thoroughly, then spray a test area (an old tin, or similar) until the technique is mastered. Cover the repair area with a thick coat of primer; the thickness should be built up using several thin layers of paint rather than one thick one. Using 400 grade wet-and-dry paper, rub down the surface of the primer until it is really smooth. While doing this, the work area should be thoroughly doused with water and the wet-and-dry paper periodically rinsed in water. Allow to dry before spraying on more paint.

Spray on the top coat using Holts Dupli-Color Autospray, again building up the thickness by using several thin layers of paint. Start spraying in the centre of the repair area and then, with a side-to-side motion, work outwards until the whole repair area and about 2 inches of the surrounding original paintwork is covered. Remove all masking material 10 to 15 minutes after spraying on the final coat of paint.

Allow the new paint at least two weeks to harden, then, using a paintwork renovator, such as Turtle Wax New Color Back, or a very fine cutting paste, like Holts Body + Plus Rubbing Compound, blend the edges of the paint into the existing paintwork. Finally, apply wax polish from one of the Turtle Wax range of wax polishes.

Plastic components

With the use of more and more plastic body components by the vehicle manufacturers (eg bumpers, spoilers and in some cases major body panels), rectification of more serious damage to such items has become a matter of either entrusting repair work to a specialist in this field, or renewing complete components. Repair of such damage by the DIY owner is not really feasible owing to the cost of the equipment and materials required for effecting such repairs. The basic technique involves making a groove along the line of the crack in the plastic using a rotary burr in a power drill. The damaged part is then welded back together by using a hot air gun to heat up and fuse a plastic filler rod into the groove. Any excess plastic is then removed and the area rubbed down to a smooth finish. It is important that a filler rod of the correct plastic is used, as body components can be made of a variety of different types (eg polycarbonate, ABS, polypropylene).

Damage of a less serious nature (abrasions, minor cracks etc) can be repaired by the DIY owner using a two-part epoxy filler repair material such as Holts Body + Plus, or Holts No Mix which can be used directly from the tube. Once mixed in equal proportions (or applied direct from the tube in the case of Holts No Mix), this is used in similar fashion to the bodywork filler used on metal panels. The filler is usually cured in twenty to thirty minutes, ready for sanding and painting.

If the owner is renewing a complete component himself, or if he has repaired it with epoxy filler, he will be left with the problem of finding a suitable paint for finishing which is compatible with the type of plastic used. At one time the use of a universal paint was not possible owing to the complex range of plastics encountered in body component applications. Standard paints, generally speaking, will not bond satisfactorily to plastic or rubber, but Holts Professional Spraymatch paints to match any plastic or rubber finish can be obtained from dealers. However, it is now possible to obtain a plastic body parts finishing kit which consists of a pre-primer treatment, a primer and coloured top coat. Full instructions are normally supplied with a kit, but

basically the method of use is to first apply the pre-primer to the component concerned and allow it to dry for up to 30 minutes. Then the primer is applied and left to dry for about an hour before finally applying the special coloured top coat. The result is a correctly-coloured component where the paint will flex with the plastic or rubber, a property that standard paint does not normally possess.

3 Major body damage – repair

Where serious damage has occurred, or large areas need renewal due to neglect, it means that complete new panels will need welding in; this is best left to professionals. If the damage is due to impact, it will also be necessary to check completely the alignment of the bodyshell; this can only be carried out accurately by a Rover dealer using special jigs. If the body is left misaligned, it is primarily dangerous as the car will not handle properly and secondly, uneven stresses will be imposed on the steering, suspension and possibly transmission, causing abnormal wear or complete failure, particularly to items such as the tyres.

4 Front wings – removal and refitting

Removal

1   Remove the wheel arch liner and the side rubbing strip (Sec 8).
2   Remove the direction indicator side repeater lamp; while not strictly necessary, it is advisable also to remove the front direction indicator lamp (Chapter 12).
3   Remove the front bumper (Sec 5).
4   Open the bonnet and remove the (hex-head) screws securing the wing (Fig. 11.1).
5   Cut along the joints and remove the wing.

Refitting

6   Before fitting the new wing, clean the body mating surfaces and apply new sealant.
7   Fit the wing and adjust its position before refitting the screws, then tighten them securely.
8   Apply protective coating under the wing and anti-stone chip coating to the bottom edge, then refinish the outer surface to match the body colour and paint the anti-stone chip coating matt black (if exposed).
9   Refit all remaining components using the reverse of the removal procedure.

Fig. 11.1 Location of front wing mountings (Sec 4)

5.4 Front bumper front mounting bolts are concealed by covers under number plate

5.5 Front bumper cover-to-bonnet lock platform screws (arrows)

5.6A Front bumper cover-to-body lower mounting bolt (one arrowed)

5.6B Front bumper cover-to-body top rear mounting bolt (arrow) is behind each wheel arch liner

5.9 Disconnecting rear fog lamp wiring

5 Bumpers – removal and refitting

Removal
Front

Note: *It is possible, with care, to prise the bumper cover's rear bottom edge off each wheel arch liner locating peg and to reach up inside the bumper cover to unscrew the top rear mounting bolts. Although difficult due to lack of visibility, this shorter procedure eliminates the steps described in paragraphs 1 and 2*

1   Jack up the front of the car and support it securely on axle stands, then remove the roadwheels (see *'Jacking, towing and wheel changing'*).
2   Remove the front wheel arch liners (Sec 8).
3   Carefully prise the number plate off the self-adhesive pads; if either

the bumper or the number plate is to be re-used, clean off all traces of adhesive with white spirit.
4   Carefully prise the covers off the two bumper front mounting bolts (photo).
5   Remove the screws securing the bumper cover to the bonnet lock platform (photo).
6   Being careful to support the bumper as necessary, unscrew the six mounting bolts, then remove the bumper assembly (including, where fitted, the front spoiler) (photos).
7   If required, the bumper cover can be unbolted from the reinforcing member, the brackets can be removed and the trim inserts (where fitted) can be detached from the cover by removing their retainer clips.

Rear

8   Open the tailgate and release the luggage compartment interior trim panels sufficiently to reach the bumper mounting bolts (Sec 24).

5.10 Rear bumper cover right-hand end mounting bolt (arrow)

5.11 Cover-to-body lower mounting bracket screws on one-piece bumper (arrows)

5.12 Rear bumper mounting nut inside luggage compartment

6.2 Disconnecting windscreen washer tubing

6.4 Always have an assistant to help with bonnet removal

7.1 Bonnet lock mounting bolts and release cable connection (arrows)

9   Release the rear foglamp wiring connector from its clip in the rear right-hand corner of the body, disconnect the wiring and press the sealing grommet out of the body (photo).
10   Unscrew the bumper cover end mounting bolts (photo). On 1.1C models fitted with the three-piece bumper, the bumper end caps can now be detached.
11   On all other models, fitted with the one-piece bumper cover, remove the retaining screws to release the cover from the lower mounting brackets (photo).
12   Being careful to support the assembly as necessary, unscrew the two nuts from inside the luggage compartment (photo) then withdraw the bumper centre section (later 1.1C models) or the bumper assembly (all other models).
13   If required, remove the retaining screws, nuts or clips (as appropriate) to detach the rear foglamp, the reflector, the bumper cover (where fitted) and the trim inserts (where fitted).

Refitting

Front

14   Refitting is the reverse of the removal procedure, noting the following points.

(a) *Tighten the mounting bolts to their specified torque wrench setting.*
(b) *Ensure that the bumper cover is engaged correctly on the wheel arch liner peg.*
(c) *Use four new self-adhesive pads to secure the number plate.*

Rear

15   Refitting is the reverse of the removal procedure; tighten the nuts and bolts to their specified torque wrench settings, ensure that the sealing grommet is securely fixed in the body and check the operation of the foglamp.

6   Bonnet – removal, refitting and adjustment

Removal

1   The help of an assistant will be required for these operations. First, with the bonnet propped open, place a thick pad of cloth beneath each rear corner of the bonnet to protect the paintwork.
2   Disconnect the windscreen washer tubing (photo).
3   Mark with a pencil around the hinge arms where they meet the bonnet, then slacken the bonnet-to-hinge arm bolts.
4   Working with one person at each side (photo), support the bonnet on the shoulders, lower the stay and unscrew the bolts. Remove the bonnet.
5   The hinge arms are each retained by a single, shouldered pivot bolt; check that these are greased and securely fastened whenever the bonnet is removed.

6   The bonnet stay can be removed by working it out of its locating rubber bush in the bonnet lock platform.

Refitting

7   Refitting is the reverse of the removal procedure. If the original bonnet is being refitted align the marks made on removal; if a new bonnet is being fitted, centre the bolt holes on the hinge arms. Tighten the bonnet-to-hinge arm bolts only lightly at first, then gently close the bonnet and check that it aligns evenly with the surrounding bodywork.
8   When the fit of the bonnet is correctly adjusted (see below), tighten the bolts to the specified torque wrench setting.

Adjustment

9   If the bonnet is not aligned correctly with the front wings, slacken the bonnet-to-hinge arm bolts and reposition the bonnet on the hinge arms until the gaps are equal between each side of the bonnet and each wing, then tighten the bolts to their specified torque wrench setting.
10   If, when closed, the bonnet stands proud of, or is lower than, either front wing, screw both bonnet rubber buffers fully down into the bonnet lock platform, then close the bonnet and check its height relative to each wing. Screw the striker pin into the bonnet to lower its height, outwards to raise it; when the height is correct (ie when closed, the bonnet is exactly flush with the adjacent wings) adjust the height of the buffers until they just contact the underside of the bonnet.
11   Refer to Section 7 for details of adjustments possible with the bonnet lock.

7   Bonnet lock and release cable – removal, refitting and adjustment

Removal

Lock

1   Open the bonnet and mark with a pencil around the bonnet lock, then unscrew the two mounting bolts and withdraw the lock and guide plate until the release cable can be disconnected (photo).

Striker

2   Open the bonnet and mark with a pencil around the assembly's mounting plate, then unscrew the two mounting bolts and withdraw the striker and safety catch assembly.

Release cable and lever

3   Open the bonnet and remove the washer system reservoir retaining screws so that the reservoir can be moved clear of the working area; disconnect the pump wiring connector plug(s) if the extra reach is required.
4   Disconnect the cable from the lock and release it from the clips or ties securing it to the body, then prise the cable sealing grommet out of the bulkhead aperture.
5   Working inside the passenger compartment, release the retaining fasteners and withdraw the fusebox cover. The release lever pivot

7.5 Bonnet release lever pivot screw (arrowed) – shown with facia removed for clarity

screw is behind the fusebox panel (photo); if the panel is removed (Chapter 12) to reach the lever screw, disconnect first the battery negative terminal. Remove the pivot screw, withdraw the lever and disconnect the cable.

6   Withdraw the cable into the engine compartment.

Refitting

7   Refitting is the reverse of the removal procedure, noting the following points.

(a)   Align (where applicable) the component on the marks made on removal; if a new bonnet or bonnet lock platform has been fitted, centre the component on its bolt holes.

(b)   Tighten the component's fasteners lightly, then check carefully the operation and adjustment of all disturbed components; if adjustment is required, proceed as described below.

(c)   Tighten the bolts securely, to the specified torque wrench settings (where given).

Adjustment

8   If the operation of any part of the bonnet release mechanism requires adjustment, check first the fit of the bonnet on the body (Sec 6); while some adjustments are inter-dependent (the bonnet height adjustment being made using the lock's striker pin), the lock cannot function correctly if the bonnet is not aligned properly with the bodywork.

9   To adjust the lock and/or striker assembly, first slacken their mounting bolts, then move them as necessary until the striker pin and safety catch hook engage squarely in the centre of their respective lock apertures; tighten the bolts securely, to the specified torque wrench settings (where given).

10   When the lock and striker are correctly aligned, check that the bonnet closes securely when dropped from a height of approximately 6 inches (150 mm); there should be no trace of movement when attempting to lift the front edge of the bonnet.

11   If the bonnet does not lock when dropped, check first that the striker pin is properly lubricated (Chapter 1); some adjustment may be made by screwing the striker pin in or out, but take care that this does not alter the bonnet height (Sec 6). Renew the striker or the lock assembly as necessary if the fault is due to wear or damage of either component.

12   If there is any doubt about the safety catch's performance, the striker assembly must be renewed.

13   There is no adjustment as such of the release cable, but the cable outer stops can be bent slightly to effect minor alterations if required; renew the cable if the bonnet release is ineffective.

8   Body exterior fittings – removal and refitting

Removal
Front spoiler

1   The spoiler is in two halves, each secured to the bumper cover by five nuts and studs; the nuts can be unscrewed from behind the bumper cover. The spoiler can be removed with the bumper (Sec 5) or separately, as required.

2   Always remove the left-hand half first, since it overlaps the right-hand half (photo).

Underwing shields

3   Jack up the front of the car and support it securely on axle stands, then remove the roadwheel (see 'Jacking, towing and wheel changing').

4   Each shield is secured by three fasteners; remove each fastener's screw and prise out its outer section to release it, then withdraw the panel (photo).

Front wheel arch liners

5   Jack up the front of the car and support it securely on axle stands, then remove the roadwheel (see 'Jacking, towing and wheel changing').

6   Remove the mudflap, if fitted.

7   Remove the three screws securing the liner to the rear of the wheel arch. Release the six fasteners by removing each fastener's screw and prising out its outer section (photo). (See Fig. 11.2.) Remove the liner, releasing its locating peg from the bumper cover at its front and releasing the liner itself from the plastic clip (where fitted) at its rear inboard edge.

Mudflaps

8   The front mudflaps are each secured by three screws; the rear by two clips.

Bonnet air intakes

9   Each air intake is secured by two small nuts or clips on the underside of the bonnet; note that the unused intake has a blanking plate fitted.

Roof drip channel

10   The drip channel moulding along the roof edges is clipped in place and can be prised off if care is taken not to break it or to damage the paintwork.

Side rubbing strips

11   Apply masking tape along the edge of the strip to be removed, as an aid to correct location on refitting.

12   Using a hot air gun, heat the strip until the adhesive softens enough for the strip to be peeled off. Take care not to damage the surrounding paintwork with the hot air gun.

Fig. 11.2 Location of front wheel arch liner mountings (Sec 8)

**8.2 Removing front spoiler left-hand half –
note mounting studs (arrows)**

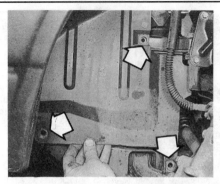

**8.4 Location of underwing shield fasteners
(arrows)**

**8.7 Removing one of the front wheel arch
liner fasteners**

**8.15 Side skirt/sill extension mountings – securing screws 'A' (two
arrowed), locating pegs 'B' (two arrowed), rear section retainer 'C'**

Fuel filler flap

13   The flap is secured by two screws.

Side skirts/sill extensions

14   These are in two sections; since the front section overlaps the rear,
always remove the front section first, as follows.

15   Remove the six screws securing the front section, then very
carefully release the section from the clip securing its front upper edge
to the wheel arch flare. Slide the section forwards to release it from the
five locating pegs, then withdraw it (photo).

16   Once the front section has been removed, the two screws which
secure the rear section can be undone; carefully release the rear section
from its retainers to remove it, noting how the rear retainer hooks into
the underbody.

Rear wheel arch flare moulding

17   Remove the rear bumper (Sec 5).

18   Remove the two retaining screws from inside the wheel arch (one
being at the bumper lower mounting), then release the three clips to
remove the moulding.

Rear spoiler

19   Taking care not to mark the spoiler, prise off the four cover plugs
from the top outside surface of the spoiler (photo), then undo the screws
beneath each.

20   Open the tailgate and prise out the sealing grommet next to each
of the rear window 'bottom' corners; unscrew the nut and remove the
sealing washer beneath each (photo).

21   Raise the wiper arm and very carefully remove the spoiler; it may
also be secured by adhesive or (especially along the lower edge) trim
clips.

Tailgate handle/number plate lamp housing

22   Remove the number plate lamp assemblies (Chapter 12).

23   Open the tailgate and remove the interior trim panel (Sec 24).

24   Remove the clip securing the lock barrel to the handle/housing,
then unscrew the four nuts securing the handle/housing to the tailgate.
Withdraw the handle/housing, noting the gasket (photo).

Badges

25   The various badges are secured with adhesives. To remove them,
either soften the adhesive using a hot air gun (taking care to avoid
damage to the paintwork) or separate the badge from the bodywork by
'sawing' through the adhesive bond using a length of nylon cord.

Refitting

Front spoiler

26   Refitting is the reverse of the removal procedure.

**8.19 Rear spoiler (outside) top edge
securing screws under cover plugs**

**8.20 Rear spoiler (inside) lower edge
securing nuts under grommets**

**8.24 Removing clip securing tailgate lock
barrel to tailgate handle/number plate lamp
housing**

Underwing shields

27   Refitting is the reverse of the removal procedure; renew any damaged fasteners.

Front wheel arch liners

28   Refitting is the reverse of the removal procedure, noting the following points.

   (a)   Ensure that the liner and the wheel arch interior are clean and dry before refitting the liner.
   (b)   Locate the liner correctly on the front bumper cover and (if fitted) the plastic clip before refitting the fasteners.
   (c)   Renew any damaged fasteners.

Mudflaps

29   Refitting is a reversal of removal.

Bonnet air intakes

30   Refitting is a reversal of removal.

Roof drip channel

31   Refitting is a reversal of removal, but make sure that the channel is pressed securely into place.

Side rubbing strips

32   Clean off all traces of adhesive using white spirit, then wash the area with warm soapy water to remove all traces of spirit. Ensure that the surface to which the new strip is to be fastened is completely clean and free from grease or dirt.
33   Use the hot air gun to soften the adhesive on the new strip, then press it firmly into position, using the masking tape as a guide. Remove the masking tape when the strip is secured.

Fuel filler flap

34   Refitting is a reversal of removal.

Side skirts/sill extensions

35   Refitting is a reversal of removal.

Rear wheel arch flare moulding

36   Refitting is a reversal of removal.

Rear spoiler

37   If adhesive was used, clean off all traces of adhesive using white spirit, then wash the area with warm soapy water to remove all traces of spirit.
38   Refitting is the reverse of the removal procedure.

Tailgate handle/number plate lamp housing

39   Refitting is the reverse of the removal procedure; tighten the nuts to the specified torque wrench setting.

Badges

40   Clean off all traces of adhesive using white spirit, then wash the area with warm soapy water to remove all traces of spirit. Ensure that the surface to which the new badge is to be fastened is completely clean and free from grease or dirt.
41   Use the hot air gun to soften the adhesive on the new badge, then press it firmly into position.

9   Windscreen, fixed rear quarterlight glasses and rear window – general information

These areas of glass are secured by the tight fit of the weatherstrip in the body aperture; although they are not fixed by the direct-bonding method used on many modern vehicles, the removal and refitting of these areas of fixed glass is still difficult, messy and time-consuming for the inexperienced. It is also difficult, unless one has plenty of practice, to obtain a secure, waterproof fit. Furthermore, the task carries a high risk of breakage; this applies especially to the laminated glass windscreen. In view of this, owners are strongly advised to have this sort of work carried out by one of the many specialist windscreen fitters.

10   Opening rear quarterlights – removal and refitting

Removal

1   Open the tailgate. Attach protective tape to the 'B' pillar rear edge to prevent damage to the paintwork.
2   Open the rear quarterlight. Have an assistant support the quarterlight, then remove the two screws securing the catch, fully open the quarterlight and release its hinge tabs from their grommets.

Refitting

3   Refitting is the reverse of the removal procedure; apply a smear of rubber lubricant to the grommets and check that the quarterlight seats correctly in its aperture before tightening the catch screws securely.

11   Sunroof – removal, refitting and adjustment

Removal

Glass panel

1   Open the sunroof and squeeze together the linkage arms of the operating handle to disconnect it from the roof latch. From outside the car, unclip the safety spring from the hook on the panel's left-hand side, then withdraw the panel until its locating lugs are clear of their sockets (photo).
2   Note that the glass panel should be stored carefully, wrapping it in a rug or blanket to prevent scratches. Each locating lug is fastened by two screws that are secured with Loctite; if either is removed, discard the gaskets and clean all traces of old thread-locking compound from the screw threads. Do not attempt to remove either the panel's seal or the safety hook; Rover state that the complete panel must be renewed if either of these are damaged. Note also that the locating lug sockets are bolted to the roof and concealed by the headlining; they should not, therefore, be disturbed except by those experienced in headlining removal and refitting.

Operating handle

3   Open the sunroof and squeeze together the linkage arms of the operating handle to disconnect it from the roof latch.
4   Remove the two retaining screws, which are secured with Loctite, to release the handle from the roof, then discard the gaskets and clean all traces of old thread-locking compound from the screw threads.

Roof latch

5   Open the sunroof and squeeze together the linkage arms of the operating handle to disconnect it from the roof latch.
6   Removing its single retaining screw, withdraw the latch cover from the roof, then unbolt the latch.

Safety spring

7   Remove the glass panel (see above); the spring is secured to the roof by a single nut.

Wind deflector

8   Remove the glass panel (see above).
9   Remove the retaining screws and withdraw the deflector hinge covers (photo).

1

This photographic sequence shows the steps taken to repair the dent and paintwork damage shown above. In general, the procedure for repairing a hole will be similar; where there are substantial differences, the procedure is clearly described and shown in a separate photograph.

2

First remove any trim around the dent, then hammer out the dent where access is possible. This will minimise filling. Here, after the large dent has been hammered out, the damaged area is being made slightly concave.

3

Next, remove all paint from the damaged area by rubbing with coarse abrasive paper or using a power drill fitted with a wire brush or abrasive pad. 'Feather' the edge of the boundary with good paintwork using a finer grade of abrasive paper.

4

Where there are holes or other damage, the sheet metal should be cut away before proceeding further. The damaged area and any signs of rust should be treated with Turtle Wax Hi-Tech Rust Eater, which will also inhibit further rust formation.

5

For a large dent or hole mix Holts Body Plus Resin and Hardener according to the manufacturer's instructions and apply around the edge of the repair. Press Glass Fibre Matting over the repair area and leave for 20-30 minutes to harden. Then ...

5A

... brush more Holts Body Plus Resin and Hardener onto the matting and leave to harden. Repeat the sequence with two or three layers of matting, checking that the final layer is lower than the surrounding area. Apply Holts Body Plus Filler Paste as shown in Step 5B.

5B

For a medium dent, mix Holts Body Plus Filler Paste and Hardener according to the manufacturer's instructions and apply it with a flexible applicator. Apply thin layers of filler at 20-minute intervals, until the filler surface is slightly proud of the surrounding bodywork.

5C

For small dents and scratches use Holts No Mix Filler Paste straight from the tube. Apply it according to the instructions in thin layers, using the spatula provided. It will harden in minutes if applied outdoors and may then be used as its own knifing putty.

6

Use a plane or file for initial shaping. Then, using progressively finer grades of wet-and-dry paper, wrapped round a sanding block, and copious amounts of clean water, rub down the filler until glass smooth. 'Feather' the edges of adjoining paintwork.

Protect adjoining areas before spraying the whole repair area and at least one inch of the surrounding sound paintwork with Holts Dupli-Color primer.

Fill any imperfections in the filler surface with a small amount of Holts Body Plus Knifing Putty. Using plenty of clean water, rub down the surface with a fine grade wet-and-dry paper – 400 grade is recommended – until it is really smooth.

Carefully fill any remaining imperfections with knifing putty before applying the last coat of primer. Then rub down the surface with Holts Body Plus Rubbing Compound to ensure a really smooth surface.

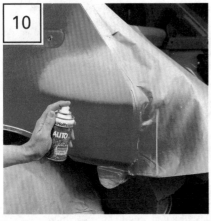

Protect surrounding areas from overspray before applying the topcoat in several thin layers. Agitate Holts Dupli-Color aerosol thoroughly. Start at the repair centre, spraying outwards with a side-to-side motion.

If the exact colour is not available off the shelf, local Holts Professional Spraymatch Centres will custom fill an aerosol to match perfectly.

To identify whether a lacquer finish is required, rub a painted unrepaired part of the body with wax and a clean cloth.

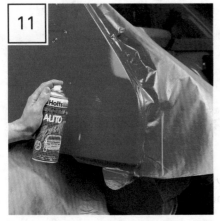

If *no* traces of paint appear on the cloth, spray Holts Dupli-Color clear lacquer over the repaired area to achieve the correct gloss level.

The paint will take about two weeks to harden fully. After this time it can be 'cut' with a mild cutting compound such as Turtle Wax Minute Cut prior to polishing with a final coating of Turtle Wax Extra.

When carrying out bodywork repairs, remember that the quality of the finished job is proportional to the time and effort expended.

11.1 Disconnecting sunroof operating handle from roof latch

11.9 Remove cover to reach wind deflector hinge screws (arrows) ...

11.10 ... noting sealing washers under securing nuts (arrows)

10   Remove the four screws and nuts securing the deflector hinges and detach the deflector from the headlining (photo); note the sealing washer under each nut.

Refitting

11   Refitting is the reverse of the removal procedure, noting the following points (photo).

 (a)   When refitting the locating lugs or the operating handle to the glass panel, apply a few drops of Loctite 222 to the screw threads and fit new gaskets. Check that the component is located correctly on the panel, then tighten the screws securely.
 (b)   Tighten the nuts and bolts to the specified torque wrench settings (where given).
 (c)   Ensure that the safety spring is engaged correctly around the hook.
 (d)   Adjust the fit of the glass panel if necessary (see below).

Adjustment

12   When the sunroof is closed, check that the glass panel sits squarely on its seal, with no sign of gaps.
13   If the fit is not correct, remove the roof latch cover (see above), slacken the two roof latch mounting bolts and adjust the position of the latch until the panel closes fully and is in full contact with the seal; tighten the two bolts to their specified torque wrench setting and refit the cover.

11.11 Ensure safety spring is engaged around hook as shown

---

12   Tailgate – removal, refitting and adjustment

Removal

Note: *The aid of an assistant will be required for this operation*

1   Open the tailgate, detach the parcel shelf straps and remove the interior trim panel (Sec 24).
2   Disconnect (where fitted) the rear window wiper motor wiring and attach a drawstring to it.
3   Prise the heated rear window wire sealing grommet from each side of the tailgate, disconnect the wires and attach drawstrings to each.
4   Disconnect (where fitted) the washer system tube from the rear window wiper motor and plug it to prevent loss of water. Disconnect the wiring for the number plate lamps and (where fitted) the central locking motor; if a luggage compartment lamp is fitted, partially withdraw the latch (Sec 14) until the two wires can be disconnected from it. Tape together the washer tube and wiring, then attach a drawstring to them.
5   Release the two harness sleeves from the tailgate 'top' corners and pull the wiring through the apertures until the drawstrings appear; untie the drawstrings, leaving them in the tailgate (Fig. 11.3).
6   Carefully prise the weatherstrip away from the body flange along the top edge of the tailgate aperture, then release the headlining from the area around the tailgate hinges.
7   Mark with a pencil around the hinges where they meet the roof and place a thick pad of cloth beneath each tailgate 'top' corner to protect the paintwork.

Fig. 11.3 Using drawstrings to assist refitting of wiring to tailgate (Sec 12)

8   Support the tailgate and remove the struts (Sec 13).
9   Unscrew the four nuts securing the tailgate hinges to the roof, then remove the tailgate. Collect the two hinge plates from their studs so that they are not lost.

Refitting

10   Clean off all traces of adhesive from the body flange using white spirit, then wash the area with warm soapy water to remove all traces of spirit.

11   Refitting is the reverse of the removal procedure, noting the following points.

(a)   *If the original tailgate is being refitted align the marks made on removal; if a new tailgate is being fitted, centre the hinges on the studs. Tighten the nuts only lightly at first, then gently close the tailgate and check that it fits correctly.*

(b)   *When the fit of the tailgate is correctly adjusted (see below), tighten the nuts to the specified torque wrench setting.*

(c)   *Use a suitable trim adhesive to secure the weatherstrip.*

Adjustment

12   When the tailgate is closed, check that it sits squarely on its weatherstrip, with no sign of gaps, also that it is aligned evenly with the surrounding bodywork.

13   If the fit is not correct, open the tailgate and carefully prise the weatherstrip away from the body flange along the top edge of the tailgate aperture, then release the headlining from the area around the tailgate hinges and slacken the hinge nuts.

14   Adjust the position of the tailgate until the gaps are equal between it and the surrounding bodywork and it sits correctly on the weatherstrip; tighten the hinge nuts to their specified torque wrench setting.

15   Clean off all traces of adhesive from the body flange using white spirit, then wash the area with warm soapy water to remove all traces of spirit and refit the headlining and, using a suitable trim adhesive, the weatherstrip.

16   Refer to Section 14 for details of adjustments possible with the tailgate striker.

13.2 Raising tailgate support strut spring clip to release mounting

13   Tailgate support struts – removal and refitting

Removal

1   Open the tailgate and support it with a piece of wood.

2   Raise the spring clip and pull the strut off each of its mountings (photo).

3   The struts are sealed, containing gas under pressure; do not attempt to dismantle them or apply any heat. If failed or damaged, the struts must be renewed. Dispose of them safely.

Refitting

4   Refitting is the reverse of the removal procedure; ensure that each end of the strut snaps securely home on its mounting.

14   Tailgate lock components – removal and refitting

Removal

Lock

1   Open the tailgate and remove the interior trim panel (Sec 24).

2   Remove (where fitted) the rear window wiper motor (Chapter 12).

3   Remove (where fitted) the plastic pin and separate the central locking motor from the lock.

4   Release the latch cable from the clip, release the cable outer from the lock abutment bracket and disconnect the cable inner from the lock lever (photos).

5   Remove the clip securing the lock barrel to the tailgate handle/number plate lamp housing, disconnect the number plate lamp wiring and unscrew the four nuts securing the handle/housing to the tailgate. Withdraw the handle/housing, noting the gasket, then remove the lock.

Latch

6   Open the tailgate and remove the interior trim panel (Sec 24).

7   Remove the two screws securing the latch to the tailgate and release the latch cable from the clip so that the latch can be withdrawn; if a luggage compartment lamp is fitted, disconnect the two wires from the latch (photo).

8   Release the cable outer from the latch abutment bracket, then disconnect the cable inner from the latch and withdraw the latch.

Latch cable

9   Remove the latch (see above).

10   Release the cable outer from the lock abutment bracket and disconnect the cable inner from the lock lever; withdraw the cable.

Striker

11   Open the tailgate and mark with a pencil around the striker, then undo the two Torx-type screws and withdraw the striker (photo).

14.4A Release latch cable outer from lock abutment bracket (arrow) ...

14.4B ... and disconnect cable inner from lock lever

14.7 Tailgate latch partially removed to allow disconnection of wiring and cable

14.11 Tailgate striker

14.13A Removing plastic pin to release central locking motor from tailgate lock ...

14.13B ... so that motor wiring connector can be disconnected and motor removed

Central locking motor

12   Open the tailgate and remove the interior trim panel (Sec 24).
13   Remove the plastic pin and separate the motor from the lock, then disconnect the motor wiring and withdraw the motor (photos).

Refitting

Lock

14   Refitting is the reverse of the removal procedure; tighten the tailgate handle/number plate lamp housing nuts to the specified torque wrench setting.

Latch

15   Refitting is the reverse of the removal procedure; lubricate all moving parts and the striker (Chapter 1).

Latch cable

16   Refitting is the reverse of the removal procedure.

Striker

17   On refitting, align the striker on the marks made on removal; if new components have been fitted, centre the striker on the screw holes, tighten the screws lightly and check the fit of the tailgate on the body (see below). When the fit is correct, tighten the screws to the specified torque wrench setting.
18   When the tailgate is closed, check that it sits squarely on its weatherstrip, with no sign of gaps, also that it is aligned evenly with the surrounding bodywork.
19   If the fit is not correct, open the tailgate and slacken the striker screws, then adjust the position of the striker until the tailgate aligns with the surrounding bodywork and the gaps are equal at all points between the tailgate and the body panels.
20   When the fit is correct, tighten the striker screws to the specified torque wrench setting and check the operation of the tailgate lock.

Central locking motor

21   Refitting is the reverse of the removal procedure.

---

15   Doors – removal, refitting and adjustment

Removal

Door

1   Remove the interior trim panel (Sec 24) and peel back the plastic sheet.
2   Disconnect all door electrical components, referring for details to the relevant Sections of this Chapter; if removing a rear door from a car with central locking fitted, note that a considerable amount of preliminary dismantling is required to reach the motor's wiring connector (Sec 16, paragraphs 25 and 26). Prise the wiring harness gaiter out of the (front) door or the sealing grommet out of the (rear) door pillar and pull the wiring clear.
3   Support the door using a block of wood or a trolley jack; ensure that the paintwork is protected with a wad of clean rag. Mark with a pencil around the hinges where they meet the door.

Fig. 11.4 Location of front door-to-hinge retaining nuts (Sec 15)

4   Unscrew the retaining nuts (see Fig. 11.4 or 11.5, as appropriate) and withdraw the door, collecting the two hinge plates.

Front door hinges

5   Remove the door (see above).
6   Remove the front wheel arch liner (Sec 8) to unscrew the bottom hinge-to-body bolt, then remove the 'A' pillar lower interior trim panel (Sec 24) and the foam insert behind to unscrew the two bottom hinge-to-body nuts.
7   Unscrew the two bolts to remove the top hinge.

Rear door hinges

8   Remove the door (see above).
9   Remove the 'B' pillar lower interior trim panel (Sec 24) and unscrew the hinge-to-body nuts.

Refitting

10   Refitting is the reverse of the removal procedure, noting the following points.

(a)   If the original door is being refitted align the marks made on removal; if a new door is being fitted, centre it on the hinge

Fig. 11.5 Location of rear door-to-hinge retaining nuts (Sec 15)

    studs. Tighten the nuts only lightly at first, then gently close the door and check that it fits correctly.
  (b) *When the fit of the door is correctly adjusted (see below), tighten the nuts and bolts to the specified torque wrench setting.*

Adjustment

11   When the door is closed, check that it fits flush with the surrounding bodywork and centrally in the body aperture.
12   If the fit is not correct, open the door, remove the interior trim panel and peel back the plastic sheet, then slacken the hinge nuts.
13   Adjust the position of the door until it fits correctly, then tighten the hinge nuts to their specified torque wrench setting.
14   Refer to Section 16 for details of adjustments possible with the door striker.

16 Door lock and handle components – removal and refitting

Removal

Front door lock

1   Open the door and fully raise the window glass, remove the interior trim panel (Sec 24), then peel back the top rear corner of the plastic sheet.
2   Release the clip to disconnect the link rod from the lock (photo).
3   Prise out the clip to release the lock from the door; remove the lock, noting the seating washer.

Exterior handle

4   Open the door and fully raise the window glass, remove the interior trim panel (Sec 24), then peel back the top rear corner of the plastic sheet.
5   On the front door, release the clip to disconnect the link rod from the handle (photo).

6   On the rear door, remove its retaining screw and move aside the window glass rear guide channel (Sec 18) to reach the handle mounting nuts (photo).
7   Unscrew the nuts and withdraw the handle; note the sealing washers.

Latch

8   Open the door and fully raise the window glass, remove the interior trim panel (Sec 24), then peel back the rear half of the plastic sheet.
9   Remove its retaining screw and withdraw the window glass rear guide channel (photos).
10   Releasing their clips as necessary, disconnect the various link rods – at either end, whichever is convenient; it may prove necessary, for example, to detach the interior handle and to remove it with the latch so that the link rod can be disconnected off the car. On the rear door, note the rubber fillet which can be removed to improve visibility and access to the latch area (photos).
11   Remove the retaining screws and withdraw the latch (photos).

Interior handle

12   Open the door and fully raise the window glass, remove the interior trim panel (Sec 24), then peel down the plastic sheet.
13   Remove the retaining screw(s) and release the link rod from the clip(s) securing it to the door (photo).
14   Either remove the handle and link rod together, disconnecting them from the latch, or disconnect the handle from the link rod, as required. Compress the spring to disconnect the rod from the handle; note the nylon bush and the washer.

Interior lock button

15   The button itself can be unscrewed from the top of its link rod with no prior dismantling being necessary.
16   If the link rod is to be removed, the door interior trim panel must be removed (Sec 24) and the plastic sheet peeled back from the top rear corner (front door) or down as far as necessary (rear door).
17   On the front door, release the clip to disconnect the link rod from the latch.
18   On the rear door, release the pin (immediately above and in front of the window regulator mounting bolts) securing the bellcrank to the door and (where fitted) release the snap-on connector to disconnect the central locking motor link rod. Disconnect the link rod from the latch and withdraw the assembly.

Striker

19   On five-door model rear doors and three-door models, the striker is screwed into the pillar; **do not** overtighten the striker or its caged retaining nut might break free inside the pillar. Mark with a pencil around the striker before unscrewing it (photo).
20   On five-door model front doors, open the door and mark with a pencil around the striker, then undo the two Torx-type screws and withdraw the striker (photo).

Central locking control unit/motor – front door

21   Open the door and fully raise the window glass, remove the interior trim panel (Sec 24), then peel back the bottom rear corner of the plastic sheet.
22   Remove the two retaining screws, disconnect the control unit/motor from the link rod and withdraw it, then unplug the wiring connector to release the control unit/motor from the door (photos).

Central locking control unit/motor – rear door

23   Open the door and fully raise the window glass, remove the interior trim panel (Sec 24), then peel back the bottom front corner of the plastic sheet.
24   Remove the two retaining screws, then disconnect the motor from the link rod (photo).
25   Prise both motor wiring sealing grommets out of the door and the 'B' pillar, then remove the 'B' pillar lower interior trim panel (Sec 24), unbolt the seat belt bottom anchorage (Sec 22) and release the floor carpet from the door sill.
26   Disconnect the motor wiring by unplugging the connector from the floor behind the front seat rear mounting, attach a drawstring to the wiring and pull it up through the pillar and door until the motor can be removed. Leave the drawstring in place to assist with refitting.

Fig. 11.6 Door lock and handle components (Sec 16)

Front door – items 1 to 11

1	Exterior handle	7	Link rod – latch-to-interior handle
2	Interior lock button	8	Latch
3	Lock	9	Central locking control unit/motor*
4	Link rod – latch-to-exterior handle	10	Link rod – latch-to-control unit/motor*
5	Link rod – latch-to-interior lock button	11	Interior handle
6	Link rod – latch-to-lock		

Rear door – items 12 to 20

12	Exterior handle	16	Interior handle
13	Link rod – latch-to-interior lock button	17	Central locking motor*
14	Latch	18	Link rod – motor*
15	Link rod – latch-to-interior handle	19	Snap-on connector*
		20	Interior lock button and bellcrank assembly
			*Not fitted to all models

16.2 Front door lock link rod clip 'A' and retaining clip 'B'

16.5 Front door exterior handle link rod clip 'A' and mounting nuts 'B

16.6 Rear door exterior handle mounting nuts

16.9A Remove retaining screw – front door shown ...

16.9B ... to remove window glass rear guide channel

16.10A Disconnecting front door exterior handle link rod

16.10B Disconnecting front door interior lock button link rod from latch

16.11A Remove latch retaining screws ...

16.11B ... and withdraw latch – with link rods, if required

16.13 Removing interior handle retaining screw

16.19 Door striker is screwed into door pillar ...

16.20 ... or secured by two screws

16.22A Remove retaining screws to release front door central locking control unit/motor from link rod ...

16.22B ... and withdraw unit/motor until wiring can be disconnected

16.24 Rear door central locking motor retaining screws (arrow)

Refitting

Front door lock
27   Refitting is the reverse of the removal procedure.

Exterior handle
28   Refitting is the reverse of the removal procedure; tighten the nuts to the specified torque wrench setting.

Latch
29   Refitting is the reverse of the removal procedure; check that the window glass slides easily up and down before tightening the guide channel screw securely.

Interior handle
30   Refitting is the reverse of the removal procedure.

Interior lock button
31   Refitting is the reverse of the removal procedure.

Striker
32   On refitting, align the striker with the marks made on removal; if new components have been fitted, centre the striker on its mounting hole(s), tighten the striker/screws lightly and check the fit of the door in the body (see below). When the fit is correct, tighten the striker/screws securely.
33   The striker can be positioned accurately only when the door is properly located in its aperture (Sec 15).
34   When the door is closed, check that it sits squarely on its weatherstrip, with no sign of gaps, so that it is flush with the surrounding bodywork and so that the door lock closes securely, with no sign of rattles.
35   If the fit is not correct, open the door and slacken the striker/screws, then adjust the position of the striker by closing the door as gently as possible, then opening it again without disturbing the position of the striker.
36   When the fit is correct, tighten the striker/screws securely and check the operation of the door lock.

Central locking control unit/motor – front door
37   Refitting is the reverse of the removal procedure.

Central locking control unit/motor – rear door
38   Refitting is the reverse of the removal procedure.

17   Central locking system – general

1   The system allows the doors and tailgate to be locked or unlocked from a central point; operating the driver's door lock, either from the outside with a key or from the inside using the interior lock button, will trigger the system.
2   Locks other than the driver's door can be operated manually, independently of the central locking system; note, however, that the system will not automatically relock these other locks if any is unlocked after the system has been operated.
3   Refer to Chapter 12 for details of the system's electrical components.

Fig. 11.7 Components of the central locking system (Sec 17)

1 *Control unit/motor*	4 *Latch*
2 *Front door lock*	5 *Tailgate lock*
3 *Interior lock button*	

4   Removal and refitting of the door control unit/motors is described in Section 16 of this Chapter, while the tailgate motor is covered in Section 14.

Fig. 11.8 Door window glass and regulator components (Sec 18)

1 Rear door window glass*
2 Weatherstrips
3 Front door window glass
4 Front and rear guide channels

5 Rear window manual regulator*
6 Front window manual regulator*

7 Front window electric regulator*
8 Electric motor*
9 Regulator channel*
10 Bezel*

11 Window manual regulator handle*
12 Electric front window switch*
*Not fitted to all models

18.2A Remove rubber fillet from rear door to improve access ...

18.2B ... and remove screw (arrow) to release window glass guide channel – rear shown, front similar

18.4A Removing door outside ...

18.4B ... and inside weatherstrips

18.5 Manoeuvring window glass out of door

18.7 Use soft rubber wedges (arrows) to hold window glass without marking it

18   Door window glass and regulator – removal and refitting

Removal

Window glass

1   Remove the regulator (see below).
2   On a rear door only, remove the rubber fillet from the rear of the door, remove their retaining screws and withdraw both the front and rear guide channels (photos).
3   If not already done, support the glass and remove the two wedges.
4   Pull off the outside and inside weatherstrips (photos).
5   Manoeuvre the glass out of the door (photo).

Manual regulator – front door

6   Open the door and fully raise the window glass, remove the interior trim panel (Sec 24), then peel down the plastic sheet.
7   Fit two soft wedges to hold the glass without marking it (photo).
8   Unscrew the three bolts securing the regulator to the door.
9   Remove its retaining screw and withdraw the front guide channel from the door.
10   Unscrew the two nuts securing the regulator channel to the door inner panel, then remove the regulator channel.
11   Support the glass and remove the two wedges, lower the glass and release the regulator from the glass bottom channels, then manoeuvre the regulator out of the door.

Manual regulator – rear door

12   Open the door and fully raise the window glass, remove the interior trim panel (Sec 24), then peel down the plastic sheet.
13   Fit two soft wedges to hold the glass without marking it (see photo 18.7).
14   Unscrew the three bolts securing the regulator to the door, then gently push the regulator into the door to release it from the door inner panel (photo).

15   Release the regulator top arms from the glass bottom channels, then manoeuvre the regulator out of the door.

Electric regulator

16   Open the door and fully raise the window glass, remove the interior trim panel (Sec 24), then peel down the plastic sheet.
17   Fit two soft wedges to hold the glass without marking it (see photo 18.7).
18   Remove its retaining screw and withdraw the front guide channel from the door (photos).
19   Release the connector from its clip, unplug the connector to disconnect the wiring, then unscrew the two motor mounting bolts (photo).
20   Unscrew the two bolts securing the regulator to the door, then manoeuvre the motor and part of the cable out of the door (photo).
21   Move the regulator towards the front of the door and release its top arms from the glass bottom channels, then manoeuvre the regulator out of the door (photo).

Refitting

Window glass

22   On refitting, manoeuvre the glass into the door and support it in the fully-raised position while the regulator is greased and refitted. Where the front and rear guide channels were disturbed, refit them with their retaining screws, but do not fully tighten the screws until the operation of the complete assembly has been checked and adjusted as described below.

Manual regulator – front door

23   On refitting, apply a smear of general-purpose grease to the regulator and glass bottom channels, then refit the regulator and its bolts, raise the glass and secure it with the wedges. Engage the regulator top arms in the glass bottom channels and its lower arm in the regulator channel, then position the regulator channel on the door inner panel and tighten the nuts to their specified torque wrench setting.
24   Remove the wedges and wind the glass to the fully-raised

18.14 Rear door window regulator mounting bolts 'A', front guide channel screw 'B' – front door similar

18.18A Unscrewing window glass front guide channel screw ...

18.18B ... to remove channel from front door

18.19 Disconnecting electric motor wiring – note motor mounting bolts (arrows)

18.20 Unscrewing electric window regulator bolts – other bolt arrowed ...

18.21 ... to remove regulator and motor assembly from door

position, refit the front guide channel and tighten its screw lightly, then lower and raise the glass several times to settle the components; if necessary, slacken the retaining screws and bolts and adjust the position of the guide channels.

25   When the setting is correct, tighten the screws and bolts securely, to their specified torque wrench settings, where given.

26   Refit the interior trim panel (Sec 24).

Manual regulator – rear door

27   On refitting, apply a smear of general-purpose grease to the regulator and glass bottom channels, raise the glass and secure it with the wedges. Refit the regulator to the door inner panel, engage the regulator top arms in the glass bottom channels (lowering the glass if necessary) and refit the regulator top mounting bolt to secure the assembly; tighten the bolt only lightly.

28   Remove the wedges and wind the glass until the remaining two regulator mounting bolt holes align then refit the bolts, tightening them only lightly.

29   Raise and lower the glass several times to settle the components; if necessary, slacken the retaining screws and bolts and adjust the position of the regulator and guide channels.

30   When the setting is correct, tighten the screws and bolts securely, to their specified torque wrench settings, where given.

31   Refit the interior trim panel (Sec 24).

Electric regulator

32   On refitting, apply a smear of general-purpose grease to the regulator and glass bottom channels. Refit the regulator; engage its top arms in the glass bottom channels and its lower arm in the regulator channel attached to the door inner panel.

33   Align the bolt holes and refit the bolts, then refit the motor and its bolts. Refit the front guide channel and tighten its screw only lightly.

34   Connect the motor and switch wiring and remove the wedges, then lower and raise the glass several times to settle the components; if necessary, slacken the retaining screws and bolts and adjust the position of the guide channels.

35   When the setting is correct, tighten the screws and bolts securely,

to their specified torque wrench settings, where given.

36   Refit the interior trim panel (Sec 24).

19 Electric front windows – general

1   Where applicable, the front windows can be raised or lowered by electric motors fitted to the regulator assemblies. The driver's door

Fig. 11.9 Electric front window components (Sec 19)

1   *Electric motor*

2   *Driver's door switch*

3   *Window regulator*

20.1 Prising exterior mirror glass and bezel from mirror casing

20.2 Removing exterior mirror inner trim panel – note fasteners

20.3 Remove retaining screws to release mirror

window can be operated only from the driver's door switch, while the passenger's door window can be operated either from the passenger's or the driver's door switch.

2   A cut-out is fitted to each motor to protect them from burning-out if the movement of either window is obstructed; if the cut-out operates at any time, clear the obstruction and wait for 15 seconds for the cut-out to reset before attempting to operate the windows. **Do not** attempt to open or close a window whose movement is obviously obstructed, or if the window is frozen in place.

3   The regulator and motor assemblies are removed and refitted as described in Section 18 of this Chapter; refer to Chapter 12 for details of the system's electrical components.

20   Mirrors – removal and refitting

Removal

Exterior mirror glass

1   Taking care not to mark the plastic and wearing gloves and suitable eye protection, carefully prise the mirror glass and bezel off the mirror casing (photo).

Exterior mirror assembly

2   Pull off the adjusting knob (where fitted). Gently prise the inner trim panel off the retaining clip at its top corner and withdraw it, unhooking it at the bottom edge (photo).

20.8 Ensure bezel is clipped firmly into casing on refitting

3   Remove the two retaining screws and withdraw the mirror and the outer trim panel (photo). Remove and discard, if fitted, the sealing pad.
4   On some early models, note that the mirror may be secured by a retaining plate which uses screws and moulded tubes through the door; note carefully how the components fit together on removal so that they can be correctly reassembled.

Interior rear view mirror

5   The mirror itself slides on to a base that is stuck to the windscreen; push upwards to remove.
6   Do not disturb the base unless absolutely necessary; it is very difficult to achieve a reliable bond. If the windscreen is to be renewed, this is a further reason for having the work carried out by a specialist windscreen fitter who will be well-versed in the removal and refitting of stick-on mirrors.
7   If the base is to be removed and is found to be glued in place, seek the advice of a Rover dealer; find out how best to remove the base (without risking cracking the windscreen) and which com-mercially-available adhesive is suitable for use on reassembly.

Refitting

Exterior mirror glass

8   Refitting is the reverse of the removal procedure; ensure the bezel is clipped securely into the casing (photo).

Exterior mirror assembly

9   Refitting is the reverse of the removal procedure; where applicable, fit a new sealing pad to the mirror.

Interior rear view mirror

10   Refitting is the reverse of the removal procedure.

21   Seats – removal and refitting

Removal

Front

1   Operate the adjuster and move the seat fully backwards, then undo the front mounting screws and remove the runner stops (photo).
2   Move the seat fully forwards and undo the rear mounting screws (photo).
3   Remove the seat.

Rear

4   Remove the parcel shelf. Release the seat belts from the seat, then fold the seat forwards.
5   Undo the seat mounting screws and remove the seat, noting the spacer under each mounting point (photo).

21.1 Front seat front mounting – note runner stop

21.2 Front seat rear mounting

21.5 Rear seat mounting points (arrows)

21.7 Removing rear seat backrest catch from parcel shelf side support

22.1 Front seat belt top anchorage, showing alternative mounting point

Refitting

Front and rear

6   Refitting is the reverse of the removal procedure; tighten the screws to the specified torque wrench setting.
7   Note that the rear seat backrest catches are located under the parcel shelf side supports and can be removed once the mounting bolts have been unscrewed (photo).

22 Seat belts – removal and refitting

Removal

Front

1   Prise off the plastic cover and unbolt the belt top anchorage (photo).
2   Unbolt the belt bottom anchorage (photo).
3   Remove the rear quarter (three-door) or the 'B' pillar lower (five-door) interior trim panel (Sec 24) and unbolt the retractor from the body (photo).
4   Prise out its retaining clip and withdraw the cover, then unbolt the stalks from the floor (photo).

Rear

5   Remove the parcel shelf. Release the belts from the seat, then fold the seat forwards.
6   Unbolt the belt bottom anchorage and buckle from the floor (photos). Note that the centre two-point belt can be unbolted completely.

22.2 Front seat belt bottom anchorage – five-door models

7   Prise off the plastic cover and unbolt the belt top anchorage (photo).
8   Remove the luggage compartment interior trim panels as necessary to reach the belt retractor mountings; on the left-hand side, this will require the removal of the luggage compartment lamp (if fitted). Unbolt the retractor from the body (photo).

22.3 Retractor is secured by a bolt, and screw, where fitted (arrows)

22.4 Front seat belt stalk mountings and cover

22.6A Rear centre seat belt mountings and side belt buckle mountings

22.6B Rear side seat belt bottom anchorage

22.7 Rear side seat belt top anchorage

22.8 Remove luggage compartment interior trim panel to reach rear side seat belt retractor mounting bolt

9   Release the belt guide from the parcel shelf side support, remove the guide from the belt and feed the belt through the support until it can be removed.

Refitting

Front and rear

10   Refitting is the reverse of the removal procedure, but ensure that the anchorages are free to move when the bolts have been securely tightened, to their respective specified torque wrench settings.

23   Parcel shelf – removal and refitting

Removal

1   Open the tailgate, detach the parcel shelf straps and push the shelf to the right until the left-hand pivot pin is released from its retainer.
2   To remove the parcel shelf side supports, remove the rear seat belt retractor (Sec 22), unbolt the rear seat catches (Sec 21), disconnect the loudspeaker wiring (if fitted) and remove the four screws securing each support.

Refitting

3   Refitting is the reverse of the removal procedure. Ensure that the parcel shelf pivot pins are located securely in their retainers.

24   Interior trim – general information

Interior trim panels

1   The interior trim panels are all secured using either screws or

Fig. 11.10 Removing the 'A' pillar upper trim panel (Sec 24)

1   Weatherstrip   2   Stud fasteners

Fig. 11.11 Removing the 'A' pillar lower trim panel (Sec 24)

1   *Weatherstrip*
2   *Door sill tread panel*
    screws

3   *Trim panel*

Fig. 11.12 Removing one-piece door trim panel (Sec 24)

Upper panel

Fig. 11.14 Removing 'B' pillar upper trim panel (Sec 24)

1   *Plastic cover*
2   *Seat belt top anchor bolt*
    and spacer

3   *Screw/rivet fasteners –*
    three-door models only
4   *Weatherstrip*
5   *Blanking plug – alternative*
    mounting point

Lower panel

Fig. 11.13 Removing two-piece door trim panel (Sec 24)

1   *Screws – front door only*
2   *Stud fasteners*

various types of trim fasteners, usually either studs or clips.
2   To remove a panel, study it carefully, noting how it is secured; usually there are some ancillary components which must be removed first such as, on door trim panels, the front door pockets and loudspeakers, the armrests/door pulls, the manual window regulator handles and door lock interior handle escutcheons (photos).
3   Once any such components have been removed, check that there are no other panels overlapping the one to be removed; usually there is a sequence that has to be followed that will become obvious on close inspection. For example, when removing two-piece door interior trim panels, the upper panel must be removed first.
4   Remove all obvious fasteners, such as screws. If the panel will not come free, it is held by hidden clips or fasteners. These are usually

24.2A Prise off armrest/door pull cover (where fitted) ...

24.2B ... and remove retaining screws to release

24.2C Prise out cover plug and unscrew (hex-head) screw ...

24.2D ... to release manual window regulator handle

24.2E Prise out cover plug ...

24.2F ... and remove screw to release door lock interior handle escutcheon

24.4A Remove obvious fasteners such as screws ...

24.4B ... and trim clips to release trim panels

24.4C Removing a panel secured by hidden clips

situated around the edge of the panel and can be prised up to release them; note, however that they can break quite easily so replacements should be available. The best way of releasing such clips is to use the correct type of tool, an example of which is shown in some of the accompanying photographs; if this is not available, an old, broad-bladed screwdriver with the edges rounded-off and wrapped in insulating tape will serve as a good substitute (photos).

5   The accompanying illustrations show typical examples of the location and number of fasteners securing most of the car's panels; note in many cases that the adjacent weatherstrip must be prised back to release a panel.

6   When removing a panel, **never** use excessive force or the panel may be damaged; always check carefully that all fasteners have been removed or released before attempting to withdraw a panel.

7   Refitting is the reverse of the removal procedure; secure the fasteners by pressing them firmly into place and ensure that all disturbed components are correctly secured to prevent rattles. If

adhesives were found at any point on removal, use white spirit to remove all traces of old adhesive, then wash off all traces of spirit using soapy water; use a suitable trim adhesive (a Rover dealer should be able to recommend a proprietary product) on reassembly.

Carpets
8   The passenger compartment floor carpet is in one piece and is secured at its edges by screws or clips, usually the same fasteners used to secure the various adjoining trim panels.

9   Carpet removal and refitting is reasonably straightforward but very time-consuming due to the fact that all adjoining trim panels must be removed first, as must components such as the seats and their mountings, the gearchange lever gaiters, the cassette storage holder and seat belt lower anchorages.

Headlining
10   The headlining is clipped to the roof and can be withdrawn only

Fig. 11.15 Removing 'B' pillar lower trim panel (Sec 24)

1   Door sill tread panel   2   Weatherstrip
    screws

Fig. 11.16 Removing rear quarter trim panel – three-door models (Sec 24)

1   Screw/rivet fasteners   2   Screws

Fig. 11.17 Location of luggage compartment trim panel fasteners (Sec 24)

Fig. 11.18 Removing 'C/D' pillar upper trim panel (Sec 24)

1   Weatherstrip   3   Stud fasteners
2   Tailgate buffer

once all fittings such as the grab handles, sun visors, roof console, sunroof (if fitted), windscreen and rear quarterlights and related trim panels have been removed and the door, tailgate and sunroof aperture weatherstrips have been prised clear.

11   Note that headlining removal requires considerable skill and experience if it is to be carried out without damage and is therefore best entrusted to an expert.

25   Sun visor – removal and refitting

Removal

1   Unclip the visor and remove the two screws securing its pivot to the roof; remove the visor. Each clip is secured by a single screw.

Refitting

2   Refitting is the reverse of the removal procedure.

Fig. 11.19 Location of tailgate trim panel fasteners (Sec 24)

28.1 Cassette storage holder retaining screws (arrows)

29.6 Glovebox (floor) securing screws 'A', lid securing screws 'B', lock retaining clip 'C'

29.7 Glovebox striker screws 'A', (ceiling) securing screws 'B', support rail screws 'C'

26 Roof console – removal and refitting

Removal

1   Remove the interior lamp from the roof (Chapter 12).
2   Release the four clips and withdraw the console.

Refitting

3   Refitting is the reverse of the removal procedure.

27 Grab handles – removal and refitting

Removal

1   Prise up the cover at each end of the handle, remove the retaining screws securing each end, then withdraw the handle.

Refitting

2   Refitting is the reverse of the removal procedure.

28 Cassette storage holder – removal and refitting

Removal

1   Remove the two retaining screws to release the holder (photo).
2   The holder bracket is secured to the floor by two (hex-head) screws.

Refitting

3   Refitting is the reverse of the removal procedure.

29 Glovebox – removal and refitting

Removal

Lid

1   Open the lid and carefully lift the edge of the glovebox floor carpet, remove the four screws and withdraw the lid.

Lock

2   Open the glovebox lid and prise out the retaining clip to release the lock.
3   The striker is secured by two screws.

Glovebox

4   Open the glovebox lid (where fitted).
5   Where fitted, remove the glovebox lamp and switch (Chapter 12).
6   Carefully lift the edge of the glovebox floor carpet and remove the three screws (photo).
7   Remove the striker (if fitted) from the glovebox ceiling. Remove the four (ceiling) retaining screws and withdraw the glovebox from the facia. If required, remove the four remaining screws to release the glovebox support rail (photo).

Refitting

Lid

8   Refitting is the reverse of the removal procedure; use white spirit to remove the old adhesive, then wash off all traces of spirit using soapy water. Use a suitable trim adhesive to secure the carpet.

Lock

9   The striker's position can be altered on the slotted mounting holes until the lid closes securely and fits properly. Tighten the screws securely.

Glovebox

10   Refitting is the reverse of the removal procedure; secure the floor carpet as described previously.

30.6 Disconnecting facia wiring

30.8A Location of facia mounting screws – front seats removed for clarity

30.8B Lower facia to floor to disconnect or remove components

30 Facia – removal and refitting

Removal

1 Disconnect the battery negative lead (Chapter 12).
2 On models with carburettor engines only, disconnect the choke cable from the facia (Chapter 4).
3 Move both front seats as far as possible to the rear.
4 Lower the steering column onto a support such as a wooden block (Chapter 10, Section 27, paragraphs 1 to 7).
5 Reaching up inside the fusebox aperture, disconnect the speedometer drive cable from the rear of the instrument panel (Chapter 12).
6 Disconnect the facia wiring by unplugging its connector plug (top row, right-hand connector, marked 'FACIA') from the fusebox panel and by unplugging the two connector plugs mounted on brackets at the left-hand end of the fusebox panel (photo).
7 Remove the cassette storage holder (Sec 28).
8 Remove the nine screws securing the facia and pull it into the passenger compartment. Do not use excessive force; it is not necessary and may damage the plastic components. If difficulty is encountered at any point check carefully that all fasteners, electrical connections and other components have been removed or disconnected as required. Lower the facia to the floor; place wads of clean rag as necessary to protect the facia surfaces (photos).
9 Remove the heater control panel (Chapter 3).
10 Disconnect, if fitted, the radio aerial and wiring (Chapter 12).
11 Remove the facia from the car.
12 The facia components can be removed now if required.

Refitting

13 Refitting is the reverse of the removal procedure. Refer where necessary to the relevant Sections of Chapters 3, 4, 10 and 12.

Chapter 12 Electrical system

Contents

Specifications

System type .... 12 volt, negative earth

Battery

Type..	Maintenance-free (sealed for life) lead-acid
Battery code (Lucas):	
All K8-engined models – standard equipment	007
All K8-engined models – cold climates, K16-engined models – standard equipment........................	063
K16-engined models – cold climates, all Police versions	063S

Battery performance:	**Cold cranking**	**Reserve capacity**
007..	280 amps	50 minutes
063..	360 amps	60 minutes
063S......................................	405 amps	70 minutes

Alternator

Type..	Lucas/Magneti Marelli A127
Output – @ 14 volts and 6000 rpm:	
GTi 16v	65 amps
All other models	55 amps
Regulated voltage	14 volts maximum
Voltage regulator..	Lucas 21TR
Brush minimum protrusion..	5 mm approx (see text)
Brush spring pressure – brush end flush with brushbox........................	1.3 to 2.7 N
Stator winding resistance – @ 20°C:	
A127/55..	0.18 ohms ± 5%
A127/65..	0.15 ohms ± 5%
Rotor field winding resistance – @ 20°C	3.2 ohms ± 5%
Drivebelt deflection	6 to 8 mm @ 10 kg pressure

Starter motor

Type	Lucas M79
Rating	0.8 kW
Commutator minimum diameter	28.8 mm
Brush minimum length	3.5 mm approx (see text)
Brush spring tension	12 to 20 N

Fuses

Fuse	Rating (amps)	Circuit(s) protected
1	10	Engine (ignition HT coil, manifold pre-heater relay, carburettor idle bypass system, fuel pump relay)
2	10	Right-hand side and tail lamps, sidelamp warning lamp, number plate lamps, electric front window switch and instrument panel illumination
3	10	Instrument (panel) feed
4	15	Electric cooling fan
5	10	Right-hand headlamp main beam, main beam warning lamp
6	10	Stop-lamps
7	–	Unused
8	–	Unused
9	10	Direction indicators, reversing lamps, heated rear window relay
10	10	Rear foglamp
11	20	Heated rear window
12	15	Central locking system, radio/cassette memory, clock, interior lamp, luggage compartment lamp, interior lamp delay/lamps-on alarm unit
13	30	Electric front windows
14	15	Heater blower motor
15	15	Windscreen wipers and washer
16	15	Rear window wiper and washer
17	10	Fuel pump
18	10	Left-hand headlamp main beam
19	20	Headlamps, sidelamps
20	15	Dim-dip
21	20	Hazard warning lamps, horn
22	15	Radio/cassette feed, cigar lighter
23	–	Unused
24	10	Right-hand headlamp dip beam
25	10	Left-hand headlamp dip beam
26	10	Left-hand side and tail lamps, number plate lamps, illumination of instrument panel switches, cigar lighter and glovebox

Fusible links

Link	Rating (amps)	Circuit(s) protected
1 (Light blue)	60	Ignition switch, ignition relay
2 (Light blue)	60	Fusebox feed
3 (Light blue)	60	Fusebox feed
4 (Light green)	30	Manifold pre-heater and starter relay (carburettor engines), relay module (fuel-injected engines)

Relays and control units

Component	Location
Starter relay – carburettor engines	Engine compartment left-hand side, in front of heater air inlet box/blower motor assembly (front relay)
Intake manifold pre-heater relay – carburettor engines	Engine compartment left-hand side, in front of heater air inlet box/blower motor assembly (rear relay)
Main relay, manifold heater relay, starter relay and fuel pump relay – fuel-injected engines	Part of relay module, in engine compartment between heater air inlet box and blower motor assembly and fuel-injection/ignition system ECU
Lambda sensor relay	Engine compartment left-hand side, next to heater air inlet box/blower motor assembly
Interior lamp delay/Lamps-on alarm unit	Fusebox panel (rear face)
Heated rear window relay	Fusebox panel (rear face)
Headlamp relay	Fusebox panel (rear face)
Ignition relay	Fusebox panel (rear face)
Electric front window/auxiliary relay	Fusebox panel (rear face)
Direction indicator/hazard warning relay	Fusebox panel (rear face)
Dim-dip unit	Fusebox panel (rear face)
Windscreen wiper relay	Fusebox panel (front face)
Rear window wiper relay	Fusebox panel (front face)

Bulbs

Fitting	Wattage
Headlamps	H4	60/55
Front sidelamps	Capless	5
Direction indicator lamps	Bayonet	21
Direction indicator side repeater lamps	Capless	5
Interior lamp	Bayonet	10
Instrument panel warning and illumination	Integral with holder	14V 1.12, 1.4 or 2W
Hazard warning indicator lamp	Capless	1.2
Glovebox lamp	Festoon	5
Luggage compartment lamp	Bayonet	10
Reversing lamps	Bayonet	21
Stop/tail lamps	Bayonet (offset pin)	21/5
Rear foglamp	Bayonet	21
Number plate lamp	Festoon	5

Torque wrench settings

	Nm	lbf ft
Battery tray and fusible link box mounting bracket bolts	9	6.5
Alternator pivot and clamp bolts:		
10 mm	45	33
8 mm	25	18.5
Alternator pulley nut	25	18.5
Alternator mounting bracket-to-cylinder block/crankcase bolts	45	33
Starter motor-to-transmission bolts	45	33
Starter motor support bracket (where fitted) fasteners:		
Bracket front half-to-motor nuts	25	18.5
Bracket front half-to-rear half bolt	45	33
Bracket rear half-to-transmission bolts	25	18.5
Oil pressure switch	12	9
Speedometer drive upper-to-lower cable nut	9	6.5
Wiper arm-to-spindle nut	11	8
Windscreen wiper motor-to-mounting bracket (hex-head) screws	10	7.5
Windscreen wiper linkage spindle housing nuts	11	8
Rear window wiper motor-to-mounting bracket (hex-head) screws	10	7.5
Rear window wiper motor mounting bracket (hex-head) screws	5	3.5
Rear window wiper motor spindle housing nut	11	8

1   General information and precautions

Warning: *Before carrying out any work on the electrical system, read through the precautions given in Safety first! at the beginning of this manual*

The electrical system is of the 12-volt negative earth type and consists of a 12-volt battery, an alternator with integral voltage regulator, a starter motor and related electrical accessories, components and wiring.

The battery is of the 'maintenance-free' (sealed for life) type and is charged by the alternator, which is belt-driven from a crankshaft-mounted pulley.

The starter motor is of the pre-engaged type, incorporating an integral solenoid. On starting, the solenoid moves the drive pinion into engagement with the flywheel ring gear before the starter motor is energised. Once the engine has started, a one-way clutch prevents the motor armature being driven by the engine until the pinion disengages from the flywheel.

Further details of the various systems are given in the relevant Sections of this Chapter. While some repair procedures are given, the usual course of action is to renew the component concerned. The owner whose interest extends beyond mere component renewal should obtain a copy of the *'Automobile Electrical & Electronic Systems Manual'*, available from the publishers of this manual.

It is necessary to take extra care when working on the electrical system to avoid damage to semi-conductor devices (diodes and transistors), and to avoid the risk of personal injury. In addition to the precautions given in *Safety first!* at the beginning of this manual, observe the following when working on the system:

Always remove rings, watches, etc before working on the electrical system. Even with the battery disconnected, capacitive discharge could occur if a component's live terminal is earthed through a metal object. This could cause a shock or nasty burn.

Do not reverse the battery connections. Components such as the alternator, fuel injection/ignition system ECU, or any other having semi-conductor circuitry could be irreparably damaged.

If the engine is being started using jump leads and a slave battery, connect the batteries *positive-to-positive* and *negative-to-negative* (see *'Booster battery (jump) starting'*). This also applies when connecting a battery charger.

Never disconnect the battery terminals, the alternator, any electrical wiring or any test instruments when the engine is running.

Do not allow the engine to turn the alternator when the alternator is not connected.

Never 'test' for alternator output by 'flashing' the output lead to earth.

Never use an ohmmeter of the type incorporating a hand-cranked generator for circuit or continuity testing.

Always ensure that the battery negative lead is disconnected when working on the electrical system.

Before using electric-arc welding equipment on the car, disconnect the battery, alternator and components such as the fuel injection/ignition system ECU to protect them.

2   Electrical fault-finding – general information

1   A typical electrical circuit consists of an electrical component, any switches, relays, motors, fuses, fusible links or circuit breakers related to that component and the wiring and connectors that link the component to both the battery and the chassis. To help you pinpoint an electrical circuit problem, wiring diagrams are included at the end of this manual.

2   Before tackling any troublesome electrical circuit, first study the appropriate wiring diagram to get a complete understanding of what components are included in that individual circuit. Trouble spots, for instance, can be narrowed down by noting if other components related to the circuit are operating properly. If several components or circuits fail at one time, the problem is probably in a shared fuse or earth connection, as more than one circuit can be routed through the same connections.

3   Electrical problems usually stem from simple causes, such as loose or corroded connections, a faulty earth, a blown fuse, a melted fusible

link or a faulty relay. Visually inspect the condition of all fuses, wires and connections in a problem circuit before testing the components. Use the diagrams to note which terminal connections will need to be checked in order to pinpoint the trouble spot.

4   The basic tools needed for electrical fault-finding include a circuit tester or voltmeter (a 12-volt bulb with a set of test leads can also be used), a continuity tester, a battery and set of test leads, and a jumper wire, preferably with a circuit breaker incorporated, which can be used to bypass electrical components. Before attempting to locate a problem with test instruments, use the wiring diagram to decide where to make the connections.

Voltage checks

5   Voltage checks should be performed if a circuit is not functioning properly. Connect one lead of a circuit tester to either the negative battery terminal or a known good earth. Connect the other lead to a connector in the circuit being tested, preferably nearest to the battery or fuse. If the tester bulb lights, voltage is present; this means that the part of the circuit between the connector and the battery is problem-free. Continue checking the rest of the circuit in the same fashion. When you reach a point at which no voltage is present the problem lies between that point and the last test point with voltage. Most problems can be traced to a loose connection. **Note:** *Bear in mind that some circuits are live only when the ignition switch is switched to a particular position.*

Finding a short circuit

6   One method of finding a short circuit is to remove the fuse and connect a test lamp or voltmeter to the fuse terminals with all the relevant electrical components switched off. There should be no voltage present in the circuit. Move the wiring from side to side while watching the test lamp. If the bulb lights there is a short to earth somewhere in that area, probably where the insulation has rubbed through. The same test can be performed on each component in the circuit, even a switch.

Earth check

7   To check whether a component is properly earthed, disconnect the battery and connect one lead of a self-powered test lamp (sometimes known as a continuity tester) to a known good earth point. Connect the other lead to the wire or earth connection being tested. If the lamp lights, the earth is sound; if not, it must be rectified.

8   The battery negative terminal is connected to 'earth' – the metal of the car body – and most systems are wired so that they only receive a positive feed, the current returning via the metal of the car's body. This means that the component mounting and the body form part of that circuit and loose or corroded mountings, therefore, can cause a range of electrical faults; note that these may range from total failure of a circuit to a puzzling partial fault. In particular, lamps may shine dimly (especially when another circuit sharing the same earth point is in operation), motors (eg wiper motors or the radiator cooling fan motor) may run slowly and the operation of one circuit may have an apparently unrelated effect on another. **Note:** *A poor earth may not cause the circuit's fuse to blow; in fact it may reduce the load on the fuse.*

9   If an earth connection is thought to be faulty, dismantle the connection and clean back to bare metal both the bodyshell and the wire terminal or the component's earth connection mating surface. Be careful to remove all traces of dirt and corrosion, then use a knife to trim away any paint, so that a clean metal-to-metal joint is made. On reassembly, tighten the joint fasteners securely; if a wire terminal is being refitted, use serrated washers between the terminal and the bodyshell to ensure a clean and secure connection. When the connection is remade, prevent the onset of corrosion in the future by applying a coat of petroleum jelly or silicone-based grease or by spraying on (at regular intervals) a proprietary ignition sealer such as Holts Damp Start or a water dispersant lubricant such as Holts Wet Start.

10   The car's wiring harness has four multiple-earth connections referred to in the wiring diagrams as Earth Header joints. Each of these serves several circuits; their locations are as follows.

   (a)   *Earth Header 1 – Attached to the front of the right-hand inner wing panel, next to the headlamp unit.*
   (b)   *Earth Header 2 – Attached to the front of the left-hand inner wing panel, next to the headlamp unit.*
   (c)   *Earth number 3 is the radio/cassette unit earth on the facia support rail.*
   (d)   *Earth Header 4 – Attached to the luggage compartment left-hand side, below the seat belt retractor.*

11   All engine/transmission-mounted electrical components are earthed by the lead attached to the starter motor upper mounting bolt, which is connected to the battery negative terminal and the main earth point on the body front panel.

Continuity check

12   A continuity check is necessary to determine if there are any breaks in a circuit. With the circuit switched off (ie no power in the circuit), a self-powered test lamp (sometimes known as a continuity tester) can be used to check the circuit. Connect the test leads to both ends of the circuit (or to the positive end and a good earth); if the test lamp lights, the circuit is passing current properly. If the lamp does not light, there is a break somewhere in the circuit.

13   The same procedure can be used to test a switch, by connecting the continuity tester to the switch terminals. With the switch in the relevant position, the test lamp should light.

Finding an open circuit

14   When checking for possible open circuits, it is often difficult to locate them by sight because oxidation or terminal misalignment are hidden by the connectors; merely moving a connector on a sensor or in the wiring harness may correct the fault. Remember this if an open circuit is indicated when fault-finding in a circuit. Intermittent problems may also be caused by oxidized or loose connections.

General

15   Electrical fault-finding is simple if you keep in mind that all electrical circuits are basically electricity flowing from the battery, through the wires, switches, relays, fuses and fusible links to each electrical component (light bulb, motor, etc.) and to earth, from where it is passed back to the battery. Any electrical problem is an interruption in the flow of electricity from the battery.

---

3   Battery – testing and charging

1   In normal use, the battery should not require charging from an external source unless very heavy use is made of electrical equipment over a series of journeys that are too short to allow the charging system to keep pace with demand. Otherwise, a need for regular recharging points to a fault either in the battery or in the charging system.

2   If, however, the car is laid up for long periods (in excess of thirty days at a time) the battery will lose approximately 1% of its charge per week. This figure is for a disconnected battery; if the battery is left connected, circuits such as the clock (where fitted) will drain it at a faster rate. To prevent this happening, always disconnect the battery negative lead whenever the car is to be laid up for a long period. To keep the battery fully charged it should be given regular 'refresher' charges every six weeks or so. This is particularly important on 'maintenance-free' batteries, which will suffer permanent reduction of charge capacity if allowed to become fully discharged.

3   If a discharged battery is suspected the simplest test for most owners is as follows. Leave the battery disconnected for at least two hours, then measure the (open circuit, or no-load) voltage using a sensitive voltmeter connected across the battery terminals. Compare the reading obtained with the following

Voltmeter reading	Charge condition
10.50 volts	*Fully discharged – battery scrap*
12.30 volts	*50% charged*
12.48 volts	*75% charged*
12.66 volts or more	*Fully charged*

4   If frequent topping-up is required and the battery case is not fractured the battery is being over-charged; the voltage regulator will have to be checked.

5   If the car covers a very small annual mileage, it is worthwhile checking the specific gravity of the electrolyte every three months to

determine the state of charge of the battery. Use a hydrometer to make the check, and compare the results with the following table

	Normal climates	Tropics
Discharged	1.120	1.080
Half charged	1.200	1.160
Fully charged	1.280	1.230

6   If the battery condition is suspect, first check the specific gravity of electrolyte in each cell. A variation of 0.040 or more between any cells indicates loss of electrolyte or deterioration of the internal plates.

7   A further test can be made only by a battery specialist using a battery heavy discharge meter. Alternatively, connect a voltmeter across the battery terminals and operate the starter motor with the ignition coil HT lead disconnected from the distributor and earthed, and with the headlamps, heated rear window and heater blower switched on. If the voltmeter reading remains above approximately 9.5 volts, the battery condition is satisfactory. If the voltmeter reading drops below 9.5 volts and the battery has already been charged, it is proven faulty.

8   In winter when heavy demand is placed on the battery (starting from cold and using more electrical equipment), it is a good idea occasionally to have the battery fully charged from an external source. The battery's bench charge rate depends on its code (see a Rover dealer or Lucas agent for details); for most owners the best method will be to use a trickle-charger overnight, charging at a rate of 1.5 amps. Rapid 'boost' charges which are claimed to restore the power of the battery in 1 to 2 hours are **not** recommended, as they can cause serious damage to the battery plates through overheating and may cause a sealed battery to explode.

9   Ideally, the battery should be removed from the car before charging and moved to a well-ventilated area. As a minimum precaution, both battery terminal leads must be disconnected (disconnect the negative lead first) before connecting the charger leads (Sec 1). **Warning:** *The battery will be emitting significant quantities of (highly-inflammable) hydrogen gas during charging and for approximately 15 minutes afterwards; do not allow sparks or naked flames near the battery or it may explode.*

10 Continue to charge the battery until all cells are gassing vigorously and no further rise in specific gravity or increase in no-load voltage is noted over a four-hour period. When charging is complete, turn the charger off before disconnecting the leads from the battery.

4   Battery – removal and refitting

Removal

1   First check that all electrical components are switched off to avoid a spark occurring as the negative lead is disconnected. If the radio/cassette unit has a security code, de-activate the code temporarily and re-activate it when the battery is re-connected; refer to the instructions and code supplied with the unit.

2   Slacken the terminal clamp nut, then lift the clamp and negative lead from the terminal. This is the terminal to disconnect before working on any electrical component on the car. If the terminal is tight, carefully ease it off by moving it from side to side (photo).

3   Raise the plastic cover from the positive terminal clamp and slacken the clamp nut, then lift the clamp and lead from the terminal.

4.2 Disconnecting the battery negative lead

4   Unscrew the clamp bolt and remove the clamp from the front of the battery (photo).

5   Lift the battery from the tray keeping it upright and taking care not to allow it to contact your clothing.

6   If the battery tray is to be removed, release the two wiring harness clips from the tray and remove the cable tie from the wiring, then release its two retainers and pull the fusible link box off its mounting bracket. Unscrew the five bolts securing the battery tray and fusible link mounting bracket to the body side member and remove the tray, collecting the bracket (photos).

7   Clean the battery terminal posts, clamps, tray and battery casing. If the bodywork is rusted as a result of battery acid spilling onto it, clean it thoroughly and re-paint (Chapter 1).

8   Whenever the battery is removed, check it for cracks and leakage.

Refitting

9   Refitting is the reverse of the removal procedure. Ensure that the terminal posts and leads are cleaned before re-connection. Smear petroleum jelly on the terminals after reconnecting the leads. Always connect the positive terminal clamp first and the negative terminal clamp last.

5   Charging system – testing

1   If the ignition warning lamp fails to light when the ignition is switched on, first check the alternator wiring connections for security. If satisfactory, check that the warning lamp bulb has not blown and is secure in its holder (Sec 14). If the lamp still fails to light check the continuity of the warning lamp feed wire from the alternator to the bulbholder. If all is satisfactory, the alternator is at fault and should be

4.4 Battery clamp bolt (arrow)

4.6A Battery tray/fusible link box mounting bracket upper (arrows) ...

4.6B ... and lower mounting bolts (arrows)

renewed or taken to an auto-electrician for testing and repair.

2   If the ignition warning lamp lights when the engine is running, stop the engine and check that the drivebelt is correctly tensioned (Chapter 1) and that the alternator connections are secure. If all is so far satisfactory, check the alternator brushes and commutator (Sec 7). If the fault persists, the alternator should be renewed or taken to an auto-electrician for testing and repair.

3   If the alternator output is suspect even though the warning lamp functions correctly, the regulated voltage may be checked as follows.

4   Connect a voltmeter across the battery terminals and start the engine.

5   Increase engine speed until the voltmeter reading remains steady; this should be approximately 12 to 13 volts and no more than 14 volts.

6   Switch on as many electrical accessories (eg the headlamps, heated rear window and heater blower) as possible and check that the alternator maintains the regulated voltage at around 13 to 14 volts.

7   If the regulated voltage is not as stated, the fault may be due to worn brushes, weak brush springs, a faulty voltage regulator, a faulty diode, a severed phase winding or a worn or damaged commutator. The brushes and commutator may be checked (Sec 7), but if the fault persists the alternator should be renewed or taken to an auto-electrician for testing and repair.

6   Alternator – removal and refitting

Removal

1   Disconnect the battery negative lead.

2   Remove its three retaining screws and move the washer system reservoir clear of the working area; disconnect the pump wiring connector plug(s) if the extra reach is required.

3   If a cover is fitted over the alternator left-hand end, unscrew its three retaining nuts and washers and withdraw it. Release the wire clip and unplug the connector to disconnect the alternator wiring (photo).

4   Remove the alternator drivebelt (Chapter 1).

5   If not already done, jack up the front of the car and support it securely on axle stands (see 'Jacking, towing and wheel changing') so that the steering can be turned to full right lock and the right-hand underwing shield can be removed (Chapter 11).

6   Remove the oil filter element (Chapter 1), having placed a suitable container under the filter adaptor to catch the spilt oil. Unless the filter was installed only recently, it should be discarded and a new filter should be installed on reassembly; this of course means that the engine oil should be changed at the same time.

7   Support the weight of the engine/transmission using a trolley jack, with a wooden spacer interposed to prevent damage to the sump, then unscrew the engine/transmission right-hand mounting through-bolt and nut and jack up the engine/transmission by approximately 2 to 3 inches (photos).

8   Unscrew the alternator clamp and pivot bolts and manoeuvre the alternator out of the car (photos).

9   The alternator adjuster link and mounting bracket can be unbolted from the cylinder block/crankcase if required.

10   If the alternator is to be renewed, the pulley must be transferred to the new unit. Clamp the pulley firmly in a vice with padded jaws and unscrew the pulley nut, taking care not to damage the pulley. Withdraw the pulley. On reassembly, tighten the pulley nut to its specified torque wrench setting.

Refitting

11   Refitting is the reverse of the removal procedure, noting the following points.

(a)   Tighten the alternator clamp and pivot bolts loosely, then refit the drivebelt and adjust it before tightening the bolts to their specified torque wrench settings (Chapter 1).

(b)   Connect the alternator wiring and refit the cover (where fitted).

(c)   Fit the oil filter (see paragraph 6 above).

(d)   Lower the engine/transmission and refit the mounting through-bolt and nut, tightening them to their specified torque wrench setting (Chapter 2).

(e)   Check the engine oil level and top up if necessary (Chapter 1).

6.3 Disconnecting alternator wiring

6.7A Protect sump as shown when jacking up engine ...

6.7B ... to height required to remove alternator

6.8A Removing alternator pivot bolts (one arrowed) ...

6.8B ... and removing alternator

Fig. 12.1 Exploded view of Lucas/Magneti Marelli A127 alternator (Sec 7)

1   Suppression capacitor
2   Voltage regulator and brushbox assembly
3   Slip ring end bracket
4   Slip ring end bearing
5   Rectifier diode pack
6   Phase terminal 8 mm fixings and insulating washers
7   Main terminal 10 mm fixings and insulating washers
8   Slip rings
9   Rotor
10 Stator
11 Through-bolts
12 Drive end bracket
13 Spacers
14 Drive end bearing
15 Pulley nut and lockwasher

7   Alternator brushes and voltage regulator – renewal

Note: *The vast majority of actual alternator faults are due to the voltage regulator or to the brushes. If the renewal of either of these assemblies does not cure the fault, the advice of an expert should be sought as to the best approach; for most owners the best course of action will be to renew the alternator as a complete unit. In many cases overhaul will not be viable on economic grounds alone*

1   While it is physically possible to remove the voltage regulator and brushbox assembly with the alternator in place on the car, owners are advised to remove the alternator (Sec 6) so that it can be serviced in clean working conditions.

2   Unscrew the three small screws securing the voltage regulator and brushbox assembly to the alternator. Lift off the regulator/brushbox, disconnect the electrical lead and remove the regulator/brushbox from the alternator (photo).

3   In most cases the brushes will have wear limit marks in the form of a groove etched along one face of each brush; when these marks are erased by wear, the brushes are worn out (photo). If no marks are provided, measure the protrusion of each brush from the brushbox end to the tip of the brush. No dimension is given by Rover but as a rough guide 5 mm should be regarded as a minimum. If either brush is worn to or below this amount, renew the voltage regulator and brushbox

7.2 Disconnecting wire to release voltage regulator/brushbox from alternator

7.3 When alternator brushes are worn to ends of wear limit marks (where given), they must be renewed

assembly. If the brushes are still serviceable, clean them with a solvent-moistened cloth. Check that the brush spring pressure is equal for both brushes and holds the brushes securely against the slip rings. If in doubt about the condition of the brushes and springs compare them with new components.

4   Clean the slip rings with a solvent-moistened cloth, then check for signs of scoring, burning or severe pitting. If worn or damaged, the slip rings should be attended to by an auto-electrician.

5   Refitting is the reverse of the removal procedure.

8 Starting system – testing

Note: *Refer to the warnings given in Safety first! and in Section 1 of this Chapter before starting work*

1   If the starter motor fails to operate when the switch is operated, the following may be the cause.

    (a)   The battery is faulty.
    (b)   The electrical connections between the switch, solenoid, battery and starter motor are somewhere failing to pass the necessary current from the battery through the starter to earth.
    (c)   The solenoid is faulty.
    (d)   The starter motor is mechanically or electrically defective.

2   To check the battery, switch on the headlamps. If they dim after a few seconds the battery is discharged; recharge (Sec 3) or renew the battery. If the lamps glow brightly operate the ignition switch and see what happens to the lamps. If they dim then you know that power is reaching the starter motor; therefore the starter motor must be removed and renewed or overhauled to cure the fault. If the lamps stay bright (and no clicking sound can be heard from the solenoid) there is a fault in the circuit or solenoid; see below. If the starter turns slowly when switched on, but the battery is in good condition, then either the starter must be faulty or there is considerable resistance in the circuit.

3   If the circuit is suspected, disconnect the battery terminals (including the earth connection to the body), the starter/solenoid wiring and the engine/transmission earth lead, thoroughly clean their connections and refit them, then use a meter or test lamp to check that full battery voltage is available at the solenoid terminal of the battery positive lead and that the earth is sound. Smear petroleum jelly around the battery terminals to prevent corrosion. Corroded connections are the most frequent cause of electric system malfunctions.

4   If the battery and all connections are in good condition, check the circuit first by disconnecting the wire from the solenoid blade terminal. Connect a meter or test lamp between the wire end and the terminal and check that the wire is live when the ignition switch is operated. If it is, then the circuit is sound; if not, proceed to paragraph 7.

5   The solenoid contacts can be checked by putting a voltmeter or test lamp across the main cable connection on the starter side of the solenoid and earth. When the switch is operated, there should be a reading or lighted bulb. If there is no reading or lighted bulb, the solenoid is faulty and should be renewed.

6   If the circuit and solenoid are proved sound, the fault must be in the starter motor; remove it (Sec 9) and check the brushes (Sec 10). If the fault does not lie in the brushes, the motor windings must be faulty; in this event the motor must be renewed, unless an auto-electrical

specialist can be found who will overhaul the unit at a cost significantly less than that of a new or exchange starter motor.

7   If the circuit is thought to be faulty, check it as follows using the equipment and procedures outlined in Section 2 of this Chapter, referring to the wiring diagrams for full details.

8   Disconnect the connector plug from the starter relay or relay module and use a meter or test lamp to check that the white/red wire is live when the ignition switch is operated; if it is not live, then the fault is either in the ignition switch or in the wiring between the switch and the relay. If it is live, then check that the earth connection is sound on the black wire. If the relay-energising wiring is good, proceed to the next check.

9   Using a multimeter set to the resistance function or a battery and bulb test circuit, check that there is continuity between the brown/red wire terminals on the relay connector and the solenoid; renew or repair the wire if a fault is found. Using a meter or test lamp, check that full battery voltage is available at the brown wire terminal; if not, check the feed wires back through the fusible link to the battery. If the wiring is in good condition the fault must lie in the relay itself; check it by substituting a new one. On models with fuel-injection, note that this means renewing the complete relay module.

9 Starter motor – removal and refitting

Removal

1   Disconnect the battery negative lead.

2   Disconnect the wiring from the starter motor solenoid; to prevent damage to the solenoid blade terminal, slide up the plastic sleeve and use a small pointed instrument to depress the release tag before pulling the wire off the terminal.

3   Unscrew the starter motor-to-transmission upper bolt, disconnecting the engine/transmission earth lead (photo).

4   Jack up the front of the car and support it securely on axle stands (see *'Jacking, towing and wheel changing'*).

5   Unbolt the starter motor support bracket (where fitted) from the transmission (photo).

6   Remove the two remaining starter motor-to-transmission bolts and withdraw the motor (photo).

7   If the motor is to be exchanged or renewed, remove the support bracket (where fitted).

Refitting

8   Refitting is the reverse of the removal procedure; tighten all bolts and nuts to their specified torque wrench settings.

10 Starter motor – brush and solenoid renewal

General

1   While it is physically possible to remove the solenoid and brushes with the starter motor in place on the car, owners are advised to remove the starter (Sec 9) so that it can be serviced in clean working conditions.

9.3 Starter motor-to-transmission upper bolt also secures engine earth lead

9.5 Starter motor support bracket-to-transmission bolts 'A', starter motor-to-transmission lower bolts 'B'

9.6 Removing the starter motor

Fig. 12.2 Exploded view of Lucas M79 starter motor (Sec 10)

1	Solenoid and plunger	7	Jump ring and thrust collar
2	Commutator end bracket assembly	8	Drive pinion assembly
3	Positive brushes and bus bar	9	Field coils and yoke
4	Negative brushes and brushbox	10	Drive end bush
5	Engaging lever pivot and grommet	11	Commutator end bush
6	Armature		

12	Motor drive end bracket
13	Plastic insulating plate
14	Commutator end bracket
15	C-clip and thrustwashers
16	Cover and gasket

Brushes

Removal

2   Undo the two screws and remove the cover and gasket from the commutator end bracket, then prise out the C-clip and withdraw any thrustwashers fitted (photo).

3   Noting the alignment marks between the end bracket or grommet and the yoke, unscrew the two retaining screws and withdraw the end bracket (photos).

4   Release the brush springs and withdraw the negative brushes, then unscrew the nut securing the positive brush lead to the solenoid terminal. Remove the brushbox, withdraw the plastic insulating plate and remove the positive brushes complete with the bus bar (photos).

5   In most cases the brushes will have wear limit marks in the form of a groove etched along one face of each brush; when the brushes are worn down to these marks, they are worn out and must be renewed (photo). If no marks are provided, measure the length of each brush. No dimension is given by Rover but as a rough guide 3.5 mm should be regarded as a minimum. If any brush is worn below this amount, renew the brushes as a set. If the brushes are still serviceable, clean them with a solvent-moistened cloth. Check that the brush spring pressure is equal for all brushes and holds the brushes securely against the commutator. If in doubt about the condition of the brushes and springs compare them with new components.

10.2 Removing the commutator end bracket cover – note the gasket

10.3A Note alignment marks between yoke and grommet ...

10.3B ... remove retaining screws ...

10.3C ... and withdraw commutator end bracket

10.4A Removing plastic insulating plate

10.4B Releasing brush springs

10.4C Removing positive brushes and bus bar from brushbox

10.5 Measuring length of starter motor brushes – note wear limit groove

6   Clean the commutator with a solvent-moistened cloth, then check for signs of scoring, burning, excessive wear or severe pitting. If worn or damaged, the commutator should be attended to by an auto-electrician.

Refitting

7   On refitting, place the bus bar on the brushbox, then fit the brushes and insulating plate, insert the negative brushes and fit the clips.
8   Fit the brushbox assembly to the commutator and fit the brush springs. Check that the brushes are free to move in their holders against spring pressure, then refit the commutator end bracket over the springs, engaging it with the grommet, align the marks noted on removal and tighten the retaining screws securely.
9   Refit the thrustwashers and C-clip, the gasket and the cover, tightening the two screws securely. Connect the positive brush lead to the solenoid terminal and tighten the nut securely.

Solenoid

Removal

10   Unscrew the nut, noting the lockwasher(s) and disconnect the motor (positive brush) lead from the solenoid terminal (photo).
11   Unscrew the two bolts securing the solenoid to the motor drive end bracket (photo).
12   Release the solenoid plunger from the starter engaging lever, then withdraw the solenoid, noting the spring (photo).

Refitting

13   Refitting is the reverse of the removal procedure. Clean the solenoid, its plunger and the motor/solenoid mating surfaces carefully and lubricate the plunger/starter engaging lever surfaces with a smear of grease (Rover recommend Shell Alvania).

11   Fuses, fusible links and relays – general information

Fuses

1   The fusebox is located in the passenger compartment, on the right-hand end of the facia.
2   Access is gained by using a coin to turn the two fasteners through quarter of a turn, then unhooking the cover's bottom edge from the facia. Symbols on the reverse of the cover indicate the circuits protected by the fuses and four spare fuses are supplied together with plastic tweezers to remove and fit them (photo). Further details on fuse ratings and circuits protected are given in the Specifications section of this Chapter.

10.10 Unscrew nut to disconnect motor (positive brush) lead from solenoid terminal

10.11 Unscrewing solenoid retaining bolts (one arrowed)

10.12 Removing solenoid from starter engaging lever

11.2 Symbols on fusebox cover indicate circuits protected – see Specifications for full details

11.3 Removing a fuse

11.11 Unclip box cover to expose fusible links

3   To remove a fuse, first switch off the circuit concerned (or the ignition), then fit the tweezers and pull the fuse out of its terminals (photo). Slide the fuse sideways from the tweezers. The wire within the fuse is clearly visible; if the fuse is blown it will be broken or melted.

4   Always renew a fuse with one of an identical rating; never use a fuse with a different rating from the original or substitute anything else. Never renew a fuse more than once without tracing the source of the trouble. The fuse rating is stamped on top of the fuse; note that the fuses are also colour-coded for easy recognition.

5   If a new fuse blows immediately, find the cause before renewing it again; a short to earth as a result of faulty insulation is most likely. Where a fuse protects more than one circuit, try to isolate the defect by switching on each circuit in turn (if possible) until the fuse blows again.

6   If any of the spare fuses are used, always replace them immediately so that a spare of each rating is available.

Fusebox

7   To remove the fusebox, disconnect the battery negative lead, then remove the fusebox cover from the facia.

8   Unplug the two connector plugs from the top row of the fusebox panel (marked 'IGN' and 'FACIA') and unplug the two connector plugs clipped to brackets at the left-hand end of the panel.

9   Unscrew the two bolts securing the panel, then lower it until the eight connector plugs can be disconnected from the panel's reverse (front) face. The wiring is complex but the connector locations are clearly marked on the panel; make careful notes as to the connections before disconnecting any of the wires. Remove the panel.

10   Refitting is the reverse of the removal procedure; ensure that the wiring is correctly reconnected and routed.

Fusible links

11   The fusible link box is located in the engine compartment, on the body left-hand side member next to the battery; unclip the box cover to expose the links (photo).

12   Details of link ratings and circuits protected are given in the Specifications Section of this Chapter; the links are numbered from front to rear.

13   Since the fusible links are almost identical to the fuses in form and function, refer to paragraphs 3 to 6 above for details of removal and refitting, noting that the links must be extracted and installed by hand, as a removal tool is not provided.

14   **Note:** *A blown fusible link indicates a serious wiring or system fault which must be diagnosed before the link is renewed.*

Relays

15   The Specifications Section of this Chapter gives full information on the location and function of the various relays fitted; refer to the relevant wiring diagram for details of wiring connections.

16   A relay is an electrically operated switch that is used for the following reasons.

(a)   *A relay can switch a heavy current at a distance, thus allowing the use of lighter gauge wiring and switch contacts.*

(b)   *A relay can receive more than one control input, unlike a mechanical switch.*

(c)   *A relay can have a 'timer' function – eg the windscreen or rear window wiper relays.*

17   If a circuit or system controlled by a relay develops a fault and the relay is suspect, operate the system; if the relay is functioning it should be possible to hear it click as it is energized. If this is the case the fault lies with the components or wiring of the system. If the relay is not being energized then either the relay is not receiving a main supply or a switching voltage or the relay itself is faulty. Testing is by the substitution of a known good unit but be careful; while some relays are identical in appearance and in operation, others look similar but perform different functions.

18   To renew a relay, disconnect the battery, then simply pull direct from the socket and press in the new relay. Reconnect the battery on completion (photos).

19   On models with fuel-injected engines, certain relays are contained in the relay module attached to the fuel-injection/ignition system ECU. To remove this, disconnect its two connector plugs, release the clip and slide it back to withdraw it from the mounting bracket (photos). The complete module must be renewed, even if only one of the relays is faulty.

11.18A Relays on fusebox panel rear face:

A Interior lamp delay/Lamps-on alarm unit
B Heated rear window relay
C Headlamp relay
D Ignition relay
E Electric front window/auxiliary relay
F Direction indicator/hazard warning relay
G Dim-dip unit

11.18B Relays on fusebox panel front (reverse) face:

A Windscreen wiper relay
B Rear window wiper relay

11.19A Unplug connectors (arrows) to disconnect relay module wiring ...

11.19B ... and release clip (arrow) to separate module from mounting bracket

12 Switches – removal and refitting

Note: *Disconnect the battery negative lead before removing any switch, and reconnect the lead after refitting the switch*

Ignition switch
1   Refer to Chapter 10, Section 27, for details of switch removal and refitting. A Rover dealer will be able to tell you whether the switch can be obtained separately from the steering lock.

Steering column multi-function switches
Removal
2   Remove the steering wheel and steering column nacelle, then disconnect the switch wiring as described in Chapter 10, Section 26, paragraphs 1 to 4 (photo).

3   Each individual multi-function switch can be removed by pressing together its retaining tongues and sliding the switch out of the housing (photo).

4   To remove the complete assembly, mark the location on the column of the switch centre housing, then slacken (but do not remove) the housing clamp screw and withdraw the assembly (photo).

Refitting
5   Refitting is the reverse of the removal procedure; position the housing at its marked height and ensure that it is correctly located. Tighten the clamp screw securely, until the housing is firmly clamped to the column, but do not overtighten it.

12.2 Press together locking tabs to disconnect multi-function switch wiring

12.3 Multi-function switches can be removed individually ...

12.4 ... or as a complete unit, by slackening clamp screw

12.7 Removing a switch from the instrument panel cowl – showing locking tabs

12.8 Prise off heater blower switch knob to expose switch retaining nut

12.10 Hazard warning switch is part of multi-function switch assembly

Instrument panel switches

Removal

6   The rear foglamp, heated rear window, rear window wiper and rear window wash/wipe switches are removed as follows

7   Check that the switch is in the 'off' position, then taking great care not to scratch or damage the switch or its surround, prise it out of the instrument panel cowl until the connector plug can be reached to disconnect it (photo). Note: *If a switch cannot be removed without risk of damage, remove the instrument panel cowl (Sec 19), disconnect the switch wiring and push the switch out from behind; this latter method is preferred as it minimises the risk of damage.*

8   To remove the heater blower switch, remove the instrument panel cowl (Sec 19) and disconnect the switch wiring. Prise off the switch knob and unscrew the retaining nut to release the switch (photo).

Refitting

9   Refitting is the reverse of the removal procedure.

Hazard warning switch

10   The switch is part of the left-hand multi-function switch; refer to paragraphs 2 to 5 above (photo).

Glovebox lamp switch

Removal

11   Open the glovebox lid.

12   Taking great care not to scratch or damage the switch or its surround, prise the switch out of the glovebox until the connectors can be removed to disconnect it (photo).

Refitting

13   Refitting is the reverse of the removal procedure.

Choke switch

Removal

14   Remove the ashtray and disconnect the switch wire from the

choke cable, then prise out the clip securing the cable to the facia and withdraw the cable until the switch can be removed from it.

Refitting

15   Refitting is the reverse of the removal procedure.

Electric front window switches

Removal

16   Remove the seven screws securing the door pocket to the door and withdraw the pocket until the switch connectors can be unplugged to disconnect the wiring (photos).

17   Remove the two screws to release the switch bracket, then release the switch from the bracket.

Refitting

18   Refitting is the reverse of the removal procedure.

Interior lamp switches

19   The interior lamp is controlled by a switch mounted in each (front) door pillar and by a switch in the lamp assembly itself (photo).

20   To remove a door pillar switch, remove its retaining screw and ease the switch out of the pillar, then disconnect the switch wire, taking care not to allow it to drop back into the pillar; refitting is the reverse of the removal procedure.

21   The roof-mounted switch is part of the lamp assembly; refer to Section 18 of this Chapter for details of removal and refitting.

Luggage compartment lamp switch

22   The switch consists of two contacts which are part of the tailgate latch assembly; refer to Chapter 11, Section 14.

Oil pressure switch

Removal

23   The switch is screwed into the oil filter adaptor (photo). Access is extremely awkward; either remove the switch working from

12.12 Removing glovebox lamp switch

12.16A Door pocket retaining screw locations (arrows)

12.16B Electric front window switch mounting screws (arrows)

12.19 Interior lamp door pillar switch

12.23 Oil pressure switch (arrow)

12.31 Location of throttle pedal switch (arrow)

underneath, with the car raised and supported on axle stands, or partially remove the alternator (Sec 6) so that the switch can be removed from above.

24   Release the wire clip and disconnect the switch wiring connector plug, then unscrew the switch; use clean rag to pack the opening in the adaptor, to minimise the loss of oil.

Refitting

25   On refitting, clean the switch threads and renew the sealing washer, if one is fitted; if a sealing washer is not fitted, apply a thin smear of suitable sealant to the threads.

26   Remove the packing rag and screw in the switch; tighten it securely but do not overtighten it; note the specified torque wrench setting.

Electric cooling fan thermostatic switch

27   Refer to Chapter 3, Section 6 for details of switch removal, refitting and testing.

Throttle pedal switch

Removal

28   Remove the throttle pedal (Chapter 4).

29   Disconnect the switch wiring by unplugging the connector and releasing it from its bracket, then unclip the wiring from its stud.

30   Prise out the C-clip securing the switch to its bracket, then withdraw the switch, noting the wave washer.

Refitting

31   Refitting is the reverse of the removal procedure; ensure that the wiring is routed correctly and secured clear of the pedals (photo).

Fuel cut-off inertia switch

Testing

32   If the switch is thought to be faulty, unplug its connector and bridge the connector's terminals on the wiring harness side, then switch on the ignition; if the fuel pump then works, the switch is proven faulty and must be renewed (photo).

Removal

33   Remove the two screws securing the switch to the body left-hand side member, withdraw the switch and unplug its connector to disconnect the wiring.

Refitting

34   Refitting is the reverse of the removal procedure; ensure that the switch is set before attempting to start the engine.

Inlet manifold pre-heater temperature switch

35   Refer to Chapter 3, Section 6 for details of switch removal, refitting and testing.

Reversing lamp switch

36   Refer to Chapter 7, Section 7 for details of switch removal, refitting and testing.

Stop-lamp switch

37   Refer to Chapter 9, Section 23 for details of switch removal, refitting and testing.

Handbrake switch

38   Refer to Chapter 9, Section 23 for details of switch removal, refitting and testing.

13   Bulbs (exterior lamps) – renewal

General

1   Whenever a bulb is renewed, note the following points.

    (a)   Disconnect the battery negative lead before starting work.
    (b)   Remember that if the lamp has just been in use the bulb may be extremely hot.

12.32 Fuel cut-off inertia switch is mounted on left-hand body side member

13.3 Remove rubber cover and unplug headlamp connector, then release retainer (arrows) to remove bulb

13.8 Removing front sidelamp bulbholder from headlamp unit

13.11 Pull wire ring to release spring clip ...

13.12 ... so that lamp unit can be removed from car and bulbholder detached

13.15 Direction indicator side repeater lamp detached from front wing

(c)   Always check the bulb contacts and holder, ensuring that there is clean metal-to-metal contact between the bulb and its live(s) and earth. Clean off any corrosion or dirt before fitting a new bulb.

(d)   Wherever bayonet-type bulbs are fitted (see Specifications) ensure that the live contact(s) bear firmly against the bulb contact.

(e)   Always ensure that the new bulb is of the correct rating and that it is completely clean before fitting it; this applies particularly to headlamp bulbs (see below).

Headlamp

2   Working in the engine compartment, unclip the black rubber cover from the rear of the lamp unit.

3   Unplug the wiring connector, then press together the ears of the wire retainer to release it from the rear of the bulbholder (photo).

4   Withdraw the bulb.

5   When handling the new bulb, use a tissue or clean cloth to avoid touching the glass with the fingers; moisture and grease from the skin can cause blackening and rapid failure of this type of bulb. If the glass is accidentally touched, wipe it clean using methylated spirit.

6   Refitting is the reverse of the removal procedure; ensure that the new bulb's locating tabs align with the reflector slots.

Front sidelamp

7   Working in the engine compartment, unclip the black rubber cover from the rear of the headlamp unit.

8   Pull the bulbholder from the headlamp reflector (photo).

9   Pull the capless (wedge-type) bulb out of its socket.

10   Refitting is the reverse of the removal procedure.

Front direction indicator

11   Working in the engine compartment next to the appropriate headlamp unit, pull the wire ring to release the indicator lamp unit, then pull it forwards, clear of the car (photo).

12   Twist the bulbholder anti-clockwise to remove it from the rear of the lamp unit (photo). Press the bulb into the holder, twist anti-clockwise and remove.

13.18 Unscrew plastic wing nuts (one arrowed) ...

13.19 ... so that rear lamp cluster can be detached from car and bulbholders removed

13.23 Remove two lens screws and withdraw lens ...

13.24 ... to renew rear foglamp bulb

13.25 Number plate lamps are secured by two screws

14.2 Removing interior lamp assembly from roof console

14.5 Glovebox lamp unit is clipped to glovebox ceiling

14.8 Unclip luggage compartment lamp unit to remove bulb

13   Refitting is the reverse of the removal procedure.

Direction indicator side repeater

14   Looking at the lamp unit from the side of the car, push it to the right to release it, then withdraw it from the wing.
15   Twist the bulbholder anti-clockwise and remove it from the lamp unit (photo).
16   Pull the capless (wedge-type) bulb out of its socket.
17   Refitting is the reverse of the removal procedure.

Rear lamp cluster

18   Open the tailgate and unscrew the two plastic wing nuts securing the rear lamp cluster (photo).
19   Pull the lamp cluster clear of the car, unplugging the wiring connector if the extra clearance is required, then twist the bulbholder anti-clockwise to release it from the lamp unit (photo).
20   All bulbs are bayonet-fitting; press the bulb into its holder, twist anti-clockwise and remove.
21   Refitting is the reverse of the removal procedure.

Rear foglamp

22   **Note:** *Only the right-hand foglamp unit contains a bulb and fittings; the other is a dummy that is clipped into the rear bumper cover.*
23   Remove the two screws securing the lamp lens, then withdraw the lens (photo).
24   The bulb is bayonet-fitting; press the bulb into its holder, twist anti-clockwise and remove (photo).

Number plate lamp

25   Remove the two screws securing the lamp unit, then withdraw the lamp unit (photo).
26   The bulb is a festoon type which is prised out of its spring contacts.
27   Refitting is the reverse of the removal procedure, but ensure that the contacts are sufficiently tensioned to hold the bulb firmly.

14   Bulbs (interior lamps) – renewal

General

1   Refer to Section 13, paragraph 1.

Interior lamp

2   Unclip the lamp unit by using a small flat-bladed screwdriver to prise it out of the roof console (photo).
3   The bulb is a bayonet-fitting; press the bulb into its holder, twist anti-clockwise and remove.
4   Refitting is the reverse of the removal procedure.

Glovebox lamp

5   Unclip the lamp unit by using a small flat-bladed screwdriver to prise it out of the ceiling of the glovebox (photo).
6   The bulb is a festoon type which is prised out of its spring contacts.
7   Refitting is the reverse of the removal procedure, but ensure that the contacts are sufficiently tensioned to hold the bulb firmly.

Luggage compartment lamp

8   Disconnecting the lamp's wiring if necessary to improve access, unclip the lamp unit from its mounting bracket (photo).
9   The bulb is a bayonet-fitting; press the bulb into its holder, twist anti-clockwise and remove.
10   Refitting is the reverse of the removal procedure.

Instrument panel illumination and warning lamps

11   Remove the instrument panel (Sec 19).
12   Twist the bulbholder anti-clockwise and withdraw it from the rear of the panel; see also Fig. 12.4 or 5, as appropriate (photos).
13   In some cases the bulbs are integral with their holders, but in others the bulbs can be renewed separately; seek the advice of a Rover dealer. Be very careful to ensure that the new bulbs are of the correct

14.12A Removing a bulbholder from the rear of the instrument panel

14.12B Removing a panel illuminating bulb from the instrument panel

14.15 Heater control panel illuminating bulb

14.18 Cigar lighter illuminating bulb

rating, the same as those removed; this is especially important in the case of the ignition/battery charging warning lamp.
14   Refitting is the reverse of the removal procedure.

Heater control panel illumination

15   Remove the control panel (Chapter 3, Section 10); the bulb can then be unplugged from the panel (photo).
16   No information is available at the time of writing as to the bulb's fitting or wattage; seek the advice of a Rover dealer.
17   Refitting is the reverse of the removal procedure.

Cigar lighter illumination

18   The bulb is secured in a container that is clipped to the side of the cigar lighter assembly (photo).
19   Remove the cigar lighter (Sec 22).
20   Unplug the bulbholder to remove it from the lighter body. No information is available at the time of writing as to the bulb's fitting or wattage; seek the advice of a Rover dealer.
21   Refitting is the reverse of the removal procedure.

Hazard warning indicator

22   Remove the red plastic cover and pull the capless (wedge-type) bulb out of its holder.
23   Refitting is the reverse of the removal procedure.

Switch illumination

24   The rear foglamp, heated rear window, heater blower, rear window wiper, rear window wash/wipe and electric window switches are fitted with an illuminating bulb; some are also fitted with warning bulbs to show when the circuit concerned is operating.
25   Each switch is removed and refitted as described in Section 12 of this Chapter; no information is available at the time of writing as to whether the bulb can be renewed separately from the switch or not. Seek the advice of a Rover dealer.

15   Exterior lamp units – removal and refitting

Headlamp unit

Removal

1   Either unclip the black rubber cover from the rear of the lamp unit, pull off the headlamp bulb wiring connector and unplug the sidelamp bulbholder (Sec 13), or disconnect all lamp unit wiring by unplugging its connector.
2   Remove the direction indicator lamp unit; refer to Section 13, paragraphs 11 and 12.
3   Unscrew the three nuts securing the headlamp unit and remove it (photo).
4   Release the six retaining clips to remove the headlamp lens, if required (photo).

Refitting

5   Refitting is the reverse of the removal procedure; check and adjust if necessary the headlamp aim (Sec 16).

Front direction indicator

6   Refer to Section 13, paragraphs 11 to 13.

Direction indicator side repeater

7   Refer to Section 13, paragraphs 14 and 15.

Rear lamp cluster

8   Refer to Section 13, paragraphs 18 and 19.

Rear foglamp

Removal

9   Remove the rear bumper (Chapter 11, Section 5). Remove the two retaining screws to release the lamp unit from the bumper cover (photo).

Refitting

10   Refitting is the reverse of the removal procedure.

15.3 Removing headlamp unit securing nuts (other two arrowed)

15.4 Headlamp lens is secured by clips – release as shown

15.9 Rear foglamp is secured by two screws (arrows) to rear bumper cover

Number plate lamps

11   Refer to Section 13, paragraph 25; disconnect its wires to release the lamp.

16   Headlamp beam alignment – general information

1   It is advisable to have the headlamp beam alignment checked and if necessary adjusted by a Rover dealer using optical beam setting equipment. Correct alignment of the headlamp beams is most important, not only to ensure good vision for the driver but also to protect other drivers from being dazzled.
2   The headlamp beam height may be adjusted to compensate for the load being carried by turning the white plastic knob on the rear of each headlamp unit. The normal setting is with the knobs turned (anti-clockwise) to the left; if a heavy load is carried the headlamp beams should be lowered to compensate by turning both knobs fully (clockwise) to the right. Ensure that both knobs are in the same position at all times and in the correct position for the load being carried (photo).
3   In an emergency, adjustment of the headlamps may be made by turning the adjuster screws on the rear of each headlamp unit. The upper screws (inside the plastic knobs) are for vertical adjustment and the lower screws for lateral adjustment (photo).
4   The car should be at kerb weight (see *'General dimensions and weights'*), with the driver seated, the headlamp height-setting knobs in the normal-load position (turned to the left, as described above), the tyres correctly inflated and the suspension ride heights correctly set (Chapter 10). Park the vehicle on level ground, approximately 5 metres (16 feet) in front of a flat wall or garage door and bounce it to settle the suspension.
5   Draw a vertical line on the wall or door corresponding to the centre-line of the car. (This can be determined by marking with crayon the centres of the windscreen and rear window, then viewing the wall or door from the rear of the car).

Fig. 12.3 Headlamp beam alignment chart (Sec 16)

A   Distance between
    headlamp centres
B   Light/dark boundary
C   Dipped beam centre
D   Dipped beam pattern

H   Height from ground to
    headlamp centre
O   Car's centre-line
X = 65 mm (2.5 in)

6   With the centre-line established, construct the other lines shown in Fig. 12.3.
7   Switch the headlamps on to dipped beam. Cover one headlamp with cloth. Working on the other lamp, use its two adjuster screws to bring the centre of the beam to the point 'C' on the appropriate side of the alignment chart.
8   Transfer the cloth to the adjusted headlamp and repeat the adjustment on the other.

16.2 Headlamp height-setting plastic knob (in normal-load position), with vertical alignment adjuster screw inside

16.3 Headlamp lateral alignment adjuster screw (arrow)

17.1 Dim-dip resistor (seen with front wheel arch liner removed)

19.3A Location of instrument panel cowl retaining screws (arrows)

19.3B Note connections before disconnecting switches to release cowl

19.4 Location of instrument panel retaining screws (arrows)

19.5 Showing disconnection of speedometer drive cable (panel partly removed for clarity)

19.6 Disconnecting instrument panel wiring connectors

9   While this will produce an acceptable setting, it is important to have accurate adjustments made at the earliest opportunity.

17   Dim-dip system – general information

1   The system comprises the dim-dip unit mounted on the fusebox panel (Sec 11) and a resistor bolted to the right-hand inner wing panel; remove the front wheel arch liner (Chapter 11, Section 8) to reach the resistor (photo).

2   The dim-dip unit is supplied with current from the sidelamp circuit and energised by a feed from the ignition switch. When energised, the unit allows battery voltage (via fusible link number 3 and fuse number 20) to pass through the (1 ohm) resistor to fuses number 24 and 25 controlling the headlamp dipped-beam circuits; this lights the headlamps with approximately one-sixth of their normal power so that the car cannot be driven using sidelamps alone.

18   Interior lamp units – removal and refitting

Interior lamp

1   Refer to Section 14, paragraph 2; disconnect the switch and lamp wires to remove the lamp unit, having taken note of their connections.

Glovebox lamp

2   Refer to Section 14, paragraph 5; disconnect the wires to remove the lamp unit.

Luggage compartment lamp

3   Refer to Section 14, paragraph 8; peel back the interior trim panel and remove the two screws to release the lamp mounting bracket.

19   Instrument panel – removal and refitting

Removal

1   Disconnect the battery negative lead.
2   Remove the steering wheel (Chapter 10, Section 25).
3   Remove the five retaining screws and withdraw the instrument panel cowl. Take note of the various switch connections before disconnecting them. Remove the cowl (photos).
4   Remove the four screws securing the panel (photo).
5   Disconnect the speedometer drive cable from the rear of the instrument panel (Sec 21) (photo).
6   Carefully pull the panel into the passenger compartment until the two connector plugs can be disconnected and the panel can be removed (photo).

Refitting

7   Refitting is the reverse of the removal procedure.

20   Instrument panel components – removal and refitting

General

1   Remove the instrument panel (Sec 19), then proceed as described in the relevant sub-section below.

Instruments

Testing

2   Refer to Chapter 3, Section 6 for details of tests of the coolant temperature gauge circuit. Some models are fitted with a high temperature warning lamp (actually an LED) to reinforce the warning if

**Fig. 12.4 Instrument panel components –
models without tachometer (Sec 20)**

1   Panel illuminating bulb
2   Direction indicator warning
    lamps
3   Main beam warning lamp
4   Oil pressure warning lamp
5   Sidelamp warning lamp
6   Trailer direction indicator
    warning lamp (where fitted)
7   Choke warning lamp –
    carburettor-engined models
8   Ignition/battery charging
    warning lamp
9   Brake warning lamp
10 Printed circuit
11 Ignition/battery charging
    warning lamp resistor
12 Trip control knob
13 Panel window
14 Panel faceplate
15 Panel illumination board
16 Panel illuminating bulb
    wiring harness
17 Panel (front) illuminating
    bulbs
18 Fuel and temperature gauge
    unit
19 Warning lamp panel
20 Speedometer
21 Panel housing
Note: The clock (where fitted) is
similar to that shown in Fig. 12.5

the coolant temperature rises to too high a level. The components of
this sub-system are not available separately; a fault in the sub-system
can be cured only by renewing the gauge unit or the printed circuit.
3   Refer to Chapter 4, Section 5 for details of tests of the fuel gauge
circuit. Some models are fitted with a low fuel warning lamp (actually an
LED) to reinforce the warning if the fuel level falls to too low a point. The
components of this sub-system are not available separately; a fault in
the sub-system can be cured only by renewing the gauge unit or the
printed circuit.

Removal

4   To remove either instrument, proceed as described below, referring
to Fig. 12.6 or 12.7, as appropriate, for details.
5   Remove the panel illuminating bulbs (Sec 14) and unclip the
illuminating bulb wiring harness from the panel housing, then release
the six clips and separate the panel window and faceplate from the
housing.
6   Remove the screws retaining the unit to be removed and withdraw it.

Refitting

7   Refitting is the reverse of the removal procedure.

Digital clock

Removal

8   Refer to Fig. 12.8 or 12.9, as appropriate, for details.
9   Remove the panel illuminating bulbs (Sec 14) and unclip the
illuminating bulb wiring harness from the panel housing, then release
the six clips and separate the panel window and faceplate from the
housing.
10   Remove the speedometer and the fuel/temperature gauge (and
tachometer, where fitted) unit (see above).
11   Remove the warning lamp panel.
12   Remove the retaining screws and withdraw the clock.

Refitting

13   Refitting is the reverse of the removal procedure.

Fig. 12.5 Instrument panel components – models with tachometer (Sec 20)

1   Panel illuminating bulb
2   Direction indicator warning lamps
3   Main beam warning lamp
4   Oil pressure warning lamp
5   Sidelamp warning lamp
6   Trailer direction indicator warning lamp (where fitted)
7   Choke warning lamp – carburettor-engined models
8   Ignition/battery charging warning lamp
9   Brake warning lamp
10 Printed circuit
11 Ignition/battery charging warning lamp resistor
12 Trip control knob
13 Panel window
14 Panel faceplate
15 Panel illumination board
16 Panel illuminating bulb wiring harness
17 Panel (front) illuminating bulbs
18 Fuel/temperature gauge and tachometer unit
19 Warning lamp panel
20 Speedometer
21 Digital clock
22 Panel housing

Printed circuit

Removal

14   Refer to Fig. 12.6, 12.7, 12.8 or 12.9, as appropriate, for details.
15   Remove all panel illuminating and warning lamp bulbs from the rear of the panel (Sec 14).
16   Remove the screws retaining the clock (where fitted) and the fuel/temperature gauge (and tachometer, where fitted) unit; see above.
17   Release the ignition/battery charging warning lamp resistor.
18   Release the printed circuit from its locating pins and withdraw it.

Refitting

19   Refitting is the reverse of the removal procedure.

Voltage stabilizer

20   The voltage stabiliser is an integral part of the printed circuit.

21   Speedometer drive cable – removal and refitting

General

1   The drive cable is in two parts; the lower cable runs from the transmission to a point just in front of the clutch release lever, while the upper cable runs from that point to the rear of the instrument panel.

Upper cable

Removal

2   Open the bonnet and unscrew the nut securing the cable upper-to-lower sections, then release the upper cable from any clamps or ties securing it (photo).
3   Working inside the passenger compartment, release its retaining

Fig. 12.6 Speedometer and fuel/temperature gauge unit mountings – models without tachometer (Sec 20)

1 Speedometer retaining screws
2 Fuel/temperature gauge unit
3 Fuel/temperature gauge unit retaining screws

Fig. 12.7 Speedometer and fuel/temperature gauge and tachometer unit mountings (Sec 20)

1 Speedometer retaining screws
2 Fuel/temperature gauge and tachometer unit
3 Fuel/temperature gauge and tachometer unit retaining screws

Fig. 12.8 Printed circuit and clock mountings – models without tachometer (Sec 20)

1 Printed circuit
2 Ignition/battery charging warning lamp resistor
3 Clock retaining screws
4 Fuel/temperature gauge unit retaining screws

Fig. 12.9 Printed circuit and clock mountings – models with tachometer (Sec 20)

1 Printed circuit
2 Ignition/battery charging warning lamp resistor
3 Clock retaining screws
4 Fuel/temperature gauge and tachometer unit retaining screws

fasteners and withdraw the fusebox cover.

4 Reaching up inside the fusebox aperture, depress the locking prong to disconnect the cable from the speedometer (photo).

5 Prise the sealing grommet out of the bulkhead and withdraw the cable into the engine compartment.

Refitting

6 Refitting is the reverse of the removal procedure; press the cable

upper end onto the speedometer boss to secure it. Do not overtighten the upper-to-lower cable nut; note the specified torque wrench setting.

Lower cable

Removal

7 Open the bonnet and unscrew the nut securing the cable upper-to-lower sections.

21.2 Unscrew nut to disconnect speedometer drive upper and lower cables

21.4 Speedometer drive upper cable attachment to speedometer – seen through fusebox aperture

21.9 Speedometer drive cable lower end secured by rubber dowel

21.10 Ensure dowel is fully engaged on refitting

22.2A Release clips to extract cigar lighter metal surround ...

22.2B ... then withdraw plastic body with illuminating bulb

8   Jack up the front of the car and support it securely on axle stands (see *'Jacking, towing and wheel changing'*).
9   Using a long-nosed pair of pliers, reach up above the right-hand side of the exhaust system front silencer and extract the rubber dowel retaining the cable lower end in the speedometer drive housing (photo). Withdraw the cable from above.

Refitting

10   Refitting is the reverse of the removal procedure; renew the sealing O-rings if they are worn or damaged, grease the cable lower end and ensure that the rubber dowel is fully engaged in the speedometer drive housing (photo).

22   Cigar lighter – removal and refitting

Removal

1   Disconnect the battery negative lead.
2   Remove the lighter element, then release its clips and remove the metal surround, followed by the plastic body. Note the wiring connections before disconnecting and do not allow the wiring to fall back inside the facia once disconnected (photos).

Refitting

3   Refitting is the reverse of the removal procedure.

23   Clock – removal and refitting

Refer to Sections 19 and 20.

24   Horn – removal and refitting

Removal

1   Disconnect the battery negative lead.
2   Disconnect the horn wire and unbolt the horn from the body (photo).

Refitting

3   Refitting is the reverse of the removal procedure.

25   Heater blower motor circuit – general information

1   The heating and ventilating system's blower motor is controlled by a switch mounted in the instrument panel. The blower fan and its motor

24.2 Location of horn

are mounted in the engine compartment, in the heater air inlet/blower motor assembly.
2   The blower motor is regulated to any one of three speeds by switching in elements of a resistor unit which is mounted on the heater air inlet/blower motor assembly. The circuit is supplied with current via fuse number 14 and the ignition relay.
3   Switch removal and refitting is described in Section 12 of this Chapter. Refer to Chapter 3, Section 8 for details of removal and refitting of all other components.

26   Heated rear window – general information

1   The rear window is heated by passing current through a resistive grid bonded to the inside of the glass.
2   The heater elements are fragile and the following precautions should be observed.

   (a)   *Do not allow luggage or other items to rub against the inside surface of the glass.*
   (b)   *Do not stick labels over the elements.*
   (c)   *Avoid scratching the elements when cleaning with rings on the fingers.*
   (d)   *Clean the glass with water and detergent only and rub in the direction of the elements using a soft cloth or chamois leather.*

3   Should an element be damaged so that the current is interrupted, a repair can be made using one of the conductive paints available from motor accessory shops.
4   Note that the system draws a very high current and therefore has its

own relay, the energising circuit of which is fed via fuse number 9. Operating the switch earths the circuit to energise the relay. A supply is then drawn via fusible link number 2 and fuse number 11 to feed the element and the switch warning lamp.

27   Electric front windows – general information

1   Refer to Chapter 11, Section 19 for an outline of the system's operation and of regulator and motor assembly removal and refitting.
2   The system consists of the relay, the two door switches and the regulator/motor assemblies. The relay is energised by a feed from fusible link number 1 and the ignition switch; with the relay energised, battery voltage is supplied via fusible link number 2, through the relay and fuse number 13 to the door switches. Both motors and the passenger door switch are earthed via the driver's door switch.
3   When a switch is pressed forwards to the 'down' position, power is fed to the motor so that it rotates and operates the regulator to lower the window glass. When the switch is pressed rearwards to the 'up' position, the feed's polarity is reversed so that the motor rotates in the opposite direction and the window glass is raised.
4   If the system fails completely, check the fuse, the fusible links and the feed to the relay, then check the driver's door switch earth return. If no fault is found check the relay by substituting a new one.
5   If one window fails to operate and the above checks fail to cure the fault, check the feeds to both door switches, then check the motor feed and earth, first when the 'up' switch is pressed, then when the 'down' switch is pressed. If the switches and wiring prove sound, the motor is probably faulty and must be renewed with the regulator assembly; if the switches are suspect, check them by substitution.

28   Central locking system – general information

1   The system's operation is outlined in Chapter 11, Section 17. Details of removal and refitting of the system's components are given in Chapter 11, Section 14 for the tailgate and Section 16 for the doors.
2   The system is supplied with current via fusible link number 2 and fuse number 12 to the control unit; both the feed and earth return of the other motors in the system are through the control unit.
3   On operation of the driver's door lock, the system is triggered by the control unit mounted in the driver's door, which sends full battery voltage, in the form of a short pulse, to the other door motor(s) and the tailgate motor. When the system is locked, the polarity of the pulse is such that the motor solenoids are extended, while on unlocking the polarity is reversed so that the solenoids retract.
4   If the system fails to work, check first that full battery voltage is available at the control unit and that the unit's earth is sound; if no fault is found, test the control unit by substituting a new component.
5   If an individual lock fails to operate, check that the wiring is sound between the control unit and the faulty motor; again, the motors can be tested only by substitution.

29   Lamps-on warning system – general information

1   If any exterior lamps are left on after the ignition has been switched off, a warning buzzer will sound as soon as either front door is opened; the buzzer will cease as soon as the door is closed or the lamps are switched off.
2   The system is fed via fuse number 12 and is controlled, with the interior lamp door pillar switches, by the interior lamp delay/lamps-on alarm unit mounted in the fusebox panel (Sec 11).

30   Wiper arms – removal and refitting

Removal

1   Before removing a wiper arm, stick a piece of masking tape on the glass, along the blade, to aid arm alignment on refitting.
2   To remove a wiper arm, pull the arm fully away from the glass until it locks; remove the blade only if required (Chapter 1).
3   Flip up the cover to reveal the wiper-to-spindle nut. If removing the rear window wiper arm, withdraw the washer jet (photo).
4   Unscrew the wiper arm-to-spindle nut and pull the arm from the spindle splines (photo). If necessary use a large screwdriver blade to prise off the arm.
5   Clean the splines of the arm and of the spindle.

Refitting

6   Refitting is the reverse of the removal procedure; use the masking tape to ensure that the arm is refitted in its original position and tighten the wiper arm-to-spindle nut to the specified torque wrench setting.

31   Windscreen wiper motor and linkage – removal and refitting

Motor

Removal

1   Operate the wipers, switching off the ignition to stop them when the crank/connecting rod joint is in sight (photo).
2   Prise out the clip and disconnect the connecting rods from the crank, collecting the spacer washer and bushes.
3   Unscrew the nut and remove the washer and crank from the motor spindle (photo).
4   Disconnect the battery negative lead. Unclip and separate the connector to disconnect the motor wiring (photo).
5   Unbolt the motor from its mounting bracket and withdraw it (photo).

30.3 Remove washer jet (rear window only) to reach wiper arm nut ...

30.4 ... then unscrew nut to remove arm

31.1 Remove clip (arrow) to disconnect connecting rods from crank

Fig. 12.10 Windscreen wiper components (Sec 31)

1   Wiper arm-to-spindle nut
2   Wiper arm
3   Wiper blade
4   Mounting bracket support rubber
5   Spindle housing nut
6   Washer
7   Upper rubber spacer
8   Lower rubber spacer
9   Mounting bracket
10 Clip
11 Bush
12 Connecting rod
13 Spacer washer
14 Crank
15 Nut
16 Washer
17 (Hex-head) screw
18 Wiper motor

31.3 Removing the crank from the windscreen wiper motor

31.4 Disconnecting the windscreen wiper motor wiring

31.5 Undo three (hex-head) screws to remove motor from mounting bracket

Refitting

6   Refitting is the reverse of the removal procedure, noting the following points.

   (a)   *Tighten the motor mounting (hex-head) screws to the specified torque wrench setting.*

   (b)   *Grease the motor spindle, the bushes and the spacer washers, then reconnect the motor wiring.*

   (c)   *Switch the wipers on and off, allowing the motor to return to the 'park' position; check that the arms are in the 'park' position.*

   (d)   *Refit the crank, connect the connecting rods – do not forget the spacer washer and bushes – and secure the clip to retain them, then tighten the crank nut securely.*

   (e)   *Connect the motor wiring and press the connector into its clip.*

   (f)   *Check that the wipers operate correctly.*

Motor and linkage

Removal

7   Remove both wiper arms (Sec 30).

8   Unscrew the linkage spindle housing nuts, then remove the washer and the upper rubber spacer under each.

9   Disconnect the battery negative lead. Unclip and separate the connector to disconnect the motor wiring.

10 Withdraw the motor and linkage assembly, removing if necessary the mounting bracket support rubber and collecting the lower rubber spacers (photo).

11 The assembly can now be dismantled, if required.

Refitting

12 Refitting is the reverse of the removal procedure, noting the

31.10 Removing windscreen wiper motor and linkage assembly

following points.

   (a)   *If the assembly was dismantled, refit the motor to the mounting bracket and position the crank so that it is parallel to the main length of the mounting bracket and pointing to the driver's side of the car.*

   (b)   *Grease the bushes and spacer washers.*

   (c)   *Ensure that the rubber spacers are correctly located.*

   (d)   *Tighten all nuts and screws to their specified torque wrench settings.*

   (e)   *Connect the motor wiring and press the connector into its clip.*

   (f)   *Check that the wipers operate correctly.*

32 Rear window wiper motor – removal and refitting

Removal

1   Remove the tailgate interior trim panel (Chapter 11).

2   Disconnect the battery negative lead.

3   Remove the wiper arm and blade (Sec 30).

4   Remove the rubber cover and unscrew the spindle housing nut, then remove the washer and upper rubber spacer, noting their locations (photo).

5   Disconnect the washer tube from the motor, then peel off the anti-rattle foam and separate the connector to disconnect the motor wiring (photo).

Fig. 12.11 Rear window wiper components (Sec 32)

1	Washer jet	9	Lower rubber spacer
2	Wiper arm-to-spindle nut	10	Wiper motor
3	Wiper arm	11	Ferrule
4	Wiper blade	12	Mounting bracket
5	Rubber cover	13	Mounting rubber
6	Spindle housing nut	14	Washer
7	Washer	15	(Hex-head) screw
8	Upper rubber spacer		

6   Unbolt the motor and its mounting bracket, then remove the assembly (photo).

7   The mounting bracket can be unbolted, if required; note the arrangement of the ferrules and the mounting rubbers.

32.4 Unscrew spindle housing nut, then remove washer and upper rubber spacer

32.5 Rear window washer tube 'A', motor wiring connector 'B', and mounting bracket (hex-head) screws 'C'

32.6 Removing the rear window wiper motor

**Fig. 12.12 Washer system components
(Sec 33)**

1 Washer jet*
2 Tube – non-return valve-to-rear
   window*
3 Rubber grommet*
4 Non-return valve – rear window
   washer only*
5 Tube – reservoir-to-bonnet
6 T-piece
7 Washer jet and tube
8 Grommet
9 Reservoir
10 Pump mounting bracket
11 Filler cap
12 Windscreen washer pump
13 Rear window washer pump*
14 Connector
* Not fitted to all models

Refitting

8   Refitting is the reverse of the removal procedure, noting the
following points.

   (a)   Tighten all nuts and screws to their specified torque wrench
         settings.
   (b)   Connect the motor wiring and washer tube, then check that the
         wiper and washer operate correctly.
   (c)   Ensure that the connector's wrapping is replaced to prevent
         rattles.

33   Washer system components – removal and refitting

1   Refer to Chapter 1 for details of maintenance requirements.
2   The system comprises the reservoir and a pump to direct flow to
the windscreen and (if fitted) to the rear window, as required.
3   The removal and refitting of all components is self-explanatory on
examination. Ensure that the tubes are not trapped when refitting the
reservoir and note that the connectors for the pumps are colour-coded
to aid correct reconnection on reassembly (photo).
4   If trouble is experienced at any time with the flow to the rear
window washer, check that the non-return valve is not blocked; it is
fitted in the tube next to the reservoir and should allow fluid to pass only
outwards, to the jet.

34   Radio/cassette unit – removal and refitting

Removal

1   If the radio/cassette unit has a security code, de-activate the code

temporarily and re-activate it when the battery is re-connected; refer to
the instructions and code supplied with the unit.
2   Disconnect the battery negative lead.
3   Actual removal and refitting procedures will vary according to the
type of radio fitted, but one of the following will be a reasonably
representative procedure (photo).

   (a)   If the unit has a finisher on each end of its faceplate, carefully
         prise these off and slacken the screw underneath each, then
         press the screws towards each other to release the unit's
         retaining clips; reach behind the facia to push the unit out from
         behind. Disconnect the wiring plugs and aerial lead to remove
         the unit.
   (b)   If the unit has two holes, one above the other, on each end of its
         faceplate, two standard DIN extraction tools are required to
         unlock and remove it. The tools may possibly be obtained from
         a Rover dealer or any audio accessory outlet, or can be made
         out of 3 mm (0.12 in) wire rod such as welding rod. Using the
         tools, push back the clamps on the left and right-hand sides,
         withdraw the unit and disconnect the wiring plugs and aerial.

Refitting

4   Refitting is the reverse of the removal procedure.

35   Loudspeakers – removal and refitting

Front
Removal

1   Remove the seven screws securing the door pocket to the door and
withdraw the pocket; disconnect the electric front window switch
wiring if required.

33.3 Disconnecting (windscreen) washer pump wiring – note colour-coded connections

34.3 Using DIN tools to remove radio/cassette unit

2   Remove the three screws and withdraw the loudspeaker from the door, then disconnect its wiring (photo).

Refitting
3   Refitting is the reverse of the removal procedure.

Rear
Removal
4   Open the tailgate; if removing the left-hand loudspeaker, remove first the luggage compartment lamp (Sec 18).
5   Remove the four screws and withdraw the loudspeaker from under the parcel shelf side support, then disconnect its wiring (photo).

Refitting
6   Refitting is the reverse of the removal procedure.

36   Radio aerial – removal and refitting

Removal
1   Unscrew the aerial mast from the aerial base.
2   Remove the interior lamp assembly (Sec 18).
3   Prise off the anti-radio interference shield and undo the screw securing the aerial base, then remove the base (photo).
4   Remove the radio/cassette unit (Sec 34), and disconnect the aerial lead. Tie a long length of string to the aerial lead lower end, then pull the lead up through the bodywork. Untie the string when the end of the lead appears. Leave the string in place to aid refitting.

Refitting
5   Refitting is the reverse of the removal procedure. Use the string to draw the lead down into place.

35.2 Front loudspeakers are mounted on door interior trim panels

35.5 Rear loudspeakers are fastened under parcel shelf side supports

36.3 Remove interior lamp assembly to reach aerial base mounting screw

NOTES:

1. All diagrams are divided into numbered circuits depending on function e.g. Diagram 2: Exterior lighting.
2. Items are arranged in relation to a plan view of the vehicle.
3. Items may appear on more than one diagram so are found using a grid reference e.g. 2/A1 denotes an item on diagram 2 grid location A1.
4. Complex items appear on the diagrams as blocks and are expanded on the internal connections page.
5. Header joints represent a method of common connection of many different circuits whilst reducing the number of crimped or soldered joints.
6. Feed wire colour varies dependant on the circuit supplied but all earth wires are coloured black or have a black tracer.
7. Not all items are fitted to all models.

WIRE COLOURS

B	Blue	R	Red
Bk	Black	Rs	Pink
Bn	Brown	S	Grey
LGn	Light Green	V	Violet
Gn	Green	W	White
O	Orange	Y	Yellow
P	Purple		

KEY TO SYMBOLS

PLUG-IN CONNECTOR
EARTH
BULB
LINE CONNECTOR
DIODE
FUSE

ITEM	DESCRIPTION	DIAGRAM/ GRID REF.
1	Alternator	1/A3
2	Battery	1/C7, 1a/C7, 2/C6, 2a/B6, 3/B6, 3a/C6
3	Central Locking Control Unit	3a/J1
4	Central Locking Motor LH Front	3a/J8
5	Central Locking Motor LH Rear	3a/M8
6	Central Locking Motor RH Rear	3a/M1
7	Central Locking Motor Tailgate	3a/M4
8	Choke Switch	1/J6
9	Cigar Lighter	2a/J6, 3/H7
10	Coolant Temp. Gauge Sender Unit	1/C6
11	Coolant Temp. Sensor	1a/E4
12	Cooling Fan Motor	3/A5
13	Cooling Fan Switch	3/A4
14	Crank Sensor	1a/C5
15	Direction Indicator Flasher Relay	2/G2
16	Direction Indicator LH Front	2/A8
17	Direction Indicator RH Front	2/A1
18	Direction Indicator Side Repeater LH	2/C8
19	Direction Indicator Side Repeater RH	2/C1
20	Dim/Dip Resistor	2/A3
21	Dim/Dip Unit	2/G1
22	Distributor	1/A5, 1a/A5
23	Earth Header 1	1/A1, 2/B1, 2a/A1, 3/A1, 3a/A1
24	Earth Header 2	1a/A8, 2/B8, 2a/A8, 3/A8, 3a/A8
25	Earth Header 4	2/L8, 2a/L8, 3/L8
26	Electric Window/Auxiliary Relay	3a/F2
27	Electric Window Drivers Switch 1	2a/K1, 3a/G1
28	Electric Window Drivers Switch 2	2a/K2, 3a/G2
29	Electric Window Motor LH Front	3a/H8
30	Electric Window Motor RH Front	3a/H1
31	Electric Window Passengers Switch	2a/K8, 3a/G8
32	Foglamp Rear	2/M1
33	Foglamp Switch	2/J3, 2a/G2
34	Fuel Gauge Sender	1/L4
35	Fuel Injector	1a/D3

FUSE	RATING	CIRCUIT
1	10A	Engine – Ignition Coil
2	10A	RH Side, Tail, Number Plate Lamps
3	10A	Instruments
4	15A	Cooling Fan
5	10A	RH Headlamp Main Beam
6	10A	Stop-Lamps
9	10A	Heated Rear Window Relay, Flashers, Reversing Lamps
10	10A	Rear Foglamp
11	20A	Heated Rear Window
12	15A	Central Locking, Radio Memory, Clock, Interior Lamps
13	30A	Electric Windows
14	15A	Heater Blower Motor
15	15A	Windscreen Wash/Wipe
16	15A	Rear Wash/Wipe
17	10A	Fuel Pump
18	10A	LH Headlamp Main Beam
19	20A	Headlamps, Side Lamps
20	15A	Dim/dip
21	20A	Hazard, Horn
22	15A	Radio Cassette, Cigar Lighter
24	10A	RH Headlamp Dip Beam
25	10A	LH Headlamp Dip Beam
26	10A	LH Side, Tail, Number Plate Lamps

ITEM	DESCRIPTION	DIAGRAM/ GRID REF.
36	Fuel Pump	1a/M4
37	Fuel Pump Relay	1a/E8
38	Fusebox	1/G2, 1a/J2, 2/F3, 2a/E3, 3/C2, 3a/E2
39	Fusible Link Box	1/C8, 1a/C8, 2/C7, 2a/B7, 3/B7, 3a/C7
40	Glove Box Lamp	2a/G7
41	Glove Box Lamp Switch	2a/G6
42	Handbrake Warning Switch	1/K5
43	Header Joint 1	2a/G3, 3/H3

Notes, fuses, ... diagrams

ITEM	DESCRIPTION	DIAGRAM/ GRID REF.
44	Header Joint 2	2a/G5, 3/H4
45	Header Joint 3	2/J6, 2a/E6, 3/G6
46	Header Joint 4	1/H6, 2/G5, 2a/D5, 3/F5
47	Header Joint 5	1a/H2, 2a/B2, 3a/B3
48	Headlamp Relay	2/G3
49	Headlamp Unit LH	2/A7
50	Heahlamp Unit RH	2/A2
51	Heated Rear Window	3/L4
52	Heated Rear Window Relay	3/C1
53	Heated Rear Window Switch	2a/K5, 3/K6
54	Heater Blower Motor	3/G5
55	Heater Blower Switch	2a/J5, 3/H5
56	Heater Illumination	2a/J6
57	Horn	3/A7
58	Idle Solenoid	1/C5
59	Ignition Amplifier Module	1/A5
60	Ignition Coil	1/A6, 1a/A6
61	Ignition Relay	3/G3
62	Ignition Switch	1/K1, 1a/L1, 2/J1, 2a/F2, 3/G1, 3a/G3
63	Inertia Switch	1a/K7
64	Instrument Cluster	1/J4, 1a/L4, 2/H4, 2a/J4
65	Intake Air Temp. Sensor	1a/A3
66	Interior Lamp	2a/E5
67	Interior Lamp Door Switch LH Front	2a/D8
68	Interior Lamp Door Switch RH Front	2a/D1
69	Lamp Cluster LH Rear	2/M8
70	Lamp Cluster RH Rear	2/M1
71	Lamps On Alarm Unit	2a/C3
72	Low Brake Fluid Sender	1/E2
73	Luggage Comp. Lamp	2a/M7
74	Luggage Comp. Switch	2a/M4
75	Main Relay	1a/E6
76	Manifold Heater	1/D4, 1a/C4
77	Manifold Heater Relay	1/F7, 1a/F6
78	Manifold Temp. Switch	1/D5
79	MEMS Unit	1a/J6
80	Multi-Function Switch	2/J4, 2a/K4, 3/K3
81	Number Plate Lamp	2/M4, 2/M5
82	Oil Pressure Switch	1/C2
83	Radio/Cassette Unit	3a/H6
84	Reversing Lamp Switch	2/B5
85	Relay Module	1a/F6
86	Spark Plugs	1/B4, 1a/B4
87	Speaker LH Front	3a/H7
88	Speaker LH Rear	3a/M7
89	Speaker RH Front	3a/H2
90	Speaker RH Rear	3a/M2
91	Starter Motor	1/A7

ITEM	DESCRIPTION	DIAGRAM/ GRID REF.
92	Starter Relay	1/E7, 1a/F8
93	Stepper Motor	1a/E3
94	Stop-Lamp Switch	2/E5
95	Throttle Pedal Switch	1/F4, 1a/J4
96	Throttle Potentiometer	1a/B3
97	Washer Pump Front	3/E1
98	Washer Pump Rear	3/D1
99	Washer Switch Rear	2a/H2, 3/K2
100	Wiper Motor Front	3/C3
101	Wiper Motor Rear	3/M4
102	Wiper Relay Front	3/D3
103	Wiper Relay Rear	3/E3
104	Wiper Switch Front	3/L4
105	Wiper Switch Rear	2a/H2, 3/J2

INTERNAL CONNECTION DETAILS

KEY TO INSTRUMENT CLUSTER (ITEM 64)

a = Ignition Warning Lamp
b = Oil Pressure Warning Lamp
c = Brake Warning Lamp
d = Choke Warning Lamp
e = Tachometer
f = Coolant Temp. Gauge
g = Fuel Gauge
h = Low Fuel Warning Lamp
i = High Temp. Warning Lamp
j = Clock
k = General Illumination
l = Sidelamp Warning Lamp
m = Main Beam Warning Lamp
n = LH Direction Indicator Lamp
p = RH Direction Indicator Lamp
q = Trailer Warning Lamp

Internal connection details and key to wiring diagrams continued

H24085
T.M.MARKE

Diagram 1: Starting, charging, ignition (carburettor models), warning lamps and gauges

Diagram 1a: Modular engine management – single point injection

Diagram 2: Exterior lighting – all models

KEY TO ITEMS 69 & 70

1 = DIRECTION INDICATOR LAMP
2 = STOP/TAIL LAMP
3 = REVERSING LAMP

Diagram 2a: Interior lighting – all models

Diagram 3: Ancillary circuits – wash/wipe, heater and cigar lighter

Diagram 3a: Ancillary circuits – electric windows, central locking and radio cassette

Index